8 5 ELECTRIC

MODEL #

SERIAL # J2935165

PLUG-
STEARING PARTS

JOHNSON
OUTBOARD MOTOR REPAIR AND TUNE-UP GUIDE

FULLY ILLUSTRATED

**GLENN'S
MARINE
SERIES**

JOHNSON
OUTBOARD MOTOR REPAIR AND TUNE-UP GUIDE

FULLY ILLUSTRATED

HAROLD T. GLENN

COWLES BOOK COMPANY, INC.

A Subsidiary of Henry Regnery Company
114 West Illinois Street, Chicago, Illinois 60610

Other Books by Harold T. Glenn
Youth at the Wheel
Safe Living
Automechanics
Glenn's Auto Troubleshooting Guide
Glenn's Triumph Repair and Tune-Up Guide
Exploring Power Mechanics
Glenn's Alfa Romeo Repair and Tune-Up Guide
Glenn's Austin, Austin-Healey Repair and Tune-Up Guide
Automobile Engine Rebuilding and Maintenance
Glenn's Sunbeam-Hillman Repair and Tune-Up Guide
Glenn's MG, Morris, and Magnette Repair and Tune-Up Guide
Glenn's Volkswagen Repair and Tune-Up Guide
Glenn's Volkswagen Repair and Tune-Up Guide (Spanish Edition)
Glenn's Mercedes-Benz Repair and Tune-Up Guide
Glenn's Foreign Carburetors and Electrical Systems Guide
Glenn's Renault Repair and Tune-Up Guide
Glenn's Jaguar Repair and Tune-Up Guide
Automobile Power Accessories
Glenn's Volvo Repair and Tune-Up Guide
Glenn's Peugeot Repair and Tune-Up Guide
Glenn's Auto Repair Manual
Glenn's Foreign Car Repair Manual
Glenn's Fiat Repair and Tune-Up Guide
Automotive Smog Control Manual
Honda Repair and Tune-Up Guide

FOREWORD

This is a comprehensive repair and tune-up manual for outboard motors. It is designed to be used as a classroom text or mechanic's reference book, or it can be used by a boating enthusiast who is interested in keeping his engine in tip-top shape. A quick-starting and dependable engine can contribute to an enjoyable vacation; a balky engine can spoil the fun.

This manual is organized about the conventional units of the outboard motor: the engine and the lower unit. Chapters are devoted to servicing the fuel and electrical systems. A separate chapter on engine tuning will enable the enthusiast to get all of the power from the engine that it was designed to deliver. A chapter on maintenance provides vital nontechnical information for fuel mixing and lubricating the units properly, to keep the engine operating dependably.

The first chapter deals with troubleshooting. It enables a mechanic to isolate trouble before beginning to disassemble the mechanism. It helps to pinpoint the trouble so that a mechanic will know what to look for as the unit is being disassembled. This feature can save valuable time when making repairs.

This book contains comprehensive and accurate specification tables, wiring diagrams, and exploded views of all mechanical and electrical units.

A special feature of this book is the use of many step-by-step illustrated instructions for representative types of carburetors, engines, and lower units. The illustrations and text are so closely correlated that no legends are needed. The illustrations have been especially treated to drop out the backgrounds.

The author wishes to thank Messrs. P. G. Geller and Bill King of Perry's Sporting Goods and Mr. Jim McDonald of Lane's Marine Sales & Service for their kind assistance in helping to set up some of the pictures for this book. Also, appreciation is expressed to Messrs. Edwin W. Hanson, John Tuzee, John Dobbertin, and Norman Schultz of Outboard Marine Corporation for their kind assistance in helping to set up the pictures and for furnishing information that is used in this Guide.

Especial thanks are due my wife, ANNA GLENN, for her devoted assistance in helping to proofread the text.

Harold T. Glenn

CONTENTS

CONTENTS

1
TROUBLESHOOTING

When the engine won't start, it is very important to be able to run through an organized procedure in order to pinpoint the cause of the trouble. Basically, starting troubles can be localized to either the fuel system or the ignition system. After isolating the trouble to the defective system, go through the following suggested check list to determine the exact cause.

FUEL SYSTEM TROUBLESHOOTING

First make sure that there is gasoline in the tank. Sometimes the fuel supply burns up faster than you realize. On engines with a remote fuel tank, make sure that the air vent screw on the fuel tank cap is open, and then squeeze the priming bulb in the fuel line. When the carburetor float bowl is full of gasoline, pressure will be felt on the priming bulb. However, it is possible to force fuel past the needle and seat by additional pressure so that gasoline will flow out of the carburetor throat. *CAUTION: The fuel will leak onto parts of the engine and could cause a fire.* Make sure that all the gasoline is dried up before attempting to start the engine again.

If the carburetor float bowl is dry, check the line for an obstruction. Do this by disconnecting the fuel line from the engine quick-disconnect fitting, and then depressing the check valve in the fuel line connection. Squeeze the bulb and fuel should come out of the line, if it is not obstructed.

If the fuel line to the engine is clear, the trouble could be in the line to the fuel pump or to the carburetor, usually at the fuel line strainer. To check this out, disconnect the fuel line at the carburetor and see if you can force fuel through it by squeezing the priming bulb. *CAUTION: When disconnecting a fuel line, use the proper wrenches, never a pair of pliers. CAUTION: When replacing a fuel line, don't tighten the nuts too much, especially on aluminum castings where the threads can be stripped rather easily.*

Remove a spark plug to check its condition. A wet spark plug means that the engine has been overchoked; a dry spark plug means that no fuel is reaching the combustion chamber. If the carburetor fuel bowl is full, but the spark plug is dry, the carburetor jets may be plugged.

If the spark plug is wet, go through the procedure for starting a flooded engine. Disconnect the fuel line or shut off the fuel supply completely, and then spin the flywheel several times to remove the excess fuel from the combustion chambers. Reconnect the fuel line, replace the spark plug, and then start the engine in the normal manner.

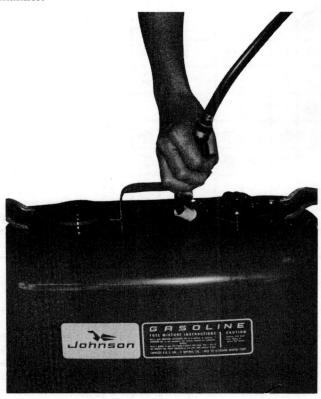

A primer bulb is used to lift fuel from a remote gas tank in order to prime the carburetor. If the carburetor runs out of fuel, the fuel pump may be defective, but the engine can be run by using the primer bulb as a fuel pump.

TROUBLESHOOTING CHART

POSSIBLE CAUSES	Engine does not start	Engine runs irregularly or misses	Engine starts and then cuts out	Engine does not idle properly	Engine speed is faster than normal	Engine speed is slower than normal	Boat speed below normal	Engine overheats
FUEL TANK EMPTY	●		●					
FUEL FILTER NEEDS CLEANING	●	●	●				●	●
CARBURETOR LOW-SPEED MIXTURE OUT OF ADJUSTMENT		●		●				
CARBURETOR HIGH-SPEED MIXTURE OUT OF ADJUSTMENT		●				●	●	●
WRONG OIL IN FUEL MIXTURE						●	●	●
WRONG GASOLINE IN FUEL MIXTURE		●				●	●	●
NOT ENOUGH OIL IN FUEL MIXTURE						●	●	●
TOO MUCH OIL IN FUEL MIXTURE	●		●			●	●	●
MOTOR FLOODED	●							
SPARK PLUGS FOULED OR DEFECTIVE	●	●		●		●	●	
WRONG TYPE SPARK PLUGS		●		●		●	●	●
NO SPARK	●							
WEAK OR INTERMITTENT SPARK		●	●	●		●	●	
MAGNETO CONTACT POINTS NEED ATTENTION		●	●	●		●	●	●
SPARK PLUG LEADS INTERCHANGED	●							
WATER PUMP DEFECTIVE								●
COOLING SYSTEM IN NEED OF CLEANING						●	●	●
CAVITATION					●		●	
PROPELLER DAMAGED						●	●	
TILT ANGLE IMPROPERLY ADJUSTED							●	
TRANSOM TOO HIGH					●		●	
TRANSOM TOO LOW							●	
AIR VENT HOLE IN FUEL CAP CLOGGED		●	●				●	●

A troubleshooting chart is often helpful to determine the general area in which to look for possible causes of trouble.

Most of the engines have a fuel pump, and the filter screen should be cleaned periodically. Always replace the gasket.

Check the fuel in the carburetor to see if water has gotten into it by catching a little of the gasoline in the palm of your hand. The water will appear as small beads or bubbles. If you blow on the mixture, the gasoline will evaporate, leaving the water behind.

FUEL SYSTEM TROUBLESHOOTING CHART

1. **No fuel in carburetor**
   1a. Empty gas tank
   1b. Clogged fuel filter
   1c. Restricted vent in gas tank
   1d. Defective fuel pump

The condition of the firing end of a spark plug can be used to determine the condition inside of the combustion chamber. This spark plug is running dry, meaning that the mixture is combustible and that the spark plug is doing its work well.

To see if the fuel pump is working, disconnect the fuel line and direct its flow into a container. You should be able to determine the condition of the pump before the carburetor fuel bowl runs out of fuel.

   1e. Main adjusting screw closed
   1f. Clogged carburetor screen
   1g. Clogged or broken fuel line
2. **Fuel in carburetor**
   2a. Flooding at carburetor
   2b. Choke not operating
   2c. Water in gasoline
   2d. Restricted carburetor jets
3. **Flooding**
   3a. Choke out of adjustment

The firing end of this spark plug is black with carbon and wet, indicating that the fuel mixture contains too much oil, the fuel mixture is too rich, or the spark plug is not firing.

To check the ignition system, hold the high-tension wire about 1/4" away from a metallic surface. Spin the flywheel and a good spark should jump from the wire to ground, if the ignition system is working properly. If the end of the high-tension wire is encased in a boot, as this one is, you can insert a screwdriver tip into the boot to make contact with the wire. Hold the screwdriver so that the shank is about 1/4" away from a good ground to check the spark.

3b. High float level
3c. Float stuck
3d. Excessive fuel pump pressure
3e. Float saturated and not buoyant

IGNITION TROUBLESHOOTING

To check the ignition system, disconnect one of the high-tension wires to a spark plug. Hold the end about 1/4" from the head and spin the flywheel. There should be a good spark from the wire to the metal; otherwise, there is trouble in the ignition system. If there is a spark from the wire to the ground, but the engine does not start because of ignition system defects, then the trouble is generally with the spark plug. Also, if the ignition timing is out of adjustment, the engine will be hard to start.

To check out a spark plug, remove it from the cylinder and connect the high-tension wire to it. Lay the spark plug on the base of the cylinder head, and then

To check out a spark plug, connect the high-tension wire to it and lay the base of the plug on the cylinder head. Spin the flywheel and the spark should jump across the spark plug gap, if the spark plug is good.

spin the flywheel. If there is no spark across the points of the plug, and there was a spark from the high-tension wire to the ground in the preceding test, then the spark plug is shorted. If the plug is good, check the gap and set it to 0.035". *CAUTION: Make the adjustment by bending the outer electrode, never the center one. NOTE: If a gap gauge is not available, you can use two thicknesses of a business card in an emergency.*

IGNITION SYSTEM TROUBLESHOOTING CHART

1. **Spark plugs**
   1a. Fouled
   1b. Wrong type for engine
   1c. Residue on porcelain, especially in salt water areas
   1d. Cracked porcelain
   1e. Loose connections
2. **Ignition coil**
   2a. Weak
   2b. Shorted

This black, pitted breaker point shows evidence of oil on the contact surface, which burned into an insulator. The oil can be placed on the contact point surface with your fingers or by using a dirty feeler gauge to measure the gap.

2c. Improperly mounted
2d. Loose wires
3. **Condenser**
3a. Weak
3b. Shorted
3c. Improperly mounted
3d. Loose wires
4. **Breaker points**
4a. Improperly adjusted
4b. Pitted or corroded
4c. Broken or weak spring
4d. Breaker point loose in its mounting
4e. Loose wires
4f. Breaker point arm binding on pivot post, which can cause sluggish action, or the plunger rod can be binding in the bracket
4g. Broken cam follower or plunger rod
5. **Wiring**
5a. Loose, corroded, or poorly soldered connections
5b. Broken wires (broken under the insulation)
5c. Oil-soaked wires that cause leaks
5d. Faulty ground or stop button connection
5e. Faulty spark suppressors (where used)
6. **Flywheel**
6a. Weak magnet

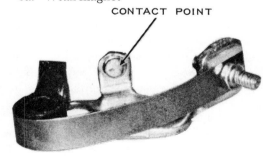

The frosted appearance of this breaker point is an indication that the ignition system was operating properly.

A compression gauge should be used to check the pressure inside of each combustion chamber. It is not possible to tune properly an engine in which the compression varies over 10 psi.

6b. Cracked magnet
6c. Improper clearance between magnet pole pieces and coil heels
6d. Magnet pole pieces sticking or rubbing on coil heels

COMPRESSION

For an engine to start properly, the compression must be good. The amount of compression depends on the ability of the piston rings to keep the gases from escaping. The condition of the cylinder walls, piston ring grooves, and the rings is a factor. Turn the flywheel by hand with the spark plugs installed to check the compression. If compression is present, it can be felt when attempting to complete one revolution of the flywheel. An engine will run with low compression, but it will be difficult to start and certainly won't develop its normal power output. *NOTE: The compression should not vary more than 10 to 15 psi between cylinders.*

COMPRESSION TROUBLESHOOTING CHART

1. **Piston rings**
   1a. Top ring striking ridge in cylinder
   1b. Worn ring grooves
   1c. Rings sticking in ring groove
   1d. Insufficient ring tension
   1e. Insufficient gap clearance
   1f. Excessive side clearance in ring groove
   1g. Undersize pistons
   1h. Scored or wavy cylinder walls

2. **Piston(s)**
   2a. Carbon accumulations in head
   2b. Broken piston, skirt, or ring land
   2c. Insufficient clearance at top of ring land
   2d. Out-of-round, tapered, or worn cylinders
   2e. Excessive piston-to-bore clearance
   2f. Inadequate lubrication

3. **Cylinder(s)**
   3a. Inadequate lubrication
   3b. Contaminated or poor oil
   3c. Exhaust ports clogged with carbon
   3d. Incomplete combustion
   3e. Incorrect type of rings
   3f. Improper cylinder wall finish
   3g. Hole in cylinder
   3h. Insufficient ring gap clearance
   3i. Distorted block or crankshaft

If the engine idles roughly, adjust the idle mixture adjusting screw to see if you can smooth out the idle. Turning the screw to the right (clockwise) leans the mixture. The high-speed adjusting screw at the base of the carburetor can be adjusted in a similar manner.

ROUGH OPERATION

An engine that is not operating smoothly can have trouble in the ignition or the fuel system. Closely allied with the fuel system is trouble with a reed valve which affects the fuel distribution to two cylinders of a multi-cylinder engine.

To check the ignition system, disconnect a spark plug wire, and then run the engine at its rough-operating point. Note the size of the spark that jumps from the wire to the terminal of the spark plug. Widen the gap to see if the spark becomes intermittent as the gap increases. This is a rather rough test, but it can be used to throw some light on the condition of the ignition system.

If the trouble is in the fuel system, it can be checked by changing the air-fuel ratio and noting its effect on the running of the engine. For example, with the engine running at its rough-operating point, close the choke valve slowly and note the effect that enriching the mixture has on the operation of the engine. If the engine smooths out with the choke valve partially closed, then the air-fuel mixture is too lean. The lean condition can be caused by a poor carburetor mixture adjustment or by dirt in one of the jets.

If the engine is running too rich, enriching the air-fuel mixture with the choke will cause the engine to slow down and run even rougher.

If the engine is running too rich, the trouble could be a leaking fuel pump diaphragm, which will allow raw fuel to enter the crankcase and mix with the carbureted fuel. This condition can be suspected if one carburetor of a multi-cylinder engine is running excessively rich. The trouble can be isolated further by removing the spark plugs to check their condition. A wet spark plug indicates an excessively rich mixture.

A defective reed valve will cause the engine to spit back through the carburetor air intake. In some cases, white smoke will come out of the carburetor throat. Hold your hand over the air intake and you may be able to feel raw gasoline being returned through the throat of the carburetor.

On a multi-cylinder engine, one reed valve block controls the air-fuel mixture of one carburetor, which may feed two cylinders. Remove the spark plugs of these two cylinders to determine which one is wet in order to pinpoint the defective reed valve.

ROUGH OPERATION
TROUBLESHOOTING CHART

1. **Engine misfires because of ignition troubles**
   1a. Incorrect spark plug gap
   1b. Defective or loose spark plugs
   1c. Spark plugs of an incorrect heat range
   1d. Sticking breaker arm
   1e. Incorrect breaker point gap
   1f. Breaker points not synchronized
   1g. Loose wire in primary circuit
   1h. Defective distributor rotor
   1i. Corroded or pitted breaker points
   1j. Cracked distributor cap
   1k. Leaking or broken high-tension wires
   1l. Weak armature magnet
   1m. Worn cam lobes on the distributor or magneto shaft
   1n. Worn distributor or magneto shaft bushings
   1o. Defective coil or condenser
   1p. Defective ignition switch
   1q. Spark timing out of adjustment

2. **Engine misfires because of fuel troubles**
   2a. Dirt or water in fuel
   2b. Reed valve stuck open or broken
   2c. Incorrect fuel level
   2d. Carburetor loose at flange
   2e. Throttle valve not closing completely
   2f. Throttle valve turned to one side or incorrectly positioned

3. **Engine misfires at high speeds**
   3a. Weak breaker arm spring
   3b. Defective coil
   3c. Coil shorts through insulation
   3d. Breaker points improperly adjusted
   3e. Poor breaker point contact
   3f. Spark plug gap set too wide
   3g. Too much spark advance
   3h. Wrong type of spark plugs
   3i. Excessive carbon in cylinders
   3j. Poor compression
   3k. Dirty carburetor
   3l. Lean carburetor adjustment
   3m. Crankcase magneto adaptor flange worn out-of-round

4. **Engine backfires through the exhaust**
   4a. Cracked spark plug porcelain
   4b. Carbon track in distributor cap
   4c. Crossed spark plug wires
   4d. Air leak at intake deflector
   4e. Improper ignition timing

5. **Engine backfires through the carburetor**
   5a. Poor quality fuel
   5b. Air-fuel mixture too lean
   5c. Excessively lean or too rich a fuel mixture
   5d. Improper ignition timing

To check the air-fuel mixture, close the choke valve slowly while the engine is running at its rough-operating point. If the engine smooths out with the choke valve partially closed, then the air-fuel mixture is too lean.

5e. Pre-ignition
5f. Improperly seated or a broken reed valve
5g. Improperly adjusted carburetor
6. **Pre-ignition**
6a. Spark advanced too far
6b. Incorrect type of spark plugs
6c. Burned spark plug electrodes
6d. Incorrect breaker point setting
6e. Excessive oil in fuel
6f. Poor grade of fuel
6g. Lean carburetor mixture
6h. Excessive engine temperature
6i. Carbon deposits in combustion chamber

HIGH FUEL CONSUMPTION

Excessively high fuel consumption is generally caused by carburetor defects. However, the efficient operation of the ignition system is essential for good utilization of the fuel that is drawn into the engine. To this extent, defects in the ignition system will cause the fuel consumption to increase.

HIGH FUEL CONSUMPTION TROUBLESHOOTING CHART

1. **Carburetor troubles**
   1a. Cracked carburetor casting
   1b. Leaking fuel line connection
   1c. Defective carburetor bowl gasket
   1d. Warped or bent bowl cover
   1e. Plugged vent hole in cover
   1f. High float level
   1g. Loose float needle valve seat
   1h. Defective needle valve seat gasket
   1i. Worn needle valve and seat
   1j. Ridge worn in lip of float
   1k. Worn float pin or bracket
   1l. Float binding in bowl
   1m. Choke lever stuck
2. **Fuel pump troubles**
   2a. Leaking around diaphragm cover
   2b. Leaking fuel pump diaphragm
   2c. Warped check valves
   2d. Dirt or sediment in valves
   2e. Corroded valve seats
   2f. High fuel pump pressure
   2g. Leakage at lines and connections
   2h. Leaking gas tank
   2i. Leakage at filler cap
3. **Ignition conditions**
   3a. Retarded spark timing

3b. Leaking high-tension wires
3c. Incorrect spark plug gap
3d. Fouled spark plugs
3e. Worn breaker points
3f. Faulty spark advance adjustment
3g. Defective condenser
2h. Weak ignition coil
3i. Pre-ignition
4. **Compression troubles**
   4a. Worn or broken piston rings
   4b. Worn pistons or cylinders
5. **Miscellaneous troubles**
   5a. Loose carburetor flange
   5b. Improperly adjusted or worn throttle linkage
   5c. Restricted exhaust system
   5d. Carbon in manifold
   5e. Overheating engine
   5f. Use of poor grade of gasoline
   5g. Sticking reed valve
   5h. Poorly seated reed valve

NOISES

Checking engine noises is one of the more difficult troubleshooting procedures because noises travel in the metal of the engine and sometimes appear to be coming from every part. However, it is possible to localize noises by using a stethoscope or a listening rod.

NOISE TROUBLESHOOTING CHART

1. **Knocking in powerhead**
   1a. Loose flywheel
   1b. Excessive bearing clearance
   1c. Spark advanced too far
   1d. Pre-ignition
   1e. Excessive end play in crankshaft
   1f. Out-of-round bearing journals
   1g. Bent or twisted crankshaft
   1h. Broken crankshaft
2. **Knocking from the connecting rods**
   2a. Excessive bearing clearance
   2b. Worn connecting rod
   2c. Misaligned connecting rods and cap
   2d. Bent or twisted connecting rod
   2e. Worn crankshaft journal
3. **Center main bearing noises**
   3a. Improperly installed main bearing
   3b. Crankshaft striking the reed stops
4. **Piston noises**
   4a. Excessive piston-to-cylinder bore clearance

4b. Out-of-round cylinder
4c. Loose piston pin
4d. Carbon in the top of the cylinder
4e. Piston pin bent
4f. Excessive clearance at the ring grooves
4g. Broken piston ring

5. **Gear housing noises**
5a. Propeller shaft worn or sprung
5b. Bearing worn
5c. Broken gears
5d. Propeller hub rubbing against the gear case cover
5e. Improperly fitted gears
5f. Worn gears
5g. Wrong conical angle
5h. Incorrect backlash
5i. Oil seal leakage
5j. Water in gear housing
5k. No grease in gear housing

MECHANICAL PROBLEMS

Generally, mechanical problems in an engine require it to be disassembled to correct the condition. The following Mechanical Troubleshooting Chart will assist in determining the possible causes of mechanical troubles.

MECHANICAL TROUBLESHOOTING CHART

1. **Reed valve breakage**
   1a. Improper valve opening
   1b. Corrosion of reed valve
   1c. Poor valve seat

2. **Excessive bearing wear caused by dirt**
   2a. Careless service methods
   2b. Contaminated oil

3. **Bearing wear caused by improper fitting**
   3a. Distorted connecting rods
   3b. Mixed connecting rod caps
   3c. Dirt between bearing and connecting rod bore
   3d. Out-of-round, tapered, or worn journal
   3e. Warped crankshaft or block
   3f. Excessive crankshaft end play
   3g. Scored bearing surface
   3h. Improper clearance
   3i. Use of wrong service tools

4. **Bearing failure caused by corrosion**
   4a. Overheating
   4b. Storage in damp place
   4c. Water entering powerhead

5. **Bearing failure caused by improper operation**
   5a. Overspeeding
   5b. Spark detonation
   5c. Improper engine break-in
   5d. Racing a cold engine
   5e. Using the wrong type or grade of oil
   5f. Using an improper fuel
   5g. Improper spark timing

6. **Bearing wear caused by lubrication problems**
   6a. Excessive engine temperatures
   6b. Insufficient engine warm-up time
   6c. Insufficient quantity of oil

7. **Engine speed faster than normal**
   7a. Cavitation
   7b. Transom too high
   7c. Propeller hub slipping
   7d. Wrong propeller pitch

8. **Engine speed slower than normal**
   8a. Carburetor out of adjustment
   8b. Too much oil in fuel mixture
   8c. Wrong oil in fuel
   8d. Wrong type of gasoline
   8e. Spark plugs fouled
   8f. Wrong type of spark plugs
   8g. Tilt angle not correctly adjusted
   8h. Transom too high
   8i. Transom too low
   8j. Cavitation
   8k. Weeds tangled on gear housing
   8l. Propeller damaged
   8m. Wrong propeller pitch

COOLING SYSTEM TROUBLESHOOTING CHART

1. **Overheating with an external leak**
   1a. Loose cylinder block cover bolts
   1b. Damaged cylinder block cover gasket
   1c. Warped cylinder block cover or block
   1d. Cracked cylinder wall
   1e. Porosity of cylinder head

2. **Overheating without a leak**
   2a. Incorrect ignition timing
   2b. Improper fuel mixture
   2c. Improperly adjusted spark advance linkage
   2d. Defective spark advance linkage
   2e. Pre-ignition

3. **Overheating caused by restricted circulation**
   3a. Pump impeller loose on shaft
   3b. Water inlet pipe seal ring not in place
   3c. Pump blades broken or worn
   3d. Water pump worn

3e.   Clogged water jacket passages
3f.   Water tube mislocated
3g.   Water tube cracked or corroded
3h.   Cover not securely tightened

ELECTRICAL SYSTEM TROUBLES

The battery supplies the current required to crank the engine. On engines with a distributor-type ignition system, the battery furnishes the current to energize this circuit. Some engines are equipped with an alternator to charge the battery. In the absence of an alternator, the battery must be charged by an outside source.

It takes specialized testing equipment and knowledge of its use to determine accurately the condition of an electrical unit. However, the following troubleshooting charts can be used for guidance in tracing out some types of electrical troubles.

BATTERY TROUBLESHOOTING CHART

1. **If frequent charging is required**
   1a.   Corroded battery terminals
   1b.   Alternator grounded or shorted
   1c.   Worn-out or inefficient battery
   1d.   Rectifier defective
   1e.   Short in charging circuit
   1f.   Excessive use of electrical units
   1g.   Short circuit in ignition switch

2. **Battery does not take a charge**
   2a.   Low water level
   2b.   Worn-out battery
   2c.   Cracked case
   2d.   Spilled electrolyte
   2e.   Internal short circuit
   2f.   Impure electrolyte

3. **High water loss**
   3a.   Too high a charging rate
   3b.   Old or inefficient battery
   3c.   Leaking battery cell
   3d.   Worn-out battery
   3e.   Cracked case
   3f.   Defective current regulation

IGNITION SYSTEM TROUBLESHOOTING CHART

1. **Oxidized breaker points**
   1a.   High charging voltage

1b.   Resistor of incorrect value
1c.   High resistance in condenser circuit
1d.   Incorrect type of ignition coil

2. **Ignition coil failures**
   2a.   Extremely high voltage
   2b.   Moisture formation
   2c.   Excessive heat from engine

3. **Spark plug troubles**
   3a.   Incorrect type of spark plug
   3b.   Too rich a fuel mixture
   3c.   Incorrect oil mixture
   3d.   Inferior grade of gasoline or oil used
   3e.   Overheated engine
   3f.   Too much carbon in combustion chamber
   3g.   Improper torque on spark plug

STARTING MOTOR TROUBLESHOOTING CHART

1. **Starter fails to crank engine**
   1a.   Poor battery ground
   1b.   Jammed or broken drive
   1c.   Broken teeth on flywheel
   1d.   Grounded switch
   1e.   Solenoid shorted or open circuited
   1f.   Burned contact points in switch
   1g.   Improperly seated brushes
   1h.   High mica between commutator segments
   1i.   Shorted armature
   1j.   Shorted field or brushes

2. **Excessive current draw**
   2a.   Broken or jammed starter drive
   2b.   Dirty or gummed armature
   2c.   Shorted armature
   2d.   Grounded armature or field
   2e.   Misaligned starting motor
   2f.   Worn armature shaft bearings
   2g.   Misaligned armature shaft
   2h.   Loose field pole pieces
   2i.   Engine turns hard

3. **Burned commutator bars**
   3a.   Excessive arcing at brushes
   3b.   Excessive voltage
   3c.   Improperly seated brushes
   3d.   Open-circuited armature coils
   3e.   Open field circuit
   3f.   Weak brush spring tension

4. **Excessive noise**
   4a.   Defective starter drive
   4b.   Chipped or broken flywheel teeth
   4c.   Insufficient lubrication
   4d.   Worn armature shaft bearings

CRANKING MOTOR TROUBLESHOOTING CHART

STEP NUMBER	METER READINGS (In Volts)			CAUSE
	As Hooked Up	With Starter Button Pushed	If It Reads	
V-1	12	10–11	12	Open Circuit
			Below 10	Weak Battery
V-2	12	0–1	Over 1	Loose Terminal Open Circuit
			Below 8	High-Resistance
V-3	0	1/2–1	Below 1	Loose Terminal Broken Wire
V-4	0	1/2–1	Over 1	Loose Terminal
V-5	0	1/2–1	Over 1	Loose Connection Corroded Connection
V-6	12	1/2–1	Over 1	Defective Solenoid
V-7	12	1/2–1	Over 1	Loose Terminal
V-8	0	0	Over 0	Poor Ground
A-9 ①	0	125	Well Over 125	Defective Cranking Motor

① An ammeter of this capacity must use a shunt. **Caution: Do not connect a small ammeter in this circuit, or you will burn it out.**

Cranking motor troubles can be caused by a defective solenoid. To check out the solenoid, use a pair of pliers to bridge the heavy contact terminals. This bypasses the solenoid entirely, and the cranking motor should work unless there are other troubles in the circuit.

4e. Misaligned starting motor
4f. Loose starter mounting
4g. Sprung armature shaft

TROUBLESHOOTING THE CRANKING MOTOR

When a cranking motor does not turn, or doesn't crank the engine, the electrical system must be checked with an accurate voltmeter and ammeter to determine the source of trouble. Use a 0–15 voltmeter and a 0–500 ammeter. The following chart is keyed to the illustration to give a useful step-by-step tracing procedure.

TROUBLESHOOTING A CD IGNITION SYSTEM

Two basic types of CD ignition systems are used on these engines. In all except the 1968, 100 Hp engine and the 1969, 115 Hp engine, breaker points are used to trigger a solid-state amplifier. In the 100 and 115 Hp engines, a pulse generator (sensor) replaces the ignition points; its generated pulse of current triggers the solid-state amplifier. Most of the troubleshooting procedures are similar for both types, and the special instructions for the 100 and 115 Hp engines (pulse-generator type) are covered at the end of this section.

Because of the higher voltages at the spark plugs, it is extremely important to observe special precautions for

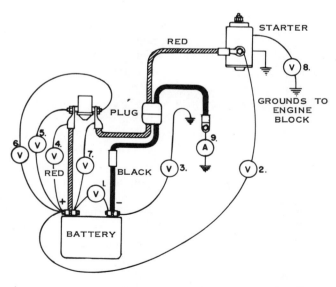

This diagram is to be used in conjunction with the Troubleshooting Chart to make accurate tests, which will determine the exact area of trouble.

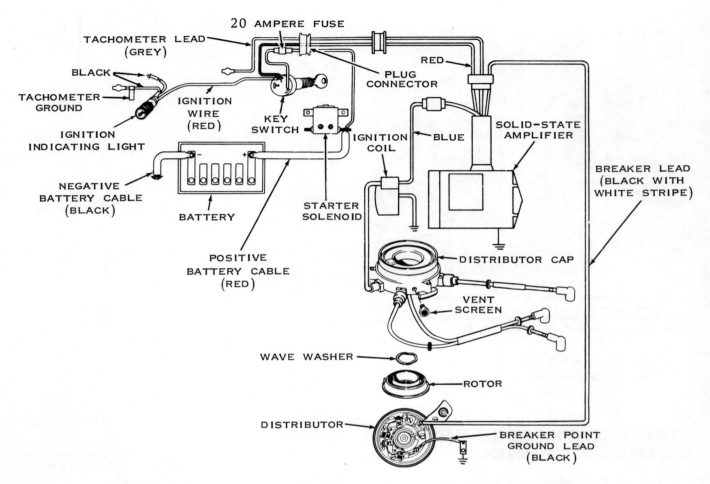

Schematic diagram for the breaker-point type of CD ignition system used on the 55, 65, and 85 Hp engines.

troubleshooting a CD ignition system. Some of the precautions are: (1) Conduct all tests with the spark plug high-tension leads connected to the spark plugs or to a good ground, unless otherwise specified. (2) When running the engine, be sure the battery is connected or damage to the ignition system will result. (3) Always hold the spark plug wire with insulated pliers when making a spark test. The high voltages in the system could result in a severe shock if you held the high-tension wire with your hand. (4) The coil lead is sealed in the ignition coil; therefore, don't attempt to remove it.

A malfunction in the ignition system will result in (1) engine misfiring, (2) engine surge, or (3) failure of the engine to run. It should be noted, too, that a malfunctioning vacuum switch may also prevent the engine from starting or cause erratic operation. Engine misfiring or surging can also be caused by a carburetor condition, and this should be checked as a possible cause of the trouble before checking the ignition system. Any ignition system malfunction should be checked in a logical order, as discussed below:

CHECKING FOR A SPARK

Use a neon tester to check for high-tension voltage at the spark plug leads, or hold the high-tension wire with a pair of insulated pliers to see if the spark jumps a small gap to the spark plug terminal when the engine is being cranked. *CAUTION: Don't hold the spark plug wire in your hand while making this check because of the high voltages in the system.*

CHECKING THE WIRING

Insert a probe, from a continuity tester using a #57 bulb, into the socket of the red lead which runs to the amplifier. Touch the other test lead to a good ground. Turn on the ignition switch and the bulb should light brightly. *NOTE: A voltmeter also can be used for this test.* No voltage to this point means that the circuit to the amplifier is open.

Check all wires associated with the system for loose or corroded connections, especially plug-in connections.

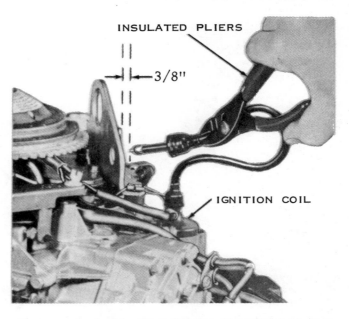

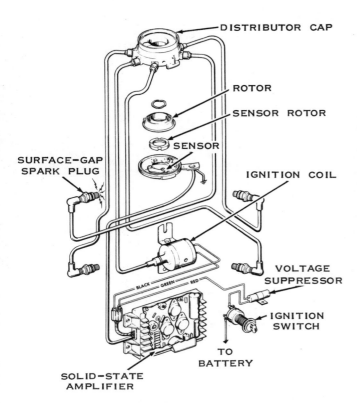

This is a schematic diagram for the pulse-generator type of CD ignition system used on the 100 and 115 Hp engines. The conventional breaker points have been replaced by a sensor and rotor (pulse generator).

Make sure that there is a clean, tight connection from the negative terminal of the ignition coil to ground. Also check for a good battery ground cable connection. Check all high-tension leads for cracks or oil-soaked insulation. The high-tension leads should also be checked with an ohmmeter for excessive resistance or an open circuit.

Always use a pair of insulated pliers to hold the high-tension wire when checking for a spark. *CAUTION: Don't hold the wire in your hand, or you can get a severe shock.*

CHECKING THE IGNITION TIMING

The timing of the engine should not change during normal operation. However, if the spark advance stop screw has been disturbed, or if the amplifier has been replaced, the ignition timing must be checked.

Connect a timing light to the spark plug lead of No. 1 cylinder, start the engine, shift into FORWARD gear, and then fully open the throttle. The straight timing mark on the flywheel must fall within the square timing mark on the ring gear guard. If necessary, move the advance stop adjustment screw for the proper setting. *NOTE: The triangular mark on the flywheel is used for timing cylinder No. 2 of a V-4 engine.*

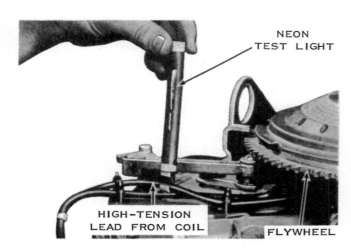

A neon tester can be used to check for high-tension voltage by holding the tester alongside of the main coil wire.

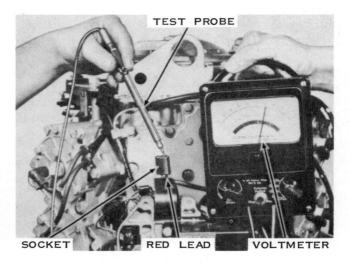

To check the wiring, use a #57 bulb or a voltmeter, as discussed in the text.

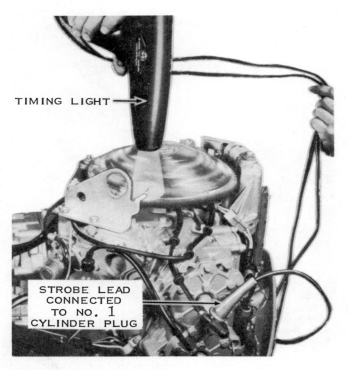

A timing light must be used to check the ignition timing.

CHECKING THE SPARK PLUGS

Remove and check the spark plugs. If the center electrode is worn to a point where it is below the ceramic, it should be replaced. Any spark plug with a cracked insulator also should be replaced.

CHECKING THE IGNITION COIL

All Except the 100 & 115 Hp Engines

Separate the black wire with the gray stripe (white stripe on the 55 Hp engine) at the connector on top of the powerhead. Connect one end of a jumper wire to

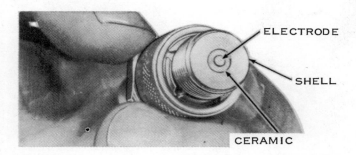

A surface-gap type of spark plug must be used with a CD ignition system. No gap adjustment is necessary, because the spark jumps from the center electrode to the shell, which is grounded.

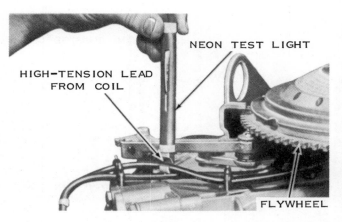

To check the output of the amplifier, hold a neon test lamp near the high-tension wire from the coil as you make and break the jumper wire connection, as discussed in the text.

the amplifier end of this lead and the other end of the jumper wire to a good ground. Hold a neon spark tester against the coil-to-distributor high-tension wire, and the neon tester should flash whenever the jumper wire is lifted from ground. If flashing does not occur, replace the ignition coil.

CHECKING THE AMPLIFIER

All Except the 100 & 115 Hp Engines

Ground all high-tension spark plug leads. Insert a probe, from a continuity tester using a #57 bulb, into the connector in the blue lead between the amplifier and the coil. *CAUTION: Don't open this connection.* Crank the engine and the bulb should glow faintly, indicating that the output of the amplifier is satisfactory. If the bulb does not glow, replace the amplifier.

100 & 115 Hp Engines

The amplifier for this system is called a "pulse pack." It performs the same function as the amplifier for the other CD ignition systems, except that a pulse of electricity is generated in the sensor as the rotating magnet interrupts the magnetic path through the sensor coil. This generated pulse of electricity is used to trigger the CD section of the solid-state amplifier.

To test the current draw of the amplifier, connect a low-reading ammeter between the white wire with the red stripe and the red wire from the voltage suppressor. Turn on the ignition switch and depress the vacuum switch diaphragm to close the ignition circuit; the ammeter should read 0.4–0.5 ampere. *CAUTION: Don't crank the engine.*

To check the output of the amplifier, connect a #57 bulb to the green lead on the positive (+) termi-

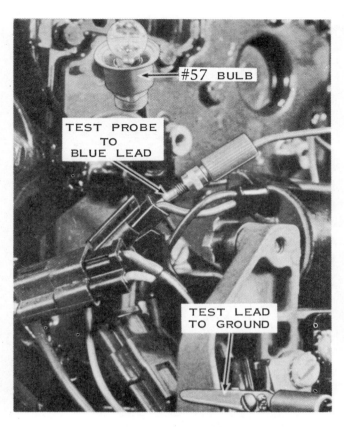

Testing the amplifier of all except the 100 and 115 Hp engines. See the text for details.

The voltage suppressor is designed to protect the amplifier from any high voltage surges; it can be tested with an ohmmeter, as discussed in the text.

nal of the ignition coil and the other lead to ground. Crank the engine and observe the bulb, which should show a glowing flicker for each firing pulse, indicating that the sensor (pulse generator) and amplifier are functioning properly. If the bulb does not flicker, the sensor or amplifier is defective.

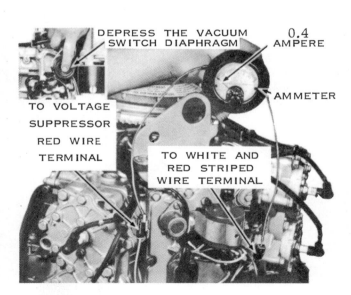

To check the current draw of the amplifier on the 100 and 115 Hp engines, connect a low-reading ammeter between the white wire and the red wire from the voltage suppressor. The meter should register 0.4 ampere with the ignition switch turned on.

To check the output of the amplifier used on the 100 and 115 Hp engines, connect a #57 bulb to the green lead on the positive terminal of the ignition coil and the other lead to ground, as discussed in the text.

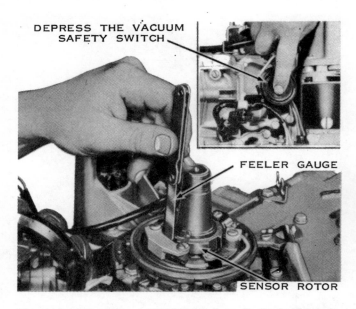

The sensor on the 100 and 115 Hp engines can be checked by positioning the sensor magnet as shown and then passing a feeler gauge blade across the gap. A spark should jump from the high-tension lead to ground, if you are generating a pulse of current by bridging the magnetic path.

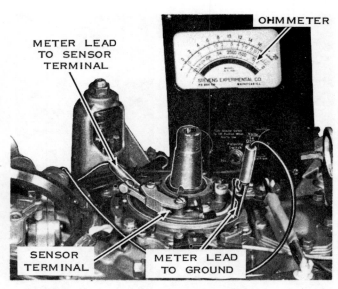

This illustration shows the sensor coil being checked for ground. The resistance of the sensor coil should be 4–6 ohms, and the coil must not be grounded.

CHECKING THE VOLTAGE SUPPRESSOR

100 & 115 Hp Engines

The voltage suppressor is designed to protect the amplifier from any high voltage surge caused by a loose connection. To test the suppressor, connect an ohmmeter between the input and output leads, and the meter should read 0.5 ohm.

To check the suppressor diode, turn the ohmmeter control knob to the high-ohms position, and then connect the test meter black lead to ground and the other test lead to the output terminal wire which goes to the amplifier. Note the meter reading, and then reverse the test leads. A normal diode should show a reading in only one direction; it must show an open circuit when the test leads are reversed.

CHECKING THE SENSOR

100 & 115 Hp Engines

The sensor (pulse generator) contains a rotating magnet with notches to interrupt the magnetic path through a coil of wire. To test the sensor, it is necessary to remove the flywheel and distributor cap to gain access to the sensor. *CAUTION: Don't lose the wave washer which stabilizes the rotor.*

Position the stator rotor as shown in the accompanying illustration. Turn on the ignition switch, depress the vacuum switch diaphragm to close the ignition circuit, hold the ignition coil high-tension lead about 3/8″ away from any metallic part of the engine, and then pass a feeler gauge blade across the sensor, as shown. A spark should jump from the high-tension lead to ground each time that the magnetic gap is bridged by the feeler gauge blade. No spark would indicate trouble in the sensor or other parts of the ignition system. *NOTE: A loose sensor would cause erratic high-speed operation.*

The sensor can be checked for continuity and ground with an ohmmeter. To do this, remove the blue and white leads from the sensor. *NOTE: These are the push-type connectors.* Check each terminal to ground, using the high-ohm scale. The reading should be infinity; if it is not, the sensor should be replaced. Using the low-ohm scale, touch the test prods to the two sensor terminals; the resistance should be 4–6 ohms.

2

MAINTENANCE

These engines are designed for a transom height of 15″ for the standard models and 20″ for the long-shaft models.

To install the engine on the transom, open the boat bracket clamp screws, and then install the unit, centering it with respect to the keel or centerline of the boat. Observe the position of the anti-cavitation plate with respect to the keel. The plate must be level with or slightly below the keel or bottom of the boat. If the anti-cavitation plate is more than one inch below the bottom of the boat, shim the engine, using 1/4″ strips of hard wood between the top of the transom and the boat brackets, as shown.

Installation of the engine on the transom should be given very careful attention. The clamp bracket not only must support the weight, but is subject to thrust, impact, inertia, and steering stresses. These forces are applied directly to the transom through the clamp bracket assembly. Therefore, to avoid damage to the transom and to prevent the engine from working loose during opera-

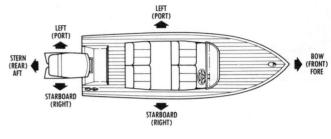

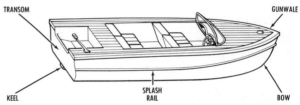

In this book, specific names are used to refer to the various sides of the boat and motor. These names are an accepted standard in the marine industry, and their usage remains the same regardless of the direction from which the boat is viewed.

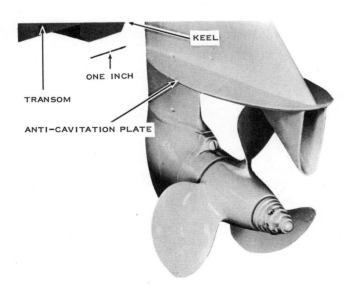

The anti-cavitation plate should be level with or slightly below the bottom of the boat when the engine is properly mounted.

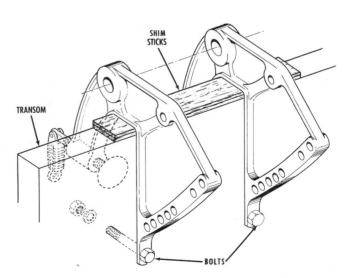

Shim sticks should be used under the motor mounting brackets if the anti-cavitation plate is more than 1″ below the bottom of the boat.

| | NO. OF MOTORS | CUTOUT WIDTH A | | | TRANSOM HEIGHT B | SPACING C | CLEARANCE LENGTH D SEE NOTE 2 | THICKNESS E | | MOTOR CLEARANCE F | COVER HT. G | DRAIN WELL H |
		X HT.	Y HT.	Z HT.				MIN.	MAX.			
1-1/2 HP THRU 5 HP	1	22"	22"	22"	15 ± 1/2" OR 20 ± 1/2"	—	15"	1-1/4"	1-3/4"	14"	18"	5-1/2" MIN.
	2	43"	45"	49"		22"						
6 HP THRU 9-1/2 HP	1	21"	23"	27"	15 ± 1/2" OR 20 ± 1/2"	—	21"	1-3/8"	1-3/4"	17"	22-1/2"	5-1/2" MIN.
	2	43"	45"	49"		22"						
20 HP THRU 40 HP	1	28"	34"	34"	15 ± 1/2" OR 20 ± 1/2"	—	21"	1-3/8"	2"	21"	29"	5-1/2" MIN.
	2	50"	56"	58"		22"						
65 HP THRU 100 HP	1	28"	35"	36"	20 ± 1/2"	26"	29-1/2"	1-5/8"	2-1/4"	28"	32-1/2"	5-1/2" MIN.
	2	54"	61"	62"								

MOUNTING DIMENSIONS

This chart shows the operating clearances and mounting dimensions for the various outboard motors made by this manufacturer.

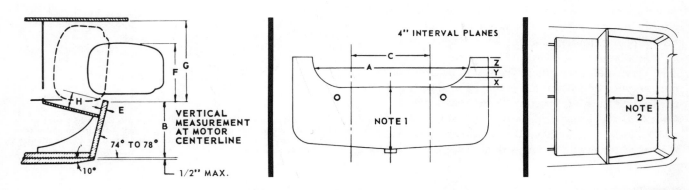

TRANSOM MOUNTING DIAGRAM

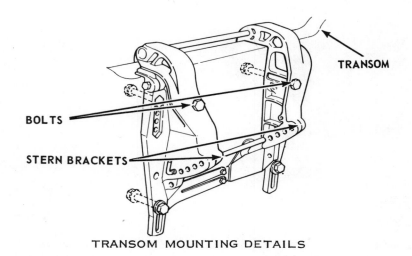

TRANSOM MOUNTING DETAILS

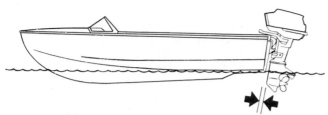

INSUFFICIENT ANGLE, BOW DIGS

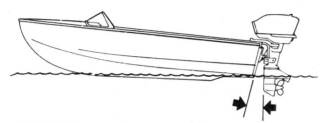

CORRECT ANGLE, TOP PERFORMANCE

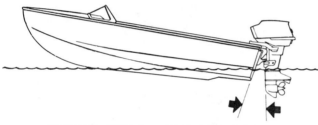

EXCESS ANGLE, TRANSOM DRAGS

For best performance, the tilt angle should be adjusted so that the engine is vertical to the surface of the water. If the lower unit is tilted out too far, the bow of the boat will ride too high. If the lower unit is tilted too close to the transom, the bow will plow, or dig into the water. NOTE: Changes in boat loading may require a change in the tilt angle.

tion, it is important that the clamp screws are tightened securely and equally and that the larger engines are secured to the transom with bolts through the brackets. *CAUTION: Failure to bolt the engine to the transom may result in damage to the boat and/or loss of the engine.* Apply a waterproof sealant to the bolts to prevent water from reaching the wood core of the transom. During operation, the clamp screws should be checked occasionally for tightness.

BOAT PERFORMANCE AND PROPELLER SELECTION

Many times the engine is blamed for inefficient operation when actually the fault lies with the boat or the installation of the engine on the boat.

Boat Speed

Consult the boat house bulletin charts for similar boat sizes and loading. These boats and engines are run with the best-suited propellers and with an optimum set-up (transom height and tilt angle, usually with an aft position of the center of gravity).

Center of Gravity

For maximum speed, move the weight aft until the boat porpoises or is about to porpoise. This reduces the wetted surface to a minimum. Only the rear half of the boat bottom should be wet.

Tilt Angle

The tilt angle should be set so that the anti-cavitation plate is about parallel to the bottom of the boat. The speed of boats that have the center of gravity located forward may be improved sometimes by tilting the lower unit out one pin hole. This will tend to raise the bow and reduce the wetted surface. If the lower unit is tilted in, the boat will ride with the bow down, wetting more of the bottom and thereby reducing speed.

Transom Height

A greater transom height will increase boat speed, but it makes cavitation more likely. The effect of transom height on speed is slight at speeds between 15–20 mph, but it becomes important at speeds of 30–35 mph and above.

Condition of Boat Bottom

For maximum speed, a boat bottom should be nearly a flat plane where it contacts the water. It should be especially straight and smooth in the fore-and-aft direction. The bottom is said to have a "hook" if it is concave in the fore-and-aft direction when viewed from below. When the boat is planing, this causes more lift on the bottom near the transom and allows the bow to drop, which greatly increases the wetted surface and reduces

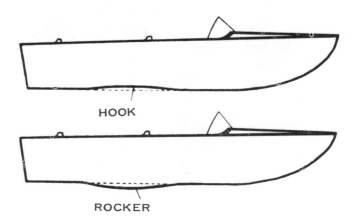

HOOK

ROCKER

For maximum speed, the bottom of the boat should be a flat plane where it contacts the water. A boat bottom with either a hook or rocker can affect the speed and operation to a large degree.

boat speed. A hook is frequently caused by supporting the boat too far forward to the transom while hauling it on a trailer or during storage. A "rocker" is the reverse of a "hook" and much less common. The boat has a rocker if the bottom is convex in the fore-and-aft direction when viewed from below. A boat with a rocker has a strong tendency to porpoise. Moss, barnacles, or other surface irregularities that increase skin friction of the boat bottom will cause a considerable loss of boat speed. Surface roughness of the gear case, caused by barnacles or corrosion, easily can result in a speed loss of 1 or 2 mph on boats in the 30 to 35 mph and higher class.

PROPELLER SELECTION

The speed at which a given boat will travel is governed mainly by the horsepower available. Use of the correct propeller will allow the engine to turn at the recommended rpm and develop full power. First, select a trial propeller, using the approximate boat length and load, if known. This usually will be the correct choice. Establish the exact transom height and tilt pin setting by test.

To check, make a trial run, using an accurate tachometer. It is important that the engine rpm remain within the recommended limits. The trial run should be made with a light load of one person. Under these conditions, it is desirable to have the engine rpm near the top of the recommended limit so that, under a heavy load, the speed will not fall below recommendations. If

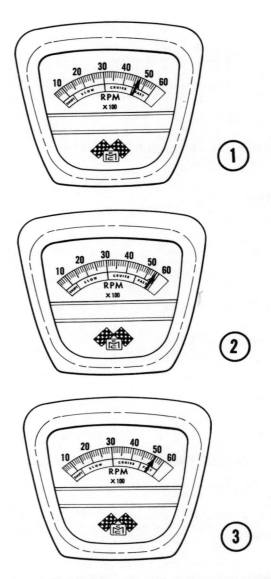

These three tachometer illustrations show the method of determining the correct propeller for a given engine-boat combination. ① The first trial run, using an 11-1/2" diameter by 14" pitch propeller, showed a tachometer reading of 4,700 rpm. The manufacturer's specification for this engine is 4,800–5,400 rpm; therefore, this propeller is loading the engine too much and should be replaced with one having less pitch. ② The second trial run, using a propeller 11-1/2" diameter by 10" pitch, shows a tachometer reading of 5,800 rpm, too fast for the load. To correct, increase the pitch. ③ The third trial run, using a propeller 11-1/2" by 12" pitch, shows a tachometer reading of 5,100 rpm, safely within the 4,800–5,400 specifications.

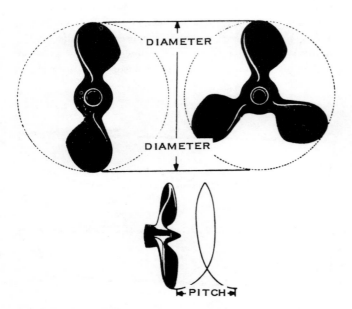

The two basic dimensions of a propeller are pitch and diameter. The pitch is the theoretical distance that a propeller advances if there is no slip. The diameter is the distance from the tip of one blade to the tip of the other.

the engine rpm is too high, try a higher pitch or the same pitch cupped. Likewise, if the rpm is low, try a lower pitch propeller. There normally is a 300–500 rpm change between propeller pitches.

For dual installation, the next higher pitch propeller may be best. For water skiing, it may be desirable to use the next lower pitch propeller; however, do not operate at full throttle when using a ski propeller and not pulling skiers. *CAUTION: If, in this connection, a propeller has too little pitch for the application, dangerous over-*

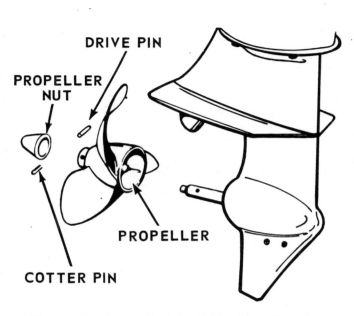

This shows how the propeller is installed for the smaller engines.

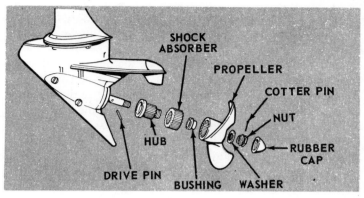

Some propellers are mounted with a shock absorber to minimize propeller damage and reduce the possibility of shearing the drive pin.

speed of the engine will result! If a propeller has too much pitch for the application, acceleration will be slow.

Light, fast boats require higher pitch propellers, while heavier boats require lower pitch propellers. Use aluminum propellers in salt water areas to reduce the electrolytic action that can result in corrosion and pitting of metal surfaces.

FUEL CONSUMPTION

For a planing boat, the maximum miles per gallon is obtained with an engine that will just plane the boat (15–17 mph) at full throttle. Larger engines, or dual engines that will drive the boat faster, will give fewer miles per gallon. A given boat and engine usually will get the most miles per gallon at or near full throttle. An improper carburetor setting can reduce the miles per gallon by 10–15%.

INSTALLING THE PROPELLER

All models are equipped with a shear pin which is designed to break before the engine is damaged. The engine is equipped with a two-position lock which prevents the propeller from rising out of the water when the unit is run in reverse. The same lock can be used to tilt the powerplant all the way forward in order to change a propeller or to replace a sheared drive pin. To raise the engine, release the lock lever and then pull the engine as far forward as possible.

To replace a shear pin, pull the rubber propeller

cap off the propeller shaft. Remove the sheared pin, align the shear pin hole in the propeller hub with the hole in the propeller shaft, insert a new shear pin, and then install the rubber propeller cap.

Extra drive pins and cotter pins should be carried for spares. If these parts are used, be sure to purchase new ones as soon as possible so that you always have a spare.

Most propellers incorporate a rubber shock absorber to prevent damage and to keep the drive pin from being sheared, unless the propeller hits a solid object. The shock absorber also prevents damage to the lower unit.

TILT PIN ADJUSTMENT

Holes are provided in the clamp bracket to permit changing the location of the tilt lock pin for proper adjustment of the tilt angle. The tilt angle of the engine should be set so that the anti-cavitation plate is about

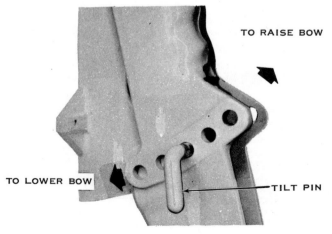

Holes are provided in the clamp bracket to allow you to change the location of the tilt lock pin in order to change the tilt angle of the engine.

parallel with the bottom of the boat. The speed of boats which have the center of gravity located forward may be improved sometimes by tilting the lower unit out one tilt pin hole. This will tend to raise the bow and reduce the amount of wetted surface. If the lower unit is tilted in, the boat will ride with the bow down, wetting more of the bottom and reducing speed. Raising the bow generally will improve operation in rough water.

Under ideal conditions, efficiency will be best with the lower unit operating in a level position, because the entire thrust will then be applied parallel to the plane of motion. With some boats, under certain unfavorable conditions of loading, there will be a tendency to ride stern high or bow high. This condition can be corrected considerably by adjusting the tilt angle so that the boat rides level. Operation with excessive tilt will reduce performance noticeably and may induce cavitation. It is preferable, therefore, to level the boat by proper loading rather than by an extreme adjustment of the tilt angle. Except in very rough water, a properly designed boat will ride level and will plane without porpoising if the tilt angle is correctly adjusted and the boat is favorably loaded. *CAUTION: Do not operate the engine with the tilt lock pin removed.*

CAVITATION

Cavitation is indicated by intermittent or continued overspeed of the engine, accompanied by violent water agitation and a sharp reduction of boat speed. Cavitation occurs when the slip stream (flow of water past the propeller) changes from a smooth, consistent flow to a turbulent one. Under conditions of cavitation, the turbulent area or cavity around the propeller causes a very noticeable loss of forward thrust. Generally, cavitation is caused by one of the following: (1) The propeller's operating too close to the surface. This may be due to the transom's being too high, to an adjustment of the tilt angle that causes the lower unit to be too high, or to the boat's riding stern-high because of improper loading. (2) Turbulence in the slip stream, which can be caused by an obstruction, such as a wide or deep keel.

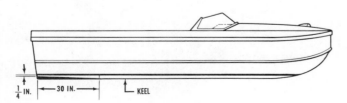

To avoid cavitation, the keel of the boat must be tapered, beginning about 30″ forward of the transom, so that it projects no more than 1/4″ below the hull at the transom end.

This can be helped in most cases by tapering the keel in both width and depth from a point about 30″ forward of the trailing edge; however, for best results, the boat should have no keel in the last 4′ of stern. (3) Fouling of the propeller by weeds, rope, etc. (4) Damaged or broken propeller blades. A broken blade is indicated usually by excessive vibration.

CAUTION FOR SHALLOW WATER OPERATION

When the shift lever is in REVERSE, the lower unit is locked in its normal operating position. The shock load of an impact could cause transom breakage, particularly when the boat is backing up. Proceed cautiously when in reverse motion and be careful of underwater obstructions. *CAUTION: Do not accelerate the engine to high speeds or the stern will dip and you may swamp the boat.*

PERFORMANCE FACTORS

Engineers have always known that weather exerts a profound effect on the performance of internal combustion engines. Therefore, all horsepower ratings refer to the power that the engine can produce at its rated speed under a specified set of weather conditions.

Summer conditions of high temperature, low barometric pressure, and high humidity combine to reduce power. Reduced power, in turn, is reflected in decreases in boat speeds—decreases of as much as two or three mph, in some cases. Nothing can restore this loss of speed for the boatman except the coming of cool, dry weather.

To point out the practical consequences of weather: an engine running on a hot, humid summer day may encounter a loss of as much as 14% of the horsepower it can develop on a dry, brisk spring or fall day. The horsepower that an internal combustion engine can produce depends on the density of the air that it is consuming; this density, in turn, depends upon the temperature of the air, its barometric pressure, and its content of water vapor or humidity.

Accompanying this weather-inspired loss of power is a second, more subtle loss. At fitting-out time in early spring, the engine may have been equipped with a propeller which allowed it to turn at its rated speed at full throttle. With the coming of the summer weather and the consequent drop in available horsepower, this propeller will be too large. Hence, the engine will operate at less than its rated speed. Due to the horsepower-speed

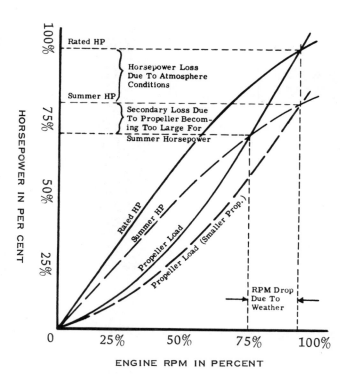

HORSEPOWER IN PER CENT

ENGINE RPM IN PERCENT

Rated HP

Horsepower Loss
Due To Atmosphere
Conditions

Summer HP

Secondary Loss Due
To Propeller Becom-
ing Too Large For
Summer Horsepower

Rated HP

Summer HP

Propeller Load

Propeller Load (Smaller Prop.)

RPM Drop
Due To
Weather

**This graph shows how the changes in temperature affect the perform-
ance of an engine.**

JOHNSON FUEL MIXING CHART

Break-in Fuel Mixture

Johnson Outboard Motor Oil	1 Pint
Gasoline (White Marine)	6 Gal.

50:1 Fuel Mixture

Johnson Outboard Motor Oil	1 Pint
Gasoline (White Marine)	6 Gal.

50:1 Fuel Mixture

Automotive SAE 30 (Type ML or MM) Oil	1 Pint
Gasoline (White Marine)	6 Gal.

characteristics of an engine, this results in a further loss of horsepower and another decrease in boat speed. This secondary loss can be regained by switching to a smaller-pitch propeller which will allow the engine to run at its rated speed again.

FUEL MIXING PROCEDURE

A marine gasoline, automotive white, and a light aircraft gasoline of 90 octane rating are the only ones recommended for outboard motor use. An outboard motor is extremely sensitive to inconsistent fuel/oil mixing and to fuel mixtures resulting from different brands of gasolines and oils. Such changes often require frequent readjustments of the carburetor.

Mix the oil with the gasoline in the following ratios: Mix a 6 oz. can of 100:1 two-cycle motor oil with each 5 gallons of gasoline. Mix a 12 oz. can of 40/50:1 two-cycle motor oil with each 5 gallons of gasoline. An approved outboard motor oil of SAE 40 weight can be mixed in the ratio of 50:1 by adding 12 ozs. of the oil to 5 gallons of gasoline. *CAUTION: Don't use multi-grade oils or other automotive oils that have a large amount of detergents. Oils which contain metallic additives are exceedingly harmful to two-cycle engines. Their use can result in piston burning and scoring. CAU-*

TION: Using less than the recommended amount of oil will result in very serious engine damage because of insufficient lubrication. Using more than the recommended amount of oil will cause spark plug fouling, erratic engine operation (poor carburetion), excessive carbon accumulation, and smoking.

Always use fresh gasoline; never store gasoline in the fuel tank over an extended period. Cracked gasolines contain ingredients that change into gums when stored for any length of time. These gums and varnish products will cause carburetor troubles and spark plug burning. Always drain the fuel from the gas tank if the engine is to be stored for any length of time.

Mix the fuel in a well-ventilated location, preferably out of doors. *CAUTION: Don't smoke while handling gasoline.* Accurately measure the required amounts of oil and gasoline. Pour the oil into a remote fuel tank, and then add an equal amount of gasoline. Mix thoroughly by shaking vigorously, and then add the balance of gasoline and mix again. *CAUTION: Cleanliness is of prime importance in mixing fuel, as even a very small particle of dirt can cause carburetor trouble.*

Automotive oils are not suitable for outboard motor use, because many of them contain a dilution inhibitor which resists thorough mixing of the oil with gasoline. The resulting separation may put a layer of oil at the bottom of the tank, with gasoline at the top and with various proportions of the mixture between. Since the fuel pick-up tube is located at the bottom of the tank, the engine may receive an excessively high proportion of oil when the tank is full and almost straight gasoline when it is nearly empty. Therefore, at first, the engine may smoke excessively and foul the spark plugs. Later on, it may overheat and score the pistons because of insufficient lubrication.

Automotive oils with metallic detergents are very

Using the wrong oils or an incorrect mixture of oil and gasoline can result in piston scoring. Follow the manufacturer's instructions to protect your outboard motor.

effective in reducing varnish formation and piston ring sticking in a four-cycle engine, where very little of the oil gets into the combustion chamber. But in a two-cycle engine, all of the oil must pass through the combustion area, where the metallic additives form deposits when they come into contact with the hot surfaces of the spark plugs, piston crowns, and combustion chamber. These deposits cause pre-ignition and detonation which result in piston crown burning, piston scuffing, and cylinder wall scoring. If the metallic particles bridge the spark plug gap, the plug will cease to fire.

WATER PUMP OPERATION

Normal operation of the water pump is indicated by a stream of water discharging from the idle relief outlet when the engine is idling. If at any time this stream is not evident, stop the engine immediately and check the hole with a piece of wire to be sure that it is not clogged. This stream indicates that the water pump is operating. *CAUTION: Avoid further operation until the water pump and cooling system have been checked.* Operation of the engine with an inoperative water pump or an obstruction in the cooling system will cause overheating and severe damage.

STOPPING

If the engine is to be ready for an immediate restart, stop by shifting into neutral and depressing the STOP button. If the engine is to remain idle for a period of time or if it is to be removed from the boat, stop it by disconnecting the fuel line and allowing the engine to run at idling speed until it stops of its own accord, indi-

cating that the carburetor is dry. Close the air vent screw on the fuel tank cap.

REMOVING THE ENGINE FROM THE BOAT

Disconnect the remote controls and steering connections, if so equipped. Disconnect the fuel line. Loosen the clamp screws and detach the safety cable or chain, if so equipped. Keep the engine in an upright position, resting on its skeg, until all water is drained from the driveshaft housing. *CAUTION: If the engine is placed on its side while the water remains trapped in the driveshaft housing, some water may drain into the powerhead and enter the cylinders through the exhaust ports.* Be sure that all water drain holes in the gear housing are open so that the water can drain completely.

MAINTENANCE

Lubrication

The lubricant in the lower unit gear housing should be checked after the first ten hours of operation and every 50 hours of operation thereafter. Add OMC Type "C" Lubricant to bring the level to the vent plug, if necessary. Drain the gear case and refill every 100 hours of operation or once each season, whichever comes first.

To replace the lubricant in the gear case, on all engines except the one-cylinder, remove the plugs and gasket assemblies marked OIL DRAIN and OIL

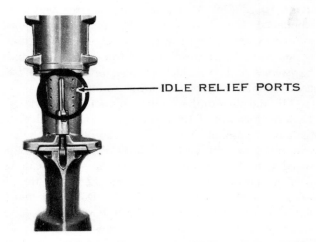

IDLE RELIEF PORTS

With the engine idling, there should be a stream of water discharging from the idle relief ports.

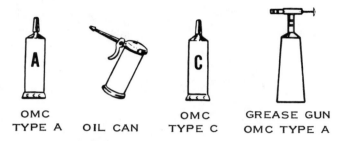

Types of OMC lubricants mentioned in the lubrication charts.

LEVEL from the port side of the gear case. With the propeller shaft in a horizontal position, allow the oil to drain completely.

To refill the unit, insert the lubricant filler hose into the oil drain hole and inject lubricant until it runs out of the oil level hole. Install the oil level plug before removing the filler hose from the drain hole to create an air lock, and then withdraw the filler hose and install the drain hole plug. If a filler-type can is not available, install the drain plug and slowly fill the gear case through the oil level hose. Do this slowly enough to allow all of the trapped air to escape, and then install the oil level plug.

On the one-cylinder engine, remove the plug and

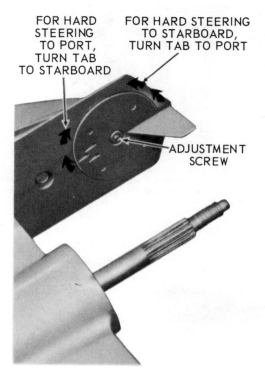

On the 55 Hp engine, an adjustable trim tab is used to achieve better steering control. If the boat steers hard to starboard, adjust the trim tab to port.

LUBRICATION POINT	LUBRICANT	FREQUENCY (PERIOD OF OPERATION)	
		FRESH WATER	#SALT WATER
1. Carburetor and Choke Linkage	OMC Type "A"	60 days	30 days
2. Throttle Linkage	OMC Type "A"	60 days	30 days
3. Clamp Screws	OMC Type "A"	60 days	30 days
4. Friction Ratchet	OMC Type "A"	60 days	30 days
5. Tilt Adjust Rack and Pinion	OMC Type "A"	60 days	30 days
6. Gearcase	OMC Type "C" Capacity 9.7 ozs.	Check level after first 10 hours of operation and every 50 hours of operation thereafter. Add lubricant if necessary. Drain and refill every 100 hours of operation or once each season, whichever occurs first.	Same as Fresh Water
7. Swivel Bracket (2 Fittings)	OMC Type "A"	60 days	30 days
8. Throttle Shaft (3 Fittings)	OMC Type "A"	60 days	30 days
9. Shift Lever (2 Fittings)	OMC Type "A"	60 days	30 days

Some areas may require more frequent lubrication.

Lubrication chart for the 9.5 Hp engine.

TILT
TENSION
NUT

REVERSE
LOCK LEVER

TILT
LOCK

TILT
ADJUSTING
ROD

Tighten the tilt tension nut only enough to hold the engine in any position of tilt. Overtightening will increase the pressure required to release the reverse lock, and this could prevent the engine from tilting when an obstruction is hit.

gasket from the starboard side of the gear case. Turn the engine over, with the starboard side facing down, and allow the oil to drain completely. To refill the unit, turn the engine over and fill with OMC Type "C" Lubricant until it appears at the hole and all trapped air has escaped.

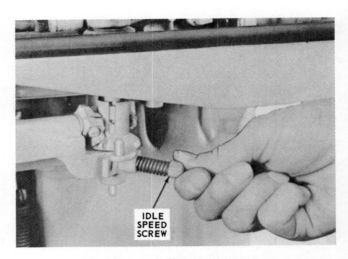

IDLE
SPEED
SCREW

After the engine is thoroughly warmed, adjust the idle speed screw in or out for the desired idling speed.

LUBRICATION POINT	LUBRICANT	FREQUENCY (PERIOD OF OPERATION)	
		FRESH WATER	#SALT WATER
1. Gearcase	OMC Type "C" Capacity 13.9 ozs.	Check level after first 10 hours of operation and every 50 hours of operation thereafter. Add lubricant if necessary. Drain and refill every 100 hours of operation or once each season, whichever occurs first.	Same as Fresh Water Same as Fresh Water
2. Cam Follower, Carburetor and Choke Linkage	OMC Type "A"	60 days	30 days
3. Clamp Screws	OMC Type "A"	60 days	30 days
4. Throttle Shaft Bearings	SAE 90 Oil	60 days	30 days
5. Throttle Shaft Gears	OMC Type "A"	60 days	30 days
6. Gear Shift Lever and Shaft	OMC Type "A"	60 days	30 days
7. Locking Lever	OMC Type "A"	60 days	30 days
8. Swivel Bracket Fitting	OMC Type "A"	60 days	30 days
9. Tilt Lock Pin	OMC Type "A"	60 days	30 days
10. Starter Pinion Gear Shaft (Electric only)	SAE 10 Oil	60 days	30 days

#Some areas may require more frequent lubrication.

Lubrication chart for the 40 Hp engine with manual shift.

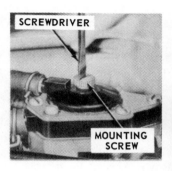
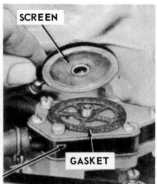

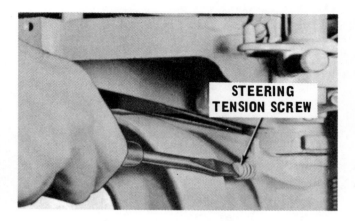

The fuel filter on top of the fuel pump should be cleaned periodically. Always use a new gasket to prevent leaks.

The steering friction adjustment screw should be tightened so that a slight drag can be felt when turning the engine.

Fuel Filter

All engines have a fuel filter screen to prevent dirt particles from reaching the carburetor. The filter screen must be cleaned periodically. On the one-cylinder engine, the fuel filter is located inside of the fuel tank and is part of the fuel hose connector. A fuel shut-off valve is positioned in the fuel line directly below the filter. On the larger engines, the fuel filter is located on the fuel pump, and it can be removed by taking out the retaining screw. Always replace the gasket to prevent leaks.

LUBRICATION POINT	LUBRICANT	FREQUENCY (PERIOD OF OPERATION)	
		FRESH WATER	#SALT WATER
1. Gearcase	OMC Type "C" Capacity 15.0 ozs.	Check level after first 10 hours of operation and every 50 hours of operation thereafter. Add lubricant if necessary. Drain and refill every 100 hours of operation or once each season, whichever occurs first.	Same as Fresh Water Same as Fresh Water
2. Locking Lever	OMC Type "A"	60 days	30 days
3. Cam Follower, Carburetor and Magneto Linkage	OMC Type "A"	60 days	30 days
4. Clamp Screws	OMC Type "A"	60 days	30 days
5. Throttle Shaft Bearing	SAE 90 Oil	60 days	30 days
6. Throttle Shaft Bushing	OMC Type "A"	60 days	30 days
7. Swivel Bracket Fitting	OMC Type "A"	60 days	30 days
8. Stern Bracket and Tilt Lock	OMC Type "A"	60 days	30 days
9. Starter Pinion Gear Shaft	SAE 10 Oil	60 days	30 days

#Some areas may require more frequent lubrication.

Lubrication chart for the 40 Hp engine with electric shift.

OPERATING IN
SALT WATER OR SILT

Operation in salt water or silt results in the accumulation of salt or mineral deposits in the cooling system water passages and around the cylinder water jackets. Unless removed regularly, these deposits will build up to the extent that circulation of the cooling water becomes restricted or cut off entirely. Also, the deposits act as an insulator, reducing the transfer of heat from the cylinders to the water. This loss of transfer will cause overheating, loss of performance, and serious damage.

Even though the interior surfaces of outboards are treated to resist corrosion, there remains a possibility of a mechanical build-up of salt and silt deposits that no form of protective coating can prevent; it can be minimized by occasional flushing with fresh water. While no complete protection for exterior surfaces is known, there are ways in which electrolysis and corrosion damage can be minimized. By following the simple steps below, you can increase materially the life of all exposed parts and decorative finishes.

An outboard motor that is to remain on a boat should be tilted out of the water. Always disconnect the negative battery terminal when in dock or in storage for any period of time.

LUBRICATION POINT	LUBRICANT	FREQUENCY (PERIOD OF OPERATION)	
		FRESH WATER	#SALT WATER
1. Starter Pinion Gear Shaft	SAE 10 Oil	60 days	30 days
2. Cam Follower, Roller Shaft	OMC Type "A"	60 days	30 days
3. Throttle Arm and Distributor Linkage	OMC Type "A"	60 days	30 days
4. Safety Switch Cam on Distributor Base	OMC Type "A"	60 days	30 days
5. Throttle and Choke Shaft Springs and Linkage	OMC Type "A"	60 days	30 days
6. Gearcase	OMC Type "C" Capacity 37.2 ozs.	Check level after first 10 hours of operation and every 50 hours of operation thereafter. Add lubricant if necessary. Drain and refill every 100 hours of operation or once each season, whichever occurs first.	Same as Fresh Water Same as Fresh Water
7. Swivel Bracket and Tilt Lock Lever	OMC Type "A"	60 days	30 days
8. Ignition - Reverse Cutoff Spring	OMC Type "D"	At time of ignition service.	

#Some areas may require more frequent lubrication.

Lubrication chart for the three-cylinder engine.

Lubricate the swivel bracket frequently and other moving parts regularly. Grease the thumb screws on the clamps to insure smooth operation. Grease the propeller shaft splines occasionally with a waterproof-type lubricant, thus enabling the propeller to be removed easily.

Spray the entire powerhead with a coating of a rust preventive to protect the finish of all parts beneath the cowl. The exterior of the engine also can be sprayed with rust preventive to keep corrosion from dulling the finish.

Attach a flushing hose and turn on the water tap. Operate the manual starter to facilitate the flow of water through the pump. *CAUTION: Do not use full pressure from a city water tap. CAUTION: During and after flushing, keep the motor in an upright position, resting on the skeg, until all water has been drained from the driveshaft housing in order to prevent water from entering the powerhead through the exhaust ports.*

AFTER SUBMERSION

An engine which has been submerged must be disassembled completely for cleaning and inspecting. This should be done as soon as possible after recovery. Delayed action will encourage rust and corrosion of internal parts. Emergency treatment may be accomplished by following the instructions below. This temporarily will retard rust and corrosion. Basically, the points to remember are these: (1) Recover the engine as quickly as possible. (2) Wash the entire unit with fresh, clean water to remove mud, weeds, etc. (3) Get as much water as possible out of the powerhead. Most of the water can be eliminated by removing the spark plugs and operating the starter with the spark plug holes facing downward. *CAUTION: If the engine does not turn freely when the*

LUBRICATION POINT	LUBRICANT	FREQUENCY (PERIOD OF OPERATION)	
		FRESH WATER	#SALT WATER
1. Gearcase	OMC Type "C" Lubricant Capacity 37.2 ozs.	Check level after first 10 hours of operation and every 50 hours of operation thereafter. Add lubricant if necessary.	Same as Fresh Water
		Drain and refill every 100 hours of operation or once each season, whichever occurs first.	Same as Fresh Water
2. Carburetor Linkage	OMC Type "A"	60 days	30 days
3. Control Shaft Lower Bushing	OMC Type "A"	60 days	30 days
4. Tilt Lever	OMC Type "A"	60 days	30 days
5. Safety Switch Cam	OMC Type "A"	60 days	30 days
6. Control Shaft Bushings and Bearings	Hypoid 90 Oil	60 days	30 days
7. Swivel Bracket Fitting	OMC Type "A"	60 days	30 days
8. Starter Pinion Gear Shaft	SAE 10 Oil (One drop)	60 days	30 days

#Some areas may require more frequent lubrication.

Lubrication chart for the V-4 engine.

starter is operated, do not force it. This may be an indication of internal damage, such as a bent connecting rod or a broken piston. (4) Pour alcohol into the cylinders because it will dissolve water, and then lubricate all the internal parts that are accessible. This can be accomplished by injecting oil into the spark plug holes, installing the spark plugs, and then operating the starter to distribute the oil. If alcohol and oil are not available, insert a rod into the fuel check unit to open the check valve, and then actuate the primer bulb, thus forcing the oil-fuel mixture into the cylinders. (5) Disassemble and clean the engine as soon as possible.

STORAGE

When storing an outboard motor for the winter, be sure that all water drain holes in the gear housing are open and that the flushing plug is removed so that the water will drain out. Trapped water may freeze and expand, thus cracking the gear housing and/or the water pump housing. Check and refill the lower unit with gear lubricant before storage to protect against possible water leakage into the gear housing, caused by a loose air vent or grease filler plug. Be sure to replace the gaskets under the vent screws.

Prior to packing at the factory, new engines are "fogged out" at the final test by injecting approximately 2 oz. of rust preventive oil through the carburetor air intake. This practice is desirable when engines are stored in a damp place, or when they are expected to stand idle for a long period of time. When an engine is started after fogging, the spark plugs should be checked and replaced, if necessary, as they may have become fouled from the rust preventive oil.

Before storage, disconnect the fuel line or turn off the fuel shut-off valve, and then allow the engine to run at idling speed until it stops of its own accord, indicating that the carburetors are dry. Drain the fuel tank and fuel lines. This will prevent gum from forming in the tank, lines, and carburetor. If an outboard motor is to remain on a boat, it should be tilted out of the water.

USING A CLEANER

Several chemical cleaners have been developed to remove the carbon deposits which reduce the power of an outboard motor. To use the cleaner, run the engine until normal operating temperature is reached. On one- and two-cylinder engines, slowly pour about 10 oz. of the cleaner through the carburetor throat while the

A properly maintained engine is a dependable source of pleasure.

engine is running at a fast idle of 1,200 rpm. Use a pump-type oil can or pressure sprayer. Increase the speed and stall the engine with the balance of the cleaner. Let the engine stand for at least 30 minutes. Start the engine and run it at full throttle for 5 minutes.

On three-cylinder models, with the engine operating at its lowest rpm above stalling, feed a sufficient quantity of the cleaner into the throat of one carburetor. Let the engine run until it is firing on all cylinders again, and then repeat the process for the other carburetors. Next, flood the entire engine through all of the carburetors and allow it to stand for 1/2 hour.

To clean a severely carbonized engine, tilt it to a horizontal position and close as many intake and exhaust ports as possible by turning the flywheel so that the pistons cover the ports. Pour the cleaner through the spark plug holes. Let it set overnight, position the engine vertically, and then pull the starter rope several times to remove the excess cleaner. Prepare the engine for running and repeat the regular cleaning process as discussed above.

WATER WISDOM

Coast Guard Regulations

To enjoy the waterways safely, it is advisable to check with authorities in regard to local, state, and federal boating regulations and restrictions. In addition, here are a few suggestions: (1) Carry one approved life jacket or buoyant cushion per person, (2) one approved fire extinguisher, (3) a flashlight or lantern, (4) an anchor, (5) a first aid kit, (6) a compass, (7) an extra propeller, and (8) enough fuel.

Rules of the Waterways

Keep practicing water safety by observing the following simple rules: (1) Do not operate your boat near swimmers, skin-divers, or fishermen. (2) Keep clear of sailing craft and rowboats, yielding the right-of-way to them. (3) Always keep to the right; show respect and courtesy at all times.

Signposts

Know the channel markers to follow a safe and confident course. When returning, keep the red buoys on your right; black buoys on your left. Black-and-white, vertically striped buoys indicate the middle of a channel; always pass as close as possible to them, on either side. Black-and-red, horizontally striped buoys indicate obstruction; give them a wide berth.

SEAMANSHIP FOR SAFETY

Stepping into the Boat

Step into the *center* of the boat. Don't carry equipment aboard; keep your hands free for steadying yourself. Equipment should be placed on the edge of the dock, and then lifted into the boat.

Casting Off

Back away *slowly* in reverse gear.

The outboard motor has opened a new frontier for leisure time activities.

Never carry equipment aboard. Equipment should be placed on the edge of the dock, and then lifted into the boat.

Weather Signals

Any flag or light which is all or part red is a warning that bad weather is developing or exists.

Rough Water

When heading into rough water, *decrease* speed but maintain plane to prevent water from entering the boat. Alter the direction of attack on the waves until it feels right.

Danger Zone

The danger zone is a 112-1/2° arc which is measured from dead ahead to off the starboard, or right-hand, side. A boat *must yield* the right-of-way to any other craft which approaches it within the danger zone.

Always carry enough approved equipment to ensure your safety.

| BLACK CAN AND SPAR BUOYS | RED NUN AND SPAR BUOYS | OBSTRUCTION MARKER | MID-CHANNEL BUOY |

Buoys are the signposts of the waterways. When returning, keep the red buoys on your right, black buoys on your left. The black-and-white, vertically striped buoys indicate the middle of the channel; always pass close to them, on either side. The black-and-red horizontally striped buoys indicate obstructions; give them a wide berth.

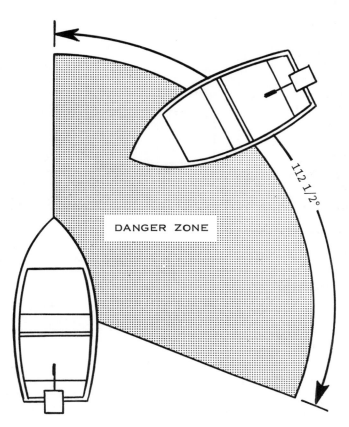

You must yield the right-of-way to any boat approaching within the danger zone.

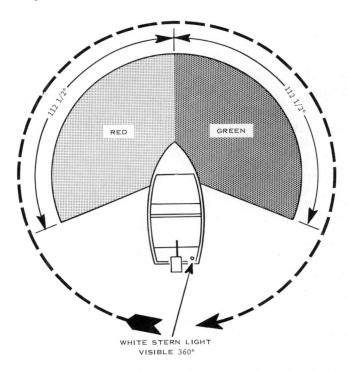

This diagram shows the direction and color of the lights that should be visible when you use the boat at night.

Overtaking

A boat which is being overtaken has the right-of-way.

Turns

Practice boat turns in order to test for the amount of stern swing of your boat.

Reverse Gear

When reversing, the stern will dip; move your passengers forward to guard against swamping the boat. When reversing, the motor will not tilt up when striking a submerged object; therefore, be alert so that the transom will not be damaged.

Skiing

The recommended procedures are: (1) Check the

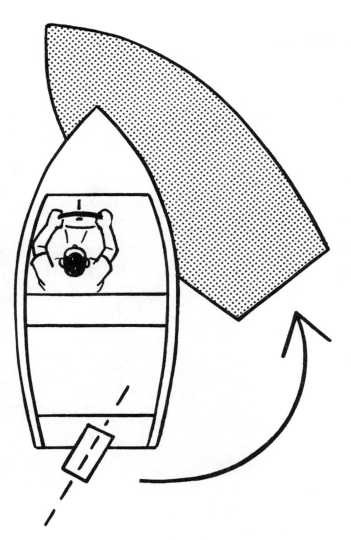

Practice turns to get used to the stern swing so that you can become an expert.

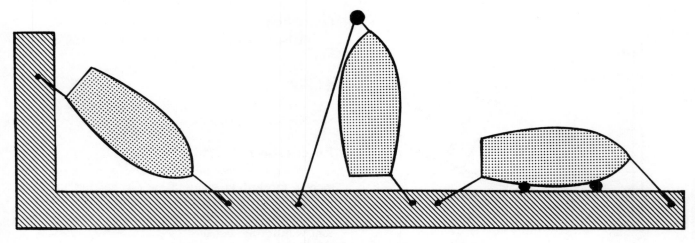

Secure your boat to the dock properly to avoid buffeting by the wind.

equipment for safe, smooth operation. (2) Know the skier's hand signals. (3) Carry an observer in the boat.

Stopping

Practice for stopping distance at various boat speeds in order to be prepared for any unusual situation.

Docking

Approach a dock slowly and, if possible, into the wind, waves, or current. Avoid buffeting by securing the boat to the dock, as shown.

Learn all Coast Guard regulations and develop skill in handling your boat so that you will enjoy your vacations.

3
TUNING FOR PERFORMANCE

The material in this chapter is divided into two basic sections, the first of which covers the general procedures that are required for servicing all ignition systems. The second section deals with each type of engine according to the number of cylinders; i.e., one, two, three, and four cylinders.

Each of the engine-type sections is a complete unit, covering the timing, linkage, and carburetor adjustments that are necessary to make the engine perform to its designed power potential.

Distributor and magneto service procedures for the larger engines will be covered in the second section of this chapter, under the tuning instructions for the three- and four-cylinder engines.

GENERAL IGNITION SERVICE PROCEDURES

SPARK PLUGS

Spark plugs are a small but vitally important component of modern gasoline engines. Without proper spark plug operation, satisfactory engine performance cannot be obtained. Outboard motors are equipped with spark plugs of a special electrode gap design.

Spark plugs are made in a number of heat ranges to satisfy a variety of possible operating conditions. Some types, having a long insulator firing end, transfer heat slowly and are used where combustion chamber temperatures are relatively low. Sustained idling, stop-and-start, and light-load operation produce this condition. The short insulator plug remains cool enough to avoid pre-ignition and excessive gap erosion.

The appearance of spark plugs will indicate whether they are too hot or too cold for the engine. The end of the spark plug is subjected to intense heat from the burning of the fuel mixture, and this heat is dissipated by conduction along the porcelain end of the spark plug and

thus to the cylinder jacket. If the porcelain part, which extends into the cylinder, is comparatively long, the heat cannot be dissipated rapidly, and the spark plug will run hot. If the porcelain is short, the heat can pass through it more quickly, and the spark plug will run cold.

The spark plug which is installed originally in the engine is the one that will give best service under normal operating conditions; however, if the speed is increased by placing the engine on a lighter hull, it may be necessary to substitute a colder spark plug. If the engine is placed on a heavier boat and the speed is decreased, a hotter spark plug may be required. If trouble arises with spark plugs fouling while trolling, changing to a hotter type of spark plug may help.

If the spark plug is operating at its most efficient temperature, the porcelain part, which projects inside of the cylinder, will be dark brown, chestnut, or coffee-

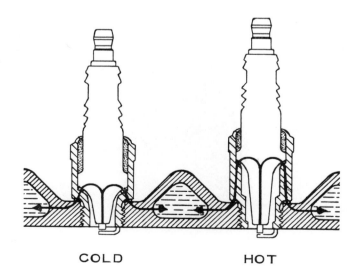

COLD   HOT

The heat range of a spark plug is determined by the length of the heat path from the tip of the insulator to the coolant or, in the case of an air-cooled engine, to the metal of the cylinder head.

Always inspect the firing end of each spark plug as it is removed from the engine. The deposits and coloration tell a story of operating conditions. This is the way that a normal spark plug should look.

OVERHEATING

This spark plug is operating too hot. Either it is of an incorrect heat range, or the engine is running too hot.

CORE BRIDGING

The electrodes are shorted out by core bridging, the result of using the wrong oil.

WET FOULING

Wet fouling can be caused by too much oil in the mixture or by a defective spark plug. This spark plug was not firing.

ALUMINUM THROW-OFF

This spark plug is shorted by aluminum throw-off, which means that particles of the piston are being deposited on the hot insulator of the spark plug.

GAP BRIDGING

Core bridging is caused by using the wrong type of motor oil.

colored. If the porcelain is chalky white or has flaky blisters, the spark plug is too hot. When an engine is operating at high speed with a spark plug that is too hot, it will run along evenly for a while, slow down, pick up speed again, and repeat this balking over and over. If a smutty or oily coating appears on the spark plug, it shows that there is incomplete fuel combustion because the plug is too cold. Hard starting generally is caused by too cold a spark plug.

The spark plug's main job is to transfer the ignition system's energy into the cylinder in the form of a spark. If a normal fuel charge fails to ignite, the spark plug is misfiring. Most misfirings result from shorting through deposits on the insulator nose surface. When these are removed either by cleaning or, in some cases, by burning them off at high speeds, the spark plug's firing ability is restored. This type of shorting is troublesome in that it can occur long before it is noticed. An owner is not always aware of a slow decrease in performance and economy because one or more cylinders are misfiring.

Spark Plug Troubles

Extensive tests have shown that spark plug life is directly related to the gasoline used in the engine. Much of the spark plug trouble is simply lead fouling, resulting from the use of automotive gasolines with tetraethyl lead. There is no practical way of removing this lead from the fuel in the field. Lead fouling may be identified by the presence of small yellow or brown globules on the plug.

Some spark plug trouble is caused by excessive carbon formation in the combustion chamber, with eventual fouling of the plug by the carbon particles. It is natural for all internal combustion engines to form some carbon during operation, but excessive amounts are caused by use of fuels which burn to a gummy residue rather than to a fluffy carbon that can pass out with the exhaust. Cracked gasolines result in fuels which give gummy deposits that remain in the combustion chamber, while straight-run gasolines are cleaner in this respect.

The use of a marine white gasoline virtually will eliminate problems with the spark plug and the carbon or varnish formation. Marine white gasolines are straight-run fuels which contain no tetraethyl lead or other metallic additives and are excellent from the standpoint of engine cleanliness. They generally have an octane rating of 75 to 80 and should not be confused with the nonmarine "whites" sold for use in gasoline lamps

The spark plug insulator should be cleaned of all foreign matter, because this could become a leakage path for the high-tension voltage.

When the dirty insulator of a spark plug gets wet, flash-over occurs, and the cylinder misfires.

and cook stoves. The 90 octane aviation gasolines, as used in light aircraft, are limited to 0.5 cc of lead and are suitable for outboard use.

In cases where spark plug or carbon difficulties are being encountered, it is suggested that a change be made to another fuel. If excessive carbon has already formed in the engine, it should be removed by disassembly or with an engine cleaner.

Many so-called spark plug troubles in reality are not traceable to faulty spark plugs. Instead, they result from poor spark plug installation, abnormal operating conditions, ignition defects, over-rich fuel mixtures, fuel mixtures with too much oil, or engines in need of an overhaul.

Used spark plugs are generally the best guide to the type and source of trouble. Therefore, it is good practice to inspect each spark plug as it is removed from the engine. A gasket which is compressed to about 3/4 of its original thickness, with smooth, parallel surfaces, indicates that the spark plug was properly installed and tightened. Gaskets which are compressed too much or too little reveal improper tightening. Rough and corroded surfaces indicate that the gasket seats were not cleaned before installation. In some cases, the resulting

One of the most important spark plug service procedures is to file the electrodes to remove the corrosion. This mechanic is passing a piece of emery cloth between the electrodes to clean the metal.

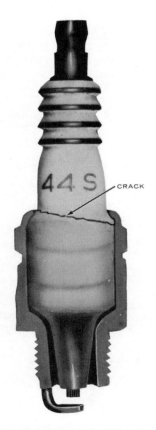

A cracked insulator can be caused only by tilting the spark plug socket.

compression leakage may have overheated the spark plugs to cause excessive electrode erosion. *NOTE: Some spark plugs have conical seats and, therefore, do not use a gasket.*

Spark plugs that are not tightened securely will cause fast electrode burning, and they may burn the piston due to detonation. Torque spark plugs to 20 ft-lbs. for a good seat.

Fuel fouling can be identified by wet, black deposits covering the entire firing end of the spark plug. These deposits result from incomplete combustion, which is traceable to an over-rich air-fuel mixture.

A crack in the insulator is sufficient cause for discarding the spark plug. Cracks in the upper portion of the insulator are caused by dropping the plug or by hitting the insulator with a wrench. For this reason, always use a deep-socket wrench of the proper size when removing or installing the spark plugs, and support the upper end with the palm of your hand to keep it from tilting enough to touch the insulator. Cracked or broken insulator firing ends result from bending the center electrode while setting the spark plug gap. To avoid damaging the insulator, bend only the side electrode.

Always bend the ground electrode to adjust the gap. If you bend the center electrode, you will crack the porcelain.

Other engine conditions can cause spark plug troubles. In general, ignition timing advanced beyond specifications will encourage overheating, thus leading to shorter spark plug life and burned pistons. Burned, pitted, or improperly set breaker points and frayed ignition cables also are sources of spark plug trouble.

It is important to keep the upper portion of the spark plug insulators free from moisture, grease, dirt, and paint. Such deposits on the outside of a spark plug can cause surface shorting or flashover from the terminal to the shell, with resulting misfire and hard starting. Spark plug insulators should be wiped off periodically with a clean rag.

Spark Plug Protectors

When installing a new set of spark plugs, inspect the spark plug protectors carefully for possible damage. No rubber will withstand indefinitely the heat of a spark plug operating under modern conditions, particularly with the high-temperature fuels now being used. When this rubber is stretched tight around the hot porcelain, the effect is to cause the rubber to dry out and crack. Once this has happened, the effectiveness of the spark plug protector as a waterproof seal is seriously impaired.

The sensitive area, where heat and stretch are greatest, is the inside bottom rim where it touches the porcelain. When this edge becomes hard, it loses its strength. The next phase is a series of fine cracks in the surface of the rubber along this same edge. It is safest to replace the spark plug protector when this edge gets hard, before it has a chance to start cracking.

The spark plug protector is not meant to be taken apart. Doing so will usually bend the prong in the spring, making it all but impossible to reassemble correctly. Don't pull the cable out of the spark plug protector except when the protector and spring are to be replaced.

When assembling a spark plug protector to a cable, make sure that the prong of the spring goes through the center of the cable to make solid contact with the ignition wire. If this is not a good electrical contact, a weak spark may result. Also, the point on this prong should always face down toward the spark plug. If it is assembled upside down, the spark plug protector may have a tendency to shake loose.

MAGNETO SERVICE PROCEDURES

ONE- AND TWO-CYLINDER ENGINES

The magneto consists of breaker points, condensers, and coils. These ignition parts are located under the flywheel; therefore, to service the ignition system of these smaller engines, it is necessary to remove the flywheel.

REMOVING THE FLYWHEEL

Remove the flywheel nut and lockwasher. Install a knock-off tool and turn it down to within two turns of the flywheel. Lift up on the edge of the flywheel, and then strike the knock-off tool with a medium-weight hammer. The blow must be centered as much as possible. *CAUTION: Don't use a heavy hammer or strike the tool too hard; you may damage the crankshaft and bearings.*

BREAKER POINT SERVICE

Generally, it is best to replace the breaker points before tuning an engine because of the load that they carry and the effect that they have on the operating efficiency of the engine. If new breaker points are not available, they can be cleaned in an emergency by folding a small strip of 320-grit emery cloth and inserting it between the points. Hold the points closed and rotate the emery cloth, using the points as a pivot. Open the points to remove the emery cloth. *CAUTION: Don't pull the cloth from between the points, or you will scrape off emery particles, which are an insulator.* Remove all traces of emery by inserting a clean piece of cardboard between the breaker points, and then (holding the points closed on the cardboard) rotate the cardboard, using the

CONTACT POINT

This black, pitted breaker point shows evidence of oil on the contact surface, which burned into an insulator. The oil can be placed on the contact point surface with your fingers or by using a dirty feeler gauge to measure the gap.

breaker points as a pivot, in order to remove the oxide and other foreign matter loosened by the emery cloth. The cardboard should be used in several spots until no further dirt can be removed.

To adjust the breaker point gap, move the throttle to the wide-open position to establish a common stationary location for setting the breaker points. Reinstall the flywheel nut so that you can turn the crankshaft with a box wrench. Rotate the crankshaft clockwise at least two full turns to establish a uniform grease film, and then rotate it enough to bring the breaker point cam follower to the high point of the cam (index line). *CAUTION: If the crankshaft is turned too far, it must be rotated an additional turn clockwise to reach the mark. Never turn the crankshaft in a counterclockwise direction to correct.*

Adjust the breaker point gap to specifications. *CAUTION: Always use a smooth, unworn feeler gauge blade and always make sure that the gaps are identical on two-cylinder engines so that the points will be synchronized. An error of 0.0015" will change the ignition timing as much as 1°. CAUTION: Always clean the feeler gauge blade before inserting it between the points to prevent depositing a layer of oil, which will cause operating difficulties later on.*

Lubricate the breaker cam, breaker plate pilot bore, cam wiper felt, and all friction surfaces of the ignition system with Rykon No. 2EP. Other types of lubricants will cause ignition troubles and operating difficulties.

BREAKER POINT SYNCHRONIZATION

On the larger two-cylinder engines, point synchronization is an important adjustment. Its purpose is to make sure that the spark occurs at precisely the same instant for each cylinder. Generally, the gap of the second set of breaker points is varied from the initial setting to obtain synchronization.

Breaker point cleaning and gapping must always precede synchronization. Changing the gap of either set of points will change both the timing and synchronization. After the breaker points are cleaned and gapped, the first set of breaker points should be timed to the top piston. Then, without moving the stator plate, the timing gauge should be transferred to the bottom cylinder and the gap of the second set of breaker points adjusted so that the spark will occur at the same position of the second piston.

Smaller engines are not sensitive to breaker point synchronization, and the manufacturer generally specifies that it is only necessary to gap the breaker points evenly. If the gaps are even, synchronization is close enough for all practical purposes. For engines on which breaker point synchronization is called for by the manufacturer, this adjustment will be covered in the second section of this chapter, under the tuning instructions for the individual engines.

IGNITION TIMING

The ignition spark must occur at precisely the instant it will do the most good. This means that the spark must occur close to TDC at idle speed and about 30° before TDC at high rpms. This ignition advance is required to compensate for the time lag between the start of combustion and the development of maximum pressure. At high engine speeds, it is necessary to start combustion about 30° BTDC so that maximum combustion chamber pressure will be reached when the piston reaches the top of the stroke.

The method of timing the engine varies, but most of the larger engines have the flywheel marked at the TDC position. In addition, some are marked at the specified Maximum Spark Advance point for setting the timing with the throttle at the wide-open position. These instructions vary with engine types and will be discussed in detail under each of the engine headings.

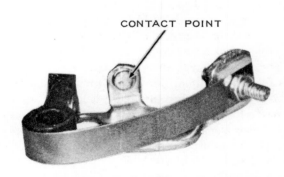

CONTACT POINT

The frosted appearance of this breaker point is an indication that the ignition system was operating properly.

CARBURETOR THROTTLE PICKUP ADJUSTMENT

The throttle control of all small outboard motors is connected to the magneto stator plate. Opening the throttle advances the stator plate (and the ignition timing). The stator plate is linked to the carburetor throttle, so that opening the throttle and advancing the stator plate opens the carburetor throttle valves at the same time. One of the most important tuning procedures is the throttle pick-up adjustment; the point of spark advance at which the throttle valves begin to open.

ONE-CYLINDER ENGINE TUNE-UP SERVICE PROCEDURES

1.5 Hp Engine

A flywheel-type magneto furnishes the ignition spark for these engines. Moving the speed-control lever shifts the entire magneto stator plate, thereby affecting the ignition timing. A throttle-actuating cam, attached to the speed-control lever, synchronizes throttle valve opening to ignition timing.

REMOVING THE FLYWHEEL

① To remove the flywheel, take off the nut. Attach a puller, Tool No. 378103, to the flywheel, and then pull the flywheel from the crankshaft.

ADJUSTING THE BREAKER POINT GAP

② Turn the crankshaft clockwise to position the breaker arm on the high point of the cam. *CAUTION:*

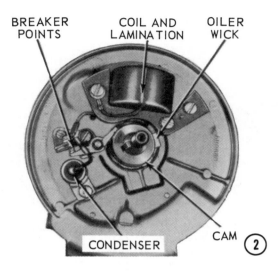

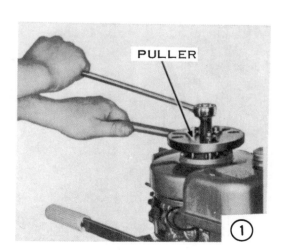

Always rotate the crankshaft clockwise to avoid damaging the water pump impeller. Loosen the locking screw, and then turn the eccentric screw to obtain a gap of 0.020″. Tighten the locking screw, and then recheck the gap, which may change as you tighten the screw. *NOTE: New breaker points should be gapped to 0.022″ to compensate for initial rubbing block wear.* Lubricate the cam and wick with OMC Type "A" lubricant.

ASSEMBLING

③ Check the crankshaft and flywheel tapers for traces of oil, which must be removed with solvent. *CAUTION: The assembly must be perfectly dry. CAUTION: Don't allow solvent to wash the oil out of the oiler wick.* The flywheel key must be installed so that it is parallel to the shaft. Replace the flywheel and nut, tightening it to 22–25 ft-lbs. of torque.

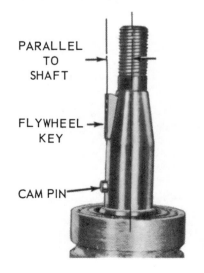

TUNE-UP SPECIFICATIONS

Models (Hp)	Cyl.	Year	Spark Plugs Type (Champion)	Gap (Inches)	Ignition System Type	Breaker Point Gap (Inches)	Condenser Capacity (Mfd.)	Idle Speed (In gear)	Full-Throttle Rpm
1.5	1	1968–69	J4J	.030	①	.020	.18–.22	550	3500–4500
3.0	2	1952–68	J4J	.030	①	.020	.18–.22	550	3500–4500
4.0	2	1969	J4J	.030	①	.020	.18–.22	550	4000–5000
5.0	2	1965–68	J4J	.030	①	.020	.18–.22	550	3500–4500
5.5	2	1956–64	J4J	.030	①	.020	.18–.22	550	3500–4500
6.0	2	1965–69	J4J	.030	①	.020	.18–.22	550	3500–4500
9.5	2	1964–69	J4J	.030	①	.020	.18–.22	550	4000–5000
18/20	2	1957–69	J4J	.030	①	.020	.25–.29	550	4000–5000
25	2	1969	J4J	.030	①	.020	.25–.29	550	5000–6000
28	2	1962–64	J4J	.030	①	.020	.25–.29	600–650	4000–5000
33	2	1965–69	J4J	.030	①	.020	.25–.29	550	4000–5000
40	2	1960–69	J4J	.030	①	.020	.25–.29	650	4000–5000
55	3	1968–69	L19V	—	① ⑤	.010	—	600–650	4500–5500
60	4	1964–67	J4J	.030	②	.020	.37–.41	600–650	4000–5000
65	4	1968	L19V	—	① ⑤	.010	—	650	4000–5000
75	4	1960–65	J4J	.030	② ③	.020	.37–.41	650	4000–5000
80	4	1966–67	J4J	.030	② ③	.020	.37–.41	600–650	4000–5000
85	4	1968–69	L19V	—	① ⑤	.010	—	650	4000–5000
90	4	1964–65	J4J	.030	③	.020	.37–.41	650	4000–5000
100	4	1966	J4J	.030	③	.020	.37–.41	650	4500–5500
100	4	1967	L19V	—	⑥ ⑤	.016 ⑦	—	650	4500–5500
100	4	1968	L19V	—	④ ⑤	.028 ⑦	—	650	4500–5500
115	4	1969	L19V	—	④ ⑤	.028 ⑦	—	650	4500–5500

① Breaker points under flywheel.
② Belt-driven magneto with breaker points.
③ Belt-driven distributor with breaker points.
④ Pulse generator (Sensor) under the flywheel.
⑤ Capacitor-Discharge type ignition system.
⑥ Belt-driven distributor with pulse generator (Sensor).
⑦ Sensor air gap.

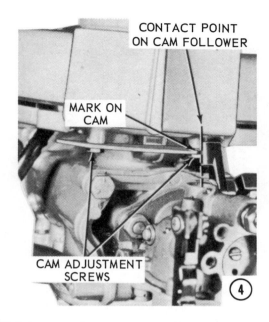

CONTACT POINT ON CAM FOLLOWER

MARK ON CAM

CAM ADJUSTMENT SCREWS

④

THROTTLE CAM SYNCHRONIZATION

④ Set the speed control lever to the STOP position. Slowly advance the control until the cam follower just begins to open the throttle. The mark on the cam and the point of contact on the cam follower should now be aligned. If an adjustment is necessary, loosen the cam adjustment screws, and then position the cam so that, with all play removed from the linkage, the throt-

IDLE MIXTURE ADJUSTING SCREW

CHOKE

STARTING INSTRUCTIONS: OPEN AIR VENT IN FUEL CAP. OPEN FUEL VALVE UNDER TANK. MOVE CONTROL LEVER TO START POSITION. PULL CHOKE. CRANK ENGINE WITH STARTER ROPE. PUSH CHOKE IN AS ENGINE WARMS. **HIGH SPEED**

HIGH-SPEED ADJUSTING SCREW

⑤

tle valve is closed. The mark on the throttle cam must now align with the flat port side of the cam follower, just as it makes contact with the cam. Tighten the cam screws.

CARBURETOR ADJUSTMENTS

⑤ Seat the high- and low-speed adjusting needles gently, and then back them out for a preliminary adjustment. *CAUTION: Don't force them into their seats, or you will damage the taper, making an accurate adjustment difficult.* Back out the high-speed adjusting needle 1/2 turn and the low-speed needle 1-1/4 turns. Start the engine and allow it to reach normal operating temperature. Run the engine at full throttle, and then adjust the high-speed needle for maximum rpm. Adjust the low-speed needle until the highest rpm consistent with smooth performance is reached. *NOTE: Allow 15 seconds for the engine to respond after each adjustment.* After making the low-speed adjustment, recheck the high-speed adjustment. Install the adjustment knobs with each boss pointing straight up.

TWO-CYLINDER ENGINE TUNE-UP SERVICE PROCEDURES

3.0, 4.0, 5.0, 5.5, 6.0, 9.5, 18/20, 25, 33 & 40 Hp Engines

A flywheel-type magneto furnishes the ignition spark for these engines. Moving the speed-control lever shifts the entire magneto stator plate, thereby affecting the ignition timing. A throttle-actuating cam, attached to the magneto stator plate, synchronizes throttle valve opening to ignition timing.

PULLER

①

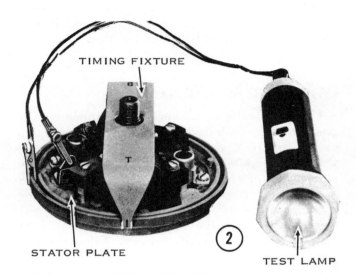

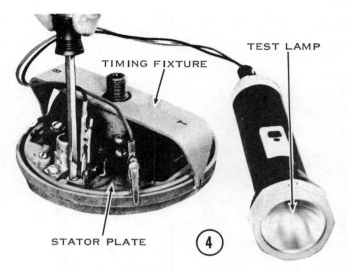

REMOVING THE FLYWHEEL

① To remove the flywheel, take off the nut. Attach a puller, Tool No. 378103, to the flywheel, and then lift the flywheel from the crankshaft.

ADJUSTING THE BREAKER POINT GAP

② Install new breaker points and adjust the gaps to 0.020″ (0.022″ for new points). Disconnect all leads from the breaker point assemblies. Connect a self-powered test lamp between the breaker plate and the forward breaker point terminal screw. Install a timing fixture, Tool No. 304667, on the crankshaft.

③ Rotate the crankshaft so that the side of the fixture marked "T" (for top) is aligned with the first projection on the stator plate. *CAUTION: To avoid damaging the water pump impeller, rotate the crank-*

shaft in a clockwise direction only. Move the timing fixture or the stator plate slowly back and forth until the exact instant at which the points open is determined, this being indicated by the test lamp going out. The breaker points should open just when the timing fixture is midway between the two projections on the stator plate. If necessary, adjust the breaker point gap until the timing is correct. *NOTE: To compensate for initial rubbing block wear, adjust the gap of new breaker points so that they just open as the fixture passes the first mark.* Tighten the breaker point lock screws, and then recheck the timing.

④ Rotate the crankshaft clockwise a full turn, and then repeat the timing procedure for the second set of breaker points. *NOTE: If a test lamp or timing fixture*

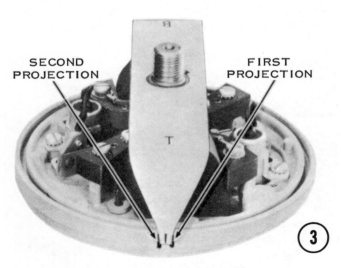

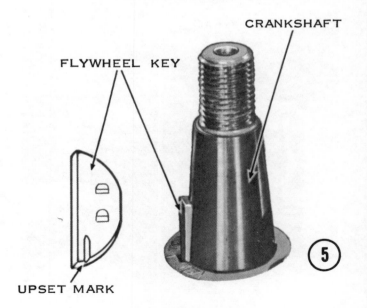

is not available, adjust the breaker point gap to 0.020"
(0.022" for new points) with the breaker arm on the
high lobe of the cam, and the timing will be fairly
accurate.

ASSEMBLING

⑤ Check the crankshaft and flywheel tapers for
traces of oil, which must be removed with solvent.
*CAUTION: The assembly must be perfectly dry. CAU-
TION: Don't allow solvent to wash the oil out of the
oiler wick.* The flywheel key must be installed so that it
is parallel to the crankshaft and with the upset mark
facing down. *CAUTION: Incorrect installation will
adversely affect the ignition timing.* Replace the flywheel
and nut, torquing it to specifications according to the
model.

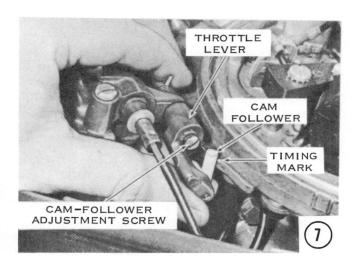

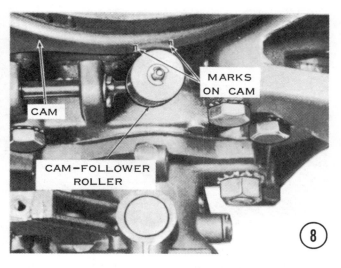

THROTTLE CAM SYNCHRONIZATION

3.0, 4.0, 5.0, 5.5 & 6.0 Hp Engines

⑥ Set the speed-control lever to the STOP position. Slowly advance the control until the cam follower
just begins to open the throttle. The timing mark on
the cam and the contact point of the cam follower
should now be aligned. If an adjustment is needed,
loosen the cam mounting screws, and then position the
cam so that, with all play removed from the linkage,
the throttle valve is closed. The mark on the throttle
cam must be aligned with the flat port side of the cam
follower just as the follower makes contact with the
cam. Tighten the cam retaining screws securely.

9.5 Hp Engine

⑦ Loosen the cam-follower adjustment screw. Move
the cam follower so that it just contacts the throttle-
control cam. Make sure that the throttle valve is fully
closed, and then rotate the throttle-lever roller against
the cam follower. Securely tighten the throttle lever to
the throttle shaft. *CAUTION: Make sure that the adjustment setting is not disturbed when tightening the
cam-follower screw.*

18/20 Hp Engine

⑧ Advance the throttle control to the position
where the cam-follower roller is centered between the
two marks on the throttle cam. The throttle valve must
be closed at this point. If it is not, adjust it by advancing
the throttle control to the position where the cam-fol-

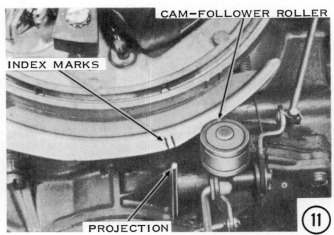

lower roller is centered between the two marks. Loosen the two hex-headed screws holding the cam to the magneto stator base, and then push the cam back toward the rear of the engine. Now, pull the cam forward until it just contacts the cam-follower roller. The throttle valve must just begin to open after the edge of the roller passes the second mark on the cam. *CAUTION: The choke knob must be all the way in.*

33 Hp Engine

⑨ Advance the throttle control so that the mark on the throttle cam is in line with the projection on the intake manifold. At this point, the throttle valve should be closed and the cam-follower roller must touch the

cam. If the throttle valve is not closed, adjust it by advancing the throttle control until the mark on the stator plate cam is in line with the raised projection on the carburetor manifold. Loosen the throttle arm clamp screw. Make sure that the throttle valve is in the closed position and that the cam-follower roller touches the cam. Tighten the screw securely. *NOTE: As the throttle is advanced, the throttle valve must just begin to open after the mark on the cam passes the projection on the intake manifold.*

⑩ To make the fuel economy adjustment, move the magneto stator plate by hand (without touching the throttle control) to the Maximum Spark Advance position. Adjust the control rod collar for 1/32" clearance from the pivot pin, as shown in the insert.

40 Hp Engine

⑪ Advance the throttle control so that the marks on the throttle cam are in line with the projection on the intake manifold. At this point, the throttle valve must be closed and the cam-follower roller must just touch the cam. If an adjustment is needed, advance the throttle control until the marks on the throttle control are aligned with the projection on the intake manifold. The cam-follower roller must just touch the cam at this point.

⑫ Loosen the throttle arm clamp screw. With the throttle valve closed, push the cam-follower roller so that it touches the cam, and then tighten the clamp screw. To make the fuel economy adjustment, move the magneto stator plate by hand (without touching the throttle control) to the Maximum Spark Advance position. Adjust the control rod collar for 1/32" clearance from the pivot pin, as shown in the insert.

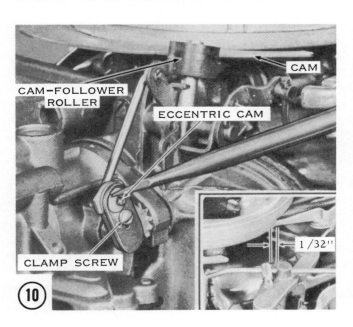

ROLLER

CLAMP SCREW

1/32"

⑫

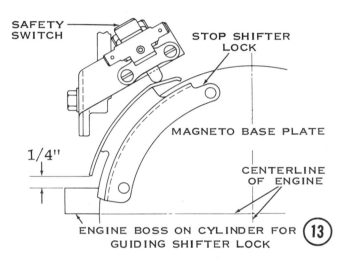

SAFETY SWITCH

STOP SHIFTER LOCK

MAGNETO BASE PLATE

1/4"

CENTERLINE OF ENGINE

ENGINE BOSS ON CYLINDER FOR GUIDING SHIFTER LOCK

⑬

VACUUM CUT-OUT SWITCH

TEST LAMP

⑭

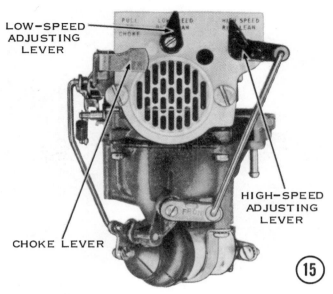

LOW-SPEED ADJUSTING LEVER

HIGH-SPEED ADJUSTING LEVER

CHOKE LEVER

⑮

ADJUSTING THE VACUUM CUTOUT AND SAFETY SWITCHES

33 & 40 Hp Engines

If the throttle is closed suddenly while the engine is running, crankcase suction (vacuum) may become abnormally high and cause erratic carburetor operation, allowing the engine speed to increase despite a closed throttle. The function of the cutout switch is momentarily to short out the breaker points for the lower cylinder whenever crankcase suction increases abnormally.

The safety switch completes the cutout switch circuit and prevents it from operating at full throttle. The safety switch also prevents the starter from being engaged with the throttle advanced too far.

⑬ To make an adjustment to the safety switch, connect a test lamp across the terminal screws, and then adjust the position of the switch on its bracket so that the circuit opens when the plunger reaches the midpoint on the slope of the shifter lock stop.

⑭ To test the vacuum cutout switch, connect a test lamp to the switch terminal and ground. Alternately apply oral suction and pressure at the switch vacuum hose connector; the light should go on and off. Check the hole in the intake manifold with a #76 drill to make sure that it is free. Check the manifold vacuum hose for a leak, which would adversely affect the operation of the switch.

ADJUSTING THE CARBURETOR

⑮ Seat the high- and low-speed adjusting needles gently, and then back them out for a preliminary ad-

The idle speed adjusting screw for the 9.5 Hp engine is located at the base of the steering handle.

The idle speed adjusting screw for the larger two-cylinder engines is located at the base of the steering handle.

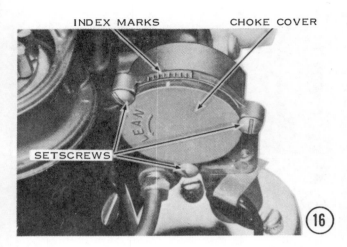

INDEX MARKS   CHOKE COVER

SETSCREWS

LEAN

16

justment. *CAUTION: Don't force them into their seats, or you will damage the taper, making an accurate adjustment difficult.* Back out the low-speed adjusting needle as follows: 1/2 turn for the 6 Hp engine; 3/4 turn for the 9.5 and 40 Hp engines; 1-1/4 turns for the 3, 5, and 33 Hp engines; and 2 turns for the 18/20 Hp models. Back out the high-speed adjusting needle 3/4 turn for all models. Start the engine and allow it to reach operating temperature. Run the engine at full throttle, and then adjust the high-speed needle for maximum rpm. Adjust the low-speed needle until the highest rpm consistent with smooth performance is reached. *NOTE: Allow 15 seconds for the engine to respond after each adjustment.* After making the low-speed adjustment, recheck the high-speed adjustment. Install the adjustment knobs.

ADJUSTING THE AUTOMATIC CHOKE

⑯ If starting is difficult in hot or cold weather, it may be necessary to adjust the automatic choke. Before disturbing the original factory setting, scribe a mark on the choke housing to serve as a reference point. To make an adjustment, loosen the setscrews, and then turn the cover one or two notches, as needed. Tighten the setscrews.

THREE-CYLINDER ENGINE TUNE-UP SERVICE PROCEDURES

55 Hp Engine

This engine is equipped with a CD (Capacitor-Discharge) type of ignition system. Two sets of breaker

FLYWHEEL PULLER

points, located under the flywheel, actuate a solid-state amplifier.

The solid-state amplifier changes the battery voltage to 300 DC volts; the voltage is stored in a capacitor for discharging through an ignition coil when the circuit is triggered by the breaker points. The capacitor discharges through a special ignition coil to generate about 25,000 volts to fire the surface-gap type spark plugs. This extremely high voltage is very successful in overcoming spark plug fouling.

REMOVING THE FLYWHEEL

① Remove the flywheel nut. Attach a puller, Tool No. 378103, to the flywheel, and then remove the flywheel.

② Disconnect the two yellow stator leads at the connector, remove the three retaining screws, and then lift off the stator. Take off the distributor cap, wave washer, and rotor to expose the breaker point plate.

ADJUSTING THE BREAKER POINT GAP

③ Turn the crankshaft clockwise to position the breaker arm on the high point of the cam. *CAUTION: Always rotate the crankshaft clockwise to avoid damaging the water pump impeller.* Loosen the locking screw,

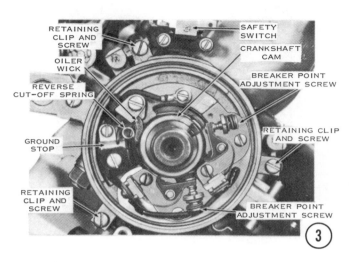

RETAINING SCREWS

CRANKSHAFT

STATOR WINDINGS ②

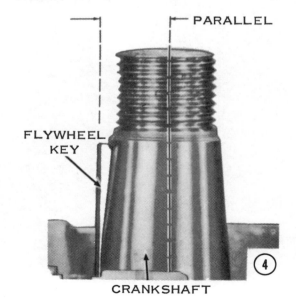

RETAINING CLIP AND SCREW
OILER WICK
REVERSE CUT-OFF SPRING
GROUND STOP
RETAINING CLIP AND SCREW
SAFETY SWITCH
CRANKSHAFT CAM
BREAKER POINT ADJUSTMENT SCREW
RETAINING CLIP AND SCREW
BREAKER POINT ADJUSTMENT SCREW

and then turn the eccentric screw to obtain a gap of 0.010″ (0.012″ for new breaker points). Make the same adjustment to the second set of breaker points.

ASSEMBLING

④ Install the rotor, wave washer, and distributor cap, making sure that the cap is seated properly. Install the stator with the screws dipped in Loctite, torquing them to 48–60 in-lbs. Check the crankshaft and flywheel tapers for traces of oil, which must be removed with solvent. *CAUTION: The assembly must be perfectly dry. CAUTION: Don't allow solvent to wash the lubricant out of the oiler.* The flywheel key must be installed parallel to the shaft. Replace the flywheel and the nut, torquing it to 70–85 ft-lbs.

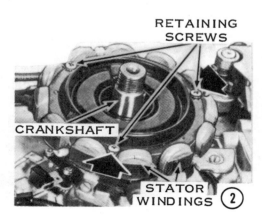

PARALLEL
FLYWHEEL KEY
CRANKSHAFT

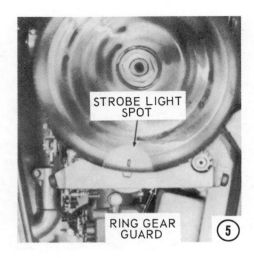

STROBE LIGHT SPOT

RING GEAR GUARD ⑤

ADJUSTING THE IGNITION TIMING

⑤ Connect a timing lamp to the spark plug lead of No. 1 cylinder, start the engine, shift into FORWARD gear, and then open the throttle wide. The straight timing mark on the flywheel must fall within the square timing mark on the ring gear guard. *NOTE: The triangular mark on the flywheel is not used for timing this engine.*

⑥ If an adjustment is necessary, turn the advance stop adjusting screw to obtain the proper setting.

SYNCHRONIZING THE CARBURETOR AND DISTRIBUTOR LINKAGE

⑦ The index mark on the throttle cam must align with the center of the cam-follower roller just as the

SPARK-ADVANCE STOP ADJUSTING SCREW

⑥

roller makes contact with the cam, and when it is just touching it. If an adjustment is required, loosen the center carburetor throttle arm screw, and then move the arm to close the throttle valves. Tighten the screw.

⑧ With the distributor base and the throttle lever at the full-throttle position against the stops, the carburetor throttle shaft must also be against its full-throttle stop. If necessary, adjust the linkage by turning the throttle cam yoke on the throttle control rod.

ADJUSTING THE SAFETY SWITCH

⑨ A safety switch prevents actuating the cranking motor with the throttle advanced too far. The switch is normally open and must close to permit starting. To adjust this switch, connect a self-powered test lamp between the switch lead and ground. Loosen the adjustment screw, and then position the switch to close on the ramp of the cam. *NOTE: A click can be heard when the switch closes.* Tighten the screw after making the adjustment.

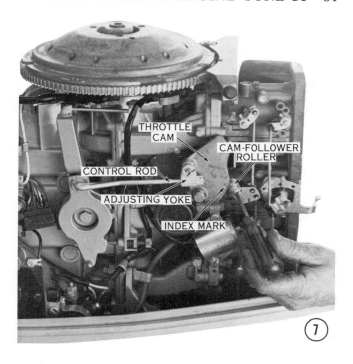

⑦

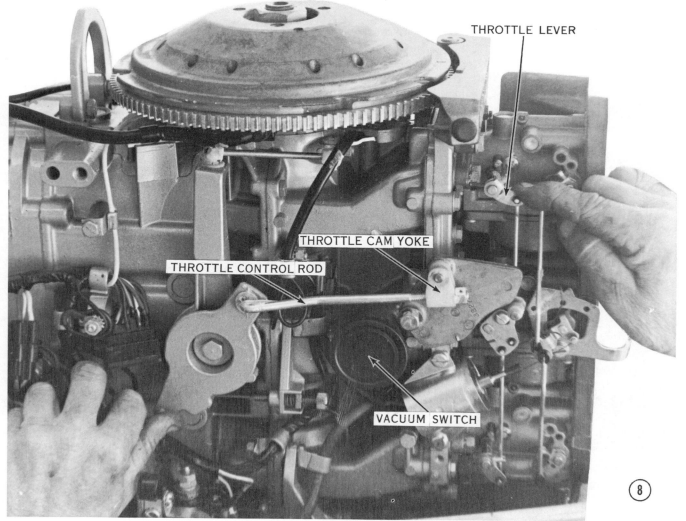

⑧

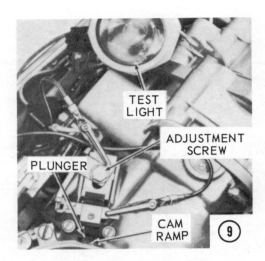

TEST LIGHT

ADJUSTMENT SCREW

PLUNGER

CAM RAMP

⑨

ADJUSTING THE CARBURETOR

⑩ To make an individual carburetor adjustment, it is necessary to take off the air silencer cover and disconnect the low-speed needle linkage. To make a preliminary adjustment, turn each low-speed adjusting needle gently into its seat, and then back each out 5/8 turn. *CAUTION: Don't force the needles into their seats, or you will damage the tapers, making an accurate adjustment difficult.* Start the engine and allow it to reach operating temperature. Shift into FORWARD gear, and then adjust one low-speed needle at a time until the highest rpm and smoothest performance are obtained. Allow ample time for the engine to respond

to each adjustment. Turn the idle speed adjusting screw so that the engine idles at 600–650 rpm in forward gear. Pull off the levers, and then connect the linkages. *CAUTION: Don't disturb the position of the adjusting needles.* Position the levers so that they are pointing straight to the starboard side, and then push them back to their original positions on the needles. Replace the air silencer cover.

FOUR-CYLINDER ENGINE TUNE-UP SERVICE PROCEDURES

60, 75 & 80 Hp Engines with Magnetos

The magneto used on the V-4 engine has a single coil, two permanent magnets cast into the magneto housing, two sets of breaker points, one condenser, a rotor, and a distributor cap. The high voltage developed in the magneto coil is distributed to each of the four spark plugs through a rotor, a distributor cap, and high-tension leads. The magneto is driven by a timing belt, which synchronizes the magneto with the crankshaft.

A double set of breaker points and one condenser are mounted on the breaker plate. The cam has two lobes, 180° apart, and the breaker points are located 90° apart on the breaker plate, thus interrupting the

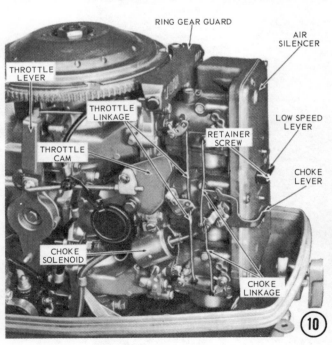

RING GEAR GUARD

AIR SILENCER

THROTTLE LEVER

THROTTLE LINKAGE

THROTTLE CAM

RETAINER SCREW

LOW SPEED LEVER

CHOKE LEVER

CHOKE SOLENOID

CHOKE LINKAGE

⑩

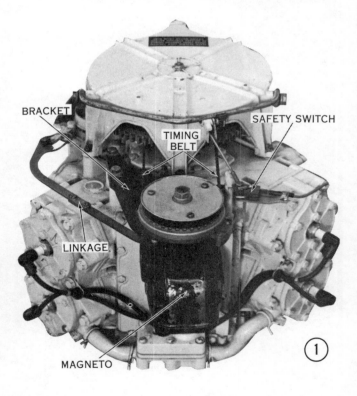

BRACKET

TIMING BELT

SAFETY SWITCH

LINKAGE

MAGNETO

①

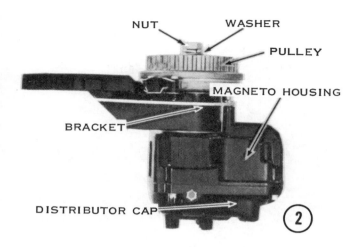

NUT WASHER
PULLEY
MAGNETO HOUSING
BRACKET
DISTRIBUTOR CAP
②

current through the magneto coils four times in each revolution. The condenser momentarily absorbs the current flowing through the primary of the coil, after the breaker points open, to hasten the collapse of the magnetic field.

REMOVING THE MAGNETO

① Disconnect the safety switch and the ground switch leads. Twist the high-tension leads off the spark plugs. Unscrew the four leads from the distributor cap. Remove the two screws from the linkage to the magneto. *NOTE: This linkage synchronizes the magneto with the carburetor throttle. CAUTION: Scribe a line on the two*

parts of the linkage before removing the screws, unless the synchronizing procedure is to be done. Remove the three bracket mounting screws, and then slide the magneto bracket forward to release belt tension. Lift the timing belt off the pulley, and then slide the magneto and bracket assembly from the powerhead.

DISASSEMBLING

② Remove the distributor shaft nut, lockwasher, and flat washer. Lift the pulley, cam, and key from the distributor shaft. Remove the screws holding the breaker plate to the housing. Separate the bearing bracket from the magneto housing. Note the positions of the washers for assembly purposes.

③ Turn the magneto over, and then take out the four screws holding the distributor cap. Remove the cap, gasket, and rotor. *CAUTION: Don't lose the carbon brush and spring.* Check the ventilating screens in the cap. To remove the coil, disconnect the primary leads from the insulated screw terminal and the retainer spring screw. Remove the retainer springs, and then lift the coil from the housing.

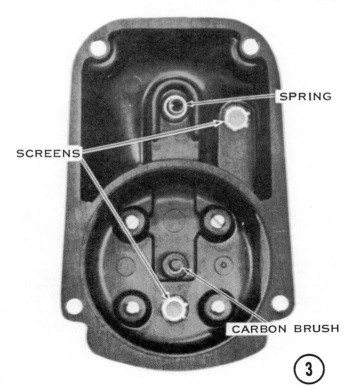

SPRING
SCREENS
CARBON BRUSH
③

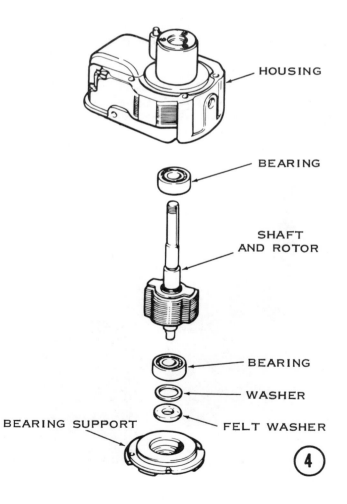

HOUSING
BEARING
SHAFT AND ROTOR
BEARING
WASHER
BEARING SUPPORT
FELT WASHER
④

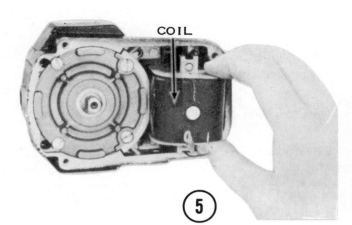

COIL

⑤

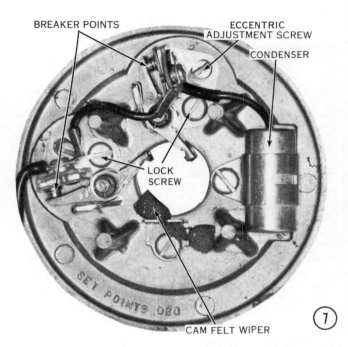

BREAKER POINTS

ECCENTRIC ADJUSTMENT SCREW

CONDENSER

LOCK SCREW

CAM FELT WIPER

⑦

④ Check the bearings by rotating the shaft. *CAUTION: Don't remove the shaft unless the bearings are damaged and need to be replaced.*

ASSEMBLING

⑤ Install the coil, with the insulators, into the housing, and then secure it with the retainer springs and screws. *CAUTION: The coil must be positioned so that the core laminations butt against the field laminations.* Connect the primary leads to the ground screw and to the insulated screw terminal.

⑥ Slide the rotor onto the shaft. Replace the distributor cap. *CAUTION: Make sure that the carbon brush and spring are in place.* Use a new gasket under the cap. Assemble the magneto housing and the breaker plate to the bearing bracket, making sure that the steel and felt washers are in place.

⑦ Replace both sets of breaker points. Install the key and cam. Replace the pulley and fasten it with the washers and nut. Screw the high-tension leads into the distributor cap.

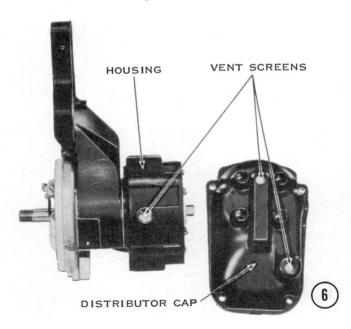

HOUSING

VENT SCREENS

DISTRIBUTOR CAP

⑥

FLYWHEEL COVER

MAGNETO BRACKET

TIMING BELT

⑧

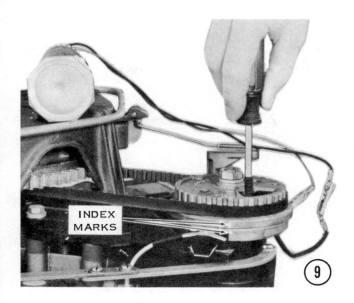

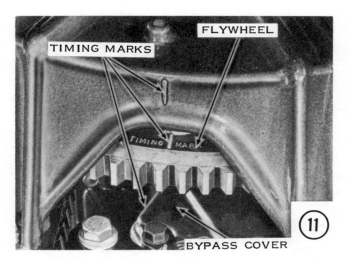

INSTALLING

⑧ Attach the magneto bearing bracket to the engine with the screws and lockwashers, tightening the screws finger-tight to allow for a belt adjustment. If a new belt is to be installed, it can be done without removing the flywheel by threading it carefully between the flywheel and starter and between the flywheel and carburetor.

ADJUSTING THE BREAKER POINT GAPS

⑨ The breaker point gaps must be adjusted before installing the timing belt. Do this by making a preliminary gap adjustment of 0.020″ for each set. Disconnect the breaker point lead from the insulated screw terminal, and then connect this wire to a self-powered test lamp. Ground the other test lamp lead. Rotate the magneto

pulley so that the index mark on the pulley lines up with the synchronizing mark on the breaker plate. Loosen the lock screw and turn the eccentric adjusting screw so that the breaker points just close, causing the test lamp to light. Tighten the lock screw. Recheck the adjustment by rotating the pulley slightly in each direction. The points must close when the two marks align.

⑩ To adjust the second set of breaker points, rotate the pulley 90° so that the index mark on the pulley lines up with the second mark on the breaker plate, as shown. Repeat the breaker point gap adjustment. *CAUTION: The breaker points must open precisely 90° apart to assure correct synchronization for all four cylinders.*

INSTALLING THE TIMING BELT

⑪ Before installing the belt, the flywheel and the magneto drive pulley must be correctly positioned. To do this, rotate the flywheel clockwise until the timing marks

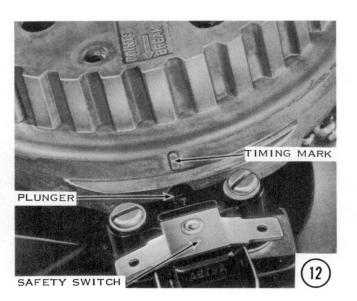

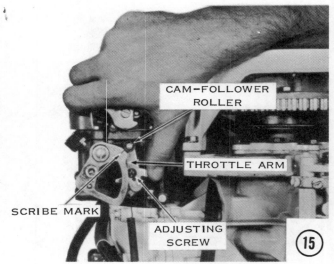

on the flywheel, starter housing, and bypass cover plate are in line. *CAUTION: Rotate the flywheel only in a clockwise direction to prevent damaging the water pump impeller. CAUTION: Remove the spark plugs and ground the high-tension leads to prevent the engine from starting accidentally while the flywheel is turned.*

⑫ Rotate the pulley so that the timing mark is in line with the center of the safety switch plunger.

⑬ Install the timing belt, and then adjust the position of the magneto bearing bracket so that the belt can be deflected 5/16″–3/8″ under a one-pound pressure applied near the center. Before tightening the bracket mounting screws, check to see that the timing marks on the flywheel are still aligned and that the mark on the timing pulley is aligned with the safety switch plunger.

SYNCHRONIZING THE MAGNETO AND CARBURETOR LINKAGE

⑭ The carburetor and magneto linkage must be synchronized so that they work in unison. To do this,

shift into FORWARD gear, and then rotate the magneto by hand to the fully advanced position. The inside surface of the control shaft arm must be parallel to the edge of the triangular projection on the control shaft bracket, when viewed from above. If it is necessary to make an adjustment, loosen the two linkage screws and make the adjustment while holding the magneto in the fully advanced position. Tighten the two linkage screws securely.

⑮ The throttle cam has a scribe mark which must be in line with the center of the cam-follower roller when the throttle valves are closed completely. If it is necessary to make an adjustment, remove the control rod to gain access to the clamp screw. *NOTE: There are two setscrews holding the rod, one above the other.* Remove the outer locking screw to gain access to the rod locking screw. Position the throttle cam so that the scribe mark is in line with the center of the cam-follower roller, and then loosen the clamp screw to move the

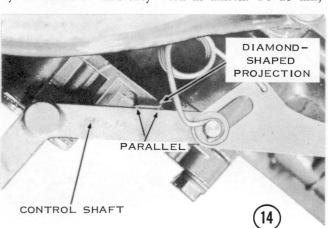

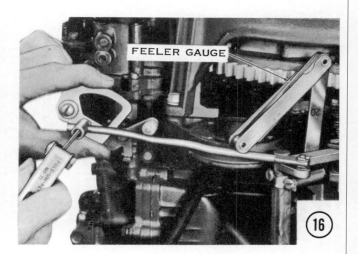

WIDE-OPEN STOPS

(17)

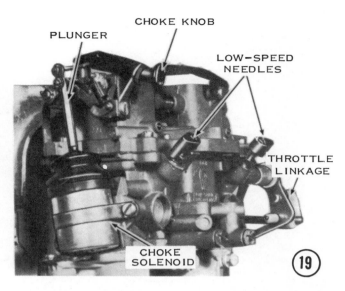

PLUNGER

CHOKE KNOB

LOW-SPEED NEEDLES

THROTTLE LINKAGE

CHOKE SOLENOID

(19)

throttle arm so as to close the throttle valves fully. Make sure that the roller is contacting the arm, and then tighten the clamp screw securely.

⑯ To adjust the length of the carburetor control rod for the wide-open throttle position, replace the carburetor control rod, leaving the setscrew loose. Shift into FORWARD gear, advance the throttle to the wide-open position, and then insert a 0.020″ feeler gauge blade between the control shaft arm and the stop on the control shaft bracket, as shown. Holding the cam in the wide-open position, tighten the setscrew. Replace the lock screw.

⑰ Check to see that all controls reach their wide-open positions at the same time by removing the feeler gauge and then moving the throttle to its wide-open position. The throttle control shaft, throttle arm, and magneto must reach their fully advanced stops at the

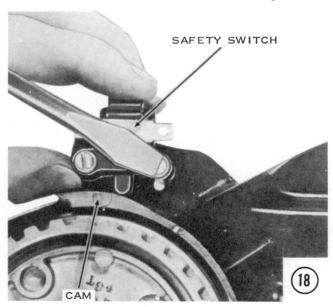

SAFETY SWITCH

CAM

(18)

same time. If they don't, repeat the preceding adjustment steps until they do.

ADJUSTING THE SAFETY SWITCH

⑱ The safety switch, mounted on the distributor bracket, prevents the engine from starting at full throttle. To adjust this switch, loosen the retaining screws, and then move the switch body so that the contacts just close at the midpoint of the cam slope. *NOTE: A click can be heard when the contacts close.*

ADJUSTING THE CARBURETOR

⑲ Remove the low-speed needle adjusting knobs and install them upside down on the needles in order to clear the stops on the carburetor. Turn each needle gently into its seat, and then back it out 3/4 turn for a preliminary adjustment. *CAUTION: Don't turn the needle into its seat too hard, or you will damage the taper, making an accurate adjustment difficult.* With the engine thoroughly warmed, shift into gear, and connect a tachometer. Run the engine at full throttle to clear it, and then retard the throttle to the fast-idle position (700–750 rpm). Slowly turn one adjusting needle clockwise (lean) until the engine spits slightly, and then back it out until the engine runs at the highest speed consistent with smooth operation. If the engine picks up speed, reset the throttle to 700–750 rpm. Adjust the second low-speed needle in a similar manner. Replace the knobs in the normal position without disturbing the setting of the needles. Turn the idle speed adjusting screw on the side of the distributor until the engine idles at 600–650 rpm while in gear.

⑳ Some of the older model carburetors had high-speed adjusting needles. To make an adjustment on this

type, lift the stem which disengages the knob from the two gears, and then turn the knob so that it faces directly forward, where it will remain disengaged.

㉑ Turn each high-speed adjusting needle in (lean), with the engine running at approximately 4,500 rpm, until it pops, and then back out the adjustment until maximum speed is reached. Do this to each adjusting needle, and then turn the adjusting knob back to engage the gears. Now that both needles are synchronized, the adjusting knob can be used to make a fine adjustment. *NOTE: Turning the knob rotates both adjusting needles an equal amount because of the gearing.*

FOUR-CYLINDER ENGINE TUNE-UP SERVICE PROCEDURES

75, 80, 90 & 100 (1966 only) Hp Engines with Battery-Ignition Systems

The battery-ignition system used on these engines has a single ignition coil and a distributor, containing two sets of breaker points, one condenser, a rotor, and a distributor cap. The high voltage developed in the ignition coil is distributed to each of the four spark plugs through the rotor, distributor cap, and high-tension leads. The distributor is driven by a timing belt, which synchronizes the distributor to the crankshaft.

A double set of breaker points and one condenser are mounted on the breaker plate. The cam has two lobes, 180° apart, and the breaker points are located 90° apart on the breaker plate, thus interrupting the battery current through the primary of the ignition coil four times in each revolution. The condenser momentarily absorbs the current flowing through the primary of the coil, after the breaker points open, to hasten the collapse of the magnetic field.

DISASSEMBLING THE DISTRIBUTOR

① Disconnect the safety switch lead and the breaker point lead. Twist the high-tension leads counterclockwise from the spark plugs. Remove the two screws from the linkage to the distributor. *NOTE: This linkage synchronizes the distributor with the carburetor throttle. CAUTION: Scribe a line on the two parts of the linkage before removing the screws unless the synchronizing procedure is to be done.* Remove the two screws holding the distributor cap in place, and then lift off the cap. *CAUTION: Don't lose the carbon rotor brush and spring in the center cavity of the cap.*

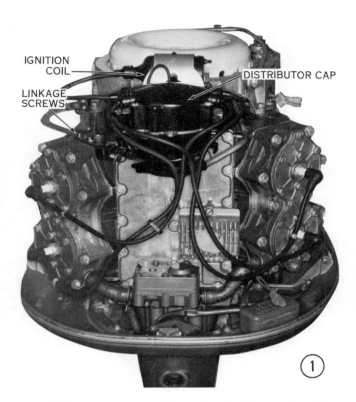

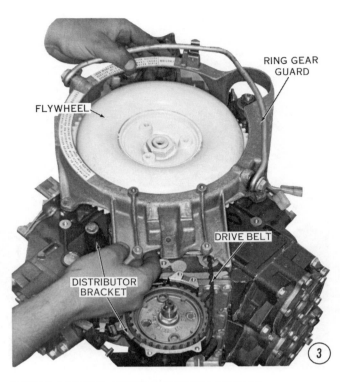

② Remove the rotor from the distributor shaft. Disconnect the breaker point lead at the ignition coil. Remove the breaker plate assembly by taking out the two screws holding it to the distributor housing. Remove the breaker points by taking out the spring clips holding the point springs to the supports. Remove both point sets and the condenser.

REPLACING THE DRIVE BELT

③ Remove the ignition coil and the flywheel ring gear guard. Loosen the distributor mounting bracket, and then slide it back to release tension on the drive belt. Remove the distributor cap, rotor, and breaker plate. Take off the ring gear guard and the flywheel. Remove the drive belt.

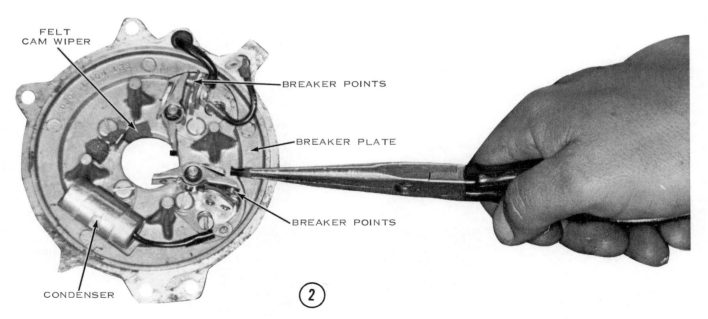

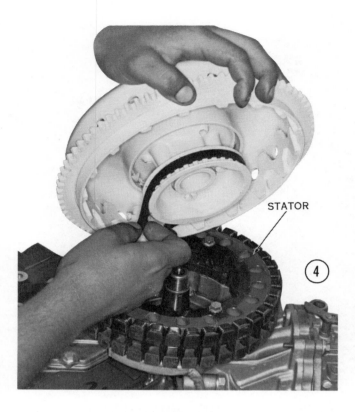

STATOR

④

④ Install a new drive belt by pushing it through the opening under the stator and then hooking it over the flywheel. Holding the belt in position around the flywheel drive gear, slide the flywheel into position, and

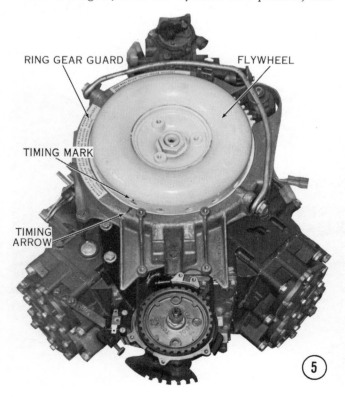

RING GEAR GUARD

FLYWHEEL

TIMING MARK

TIMING ARROW

⑤

TIMING MARKS

⑥

then replace the nut, tightening it to 70–85 ft-lbs. of torque. Replace the distributor bracket and the ring gear guard.

TIMING THE DRIVE BELT

⑤ Rotate the flywheel clockwise so that the timing marks on the flywheel and the arrow on the ring gear guard are aligned. *CAUTION: Always rotate the flywheel in a clockwise direction to prevent damaging the water pump impeller. NOTE: To relieve powerhead compression, remove the spark plugs.*

1/4" - 3/8"

⑦

⑥ With the timing mark on the flywheel aligned with the arrow on the ring gear guard, the timing marks on the distributor pulley and bracket must be in line, as shown. If they are not, loosen the mounting screws to release belt tension so that you can rotate the distributor pulley until the timing marks do align.

⑦ Adjust the distributor bracket for the proper belt tension; the tension is correct when the belt can be deflected 1/4″–3/8″ under a one-pound push applied near the center. Tighten the distributor bracket retaining screws.

INSTALLING NEW BREAKER POINTS

⑧ Always replace the breaker points. *CAUTION: Don't touch the point surface with your fingers, or you will coat them with a layer of oil, which is an insulator.* It is desirable to clean the point surfaces with carbon tetrachloride to insure cleanliness. When points are installed, the spring goes under the point support bracket and is held in place with a clip. Install the assembled breaker plate in the distributor, tightening the two retaining screws securely. Adjust the gaps of both sets of breaker points to 0.020″ for a preliminary adjustment. *CAUTION: Use a cleaned feeler gauge blade to avoid getting oil on the contact points.*

⑨ To time the first set of breaker points to piston movement, disconnect the breaker point lead, and then connect it to a self-powered test lamp. Ground the other test lamp lead to the breaker plate. Rotate the distribu-

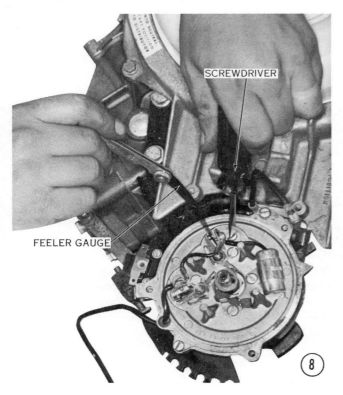

tor housing to the fully advanced position so that the boss on the housing is against the stop on the distributor bracket. *CAUTION: The distributor must be held in this position throughout the following breaker point adjustments.* Rotate the pulley so that the mark on the pulley lines up with the timing mark on the distributor housing. Adjust the gap of the breaker points so that they just close and the test lamp lights. Recheck the adjustment by rotating the pulley slightly in each direction. The points must open at the instant the pulley mark and the mark on the breaker plate are aligned. *NOTE: This times the first set of breaker points to the piston.*

⑩ To time the second set of breaker points (to fire 90° apart), rotate the flywheel so that the mark on the

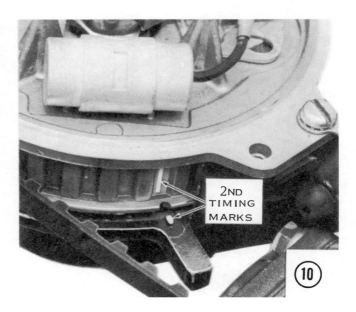

IGNITION COIL

DISTRIBUTOR CAP VENT SCREEN ⑪

pulley lines up with the second timing (synchronizing) mark on the breaker plate. Adjust the gap of the second set of breaker points until the points open as the pulley mark passes the distributor timing (synchronizing) mark.

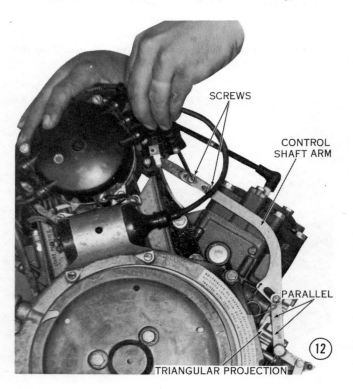

SCREWS

CONTROL SHAFT ARM

PARALLEL

⑫

TRIANGULAR PROJECTION

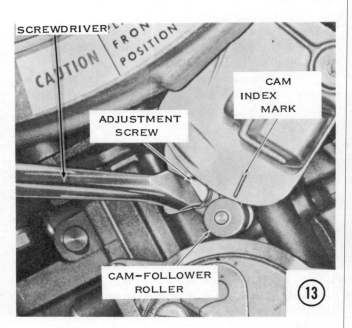

SCREWDRIVER

CAUTION FRONT POSITION

ADJUSTMENT SCREW

CAM INDEX MARK

CAM-FOLLOWER ROLLER

⑬

⑪ Replace the rotor, making sure that it engages properly with the indexing flat on the shaft and that it is fully depressed. Inspect the distributor cap to be sure that the rotor spring and brush are in place and that the brush is free. Make sure that the ventilating screen in the cap is clean to assure proper ventilation. Replace the distributor cap, making sure that the locating lugs are indexed properly. Replace the ignition coil and the high-tension wiring.

SYNCHRONIZING THE CARBURETOR AND DISTRIBUTOR LINKAGE

⑫ Attach the linkage to the distributor. Turn the distributor to the fully advanced position by hand. With the shift lever in FORWARD gear, the inside surface of the control shaft arm should be parallel to the edge of the triangular projection on the control shaft bracket. If necessary, loosen the two linkage screws and make the adjustment while holding the distributor in the fully advanced position. Tighten the two screws securely.

⑬ Check the position of the throttle cam by rotating the linkage from the closed to the wide-open position. The carburetor throttle must just begin to open as the center of the roller is opposite the index mark on the cam. If necessary, loosen the cam-adjustment screw, and then push the throttle arm to the closed position while holding the cam-follower roller in contact with the cam and correctly aligned with the index mark. Tighten the screw. Recheck the adjustment. The cam follower must just begin to move as the index mark on the cam passes the center line of the cam-follower roller.

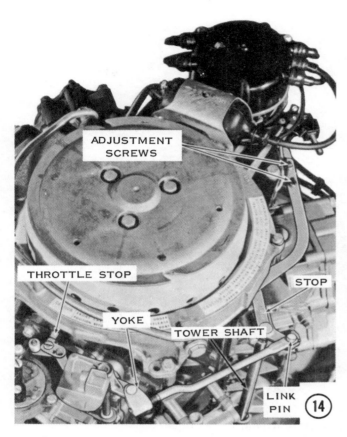

Ⓐ Turn the tower shaft to the wide-open throttle position to see that the throttle arm is against the full-throttle stop. If necessary, make an adjustment by removing the link pin and turning the throttle control rod in the yoke until the throttle control shaft and the throt-

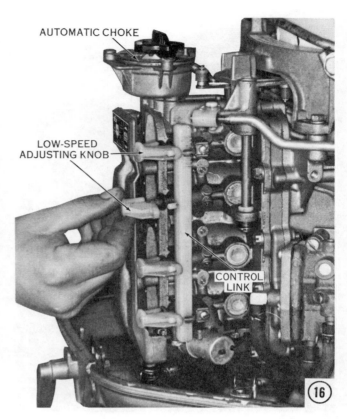

tle arm reach their wide-open positions at the same time. *NOTE: The distributor must reach the fully advanced position at the same time.*

ADJUSTING THE SAFETY SWITCH

Ⓕ The safety switch on the distributor bracket prevents the cranking motor from being actuated with the throttle fully advanced. To adjust the switch, loosen the retaining screws and position the switch so that the contact points close at the midpoint of the cam slope. *NOTE: A sharp click can be heard when the switch contacts close.* Tighten the retaining screws. *NOTE: The switch contacts are normally open and must close to complete the cranking motor solenoid circuit.* Check the operation of the switch with a self-powered test lamp. When the switch button reaches the midpoint of the cam slope, the contacts must close and the test lamp should light.

ADJUSTING THE CARBURETOR

Ⓖ Before starting the engine, center the low-speed control link, and then remove all four knobs. Make a preliminary adjustment by gently seating each low-speed adjusting needle and then backing it out 1/2 turn. Connect a tachometer, start the engine, and shift into gear.

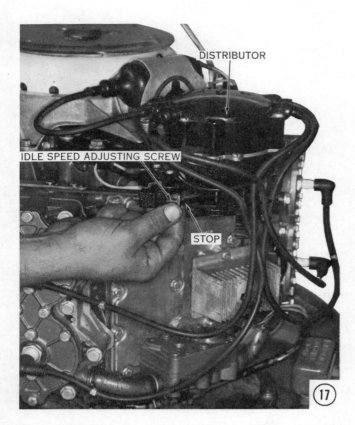

DISTRIBUTOR

IDLE SPEED ADJUSTING SCREW

STOP

⑰

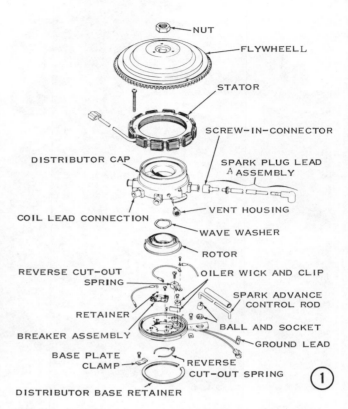

NUT

FLYWHEELL

STATOR

SCREW-IN-CONNECTOR

DISTRIBUTOR CAP

SPARK PLUG LEAD
ASSEMBLY

COIL LEAD CONNECTION

VENT HOUSING

WAVE WASHER

ROTOR

REVERSE CUT-OUT
SPRING

OILER WICK AND CLIP

SPARK ADVANCE
CONTROL ROD

RETAINER

BALL AND SOCKET

BREAKER ASSEMBLY

GROUND LEAD

BASE PLATE
CLAMP

REVERSE
CUT-OUT SPRING

DISTRIBUTOR BASE RETAINER

①

Warm the engine to operating temperature, and then run it briefly at full throttle to clear it out. Set the idle speed at 650 rpm, and then turn each low-speed adjusting needle in (lean) until the engine pops and loses speed. Back the needle out slowly until the engine runs smoothly and at the highest speed. Adjust the other low-speed needles in a similar fashion. Check to see that the low-speed control link is centralized on the 100 Hp engine, and then replace the four control knobs, being careful not to alter the setting of the adjusting needles.

⑰ Adjust the idle speed to 650 rpm with the engine in gear. Make the idle speed adjustment by turning the distributor stop screw, as shown.

FOUR-CYLINDER ENGINE TUNE-UP SERVICE PROCEDURES

65 & 85 Hp Engines with Breaker-Point Type CD Ignition Systems

These four-cylinder engines have been equipped with a CD (Capacitor-Discharge) type of ignition sys-

tem since 1968. Two sets of breaker points, located under the flywheel, actuate a solid-state amplifier.

The solid-state amplifier changes the battery voltage to 300 DC volts; the voltage is stored in a capacitor for discharging through an ignition coil when the circuit is triggered by the breaker points. The capacitor discharges through a special ignition coil to generate a 25,000-volt charge for firing the surface-gap type spark plugs. This extremely high voltage has been dramatically successful in overcoming spark plug fouling.

DISASSEMBLING THE DISTRIBUTOR

① Remove the flywheel. Disconnect the yellow stator leads at the connector, and then remove the stator. Lift off the distributor cap, wave washer, and rotor. *NOTE: This exposes the breaker point assemblies and the reverse cut-out spring.*

ASSEMBLING

② Install a new reverse cut-out spring. Use Shell EP-2 Grease to lubricate the nylon ring and assemble it to the breaker base, and then attach the assembly to the crankcase head with four retainer clips and screws.

③ Replace both breaker point sets, and then adjust the gaps to 0.012″ (0.010″ for old points).

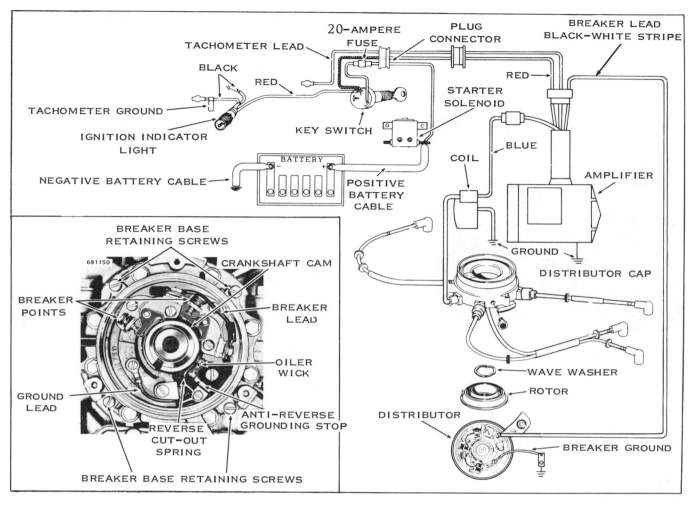

TACHOMETER LEAD

20-AMPERE FUSE

PLUG CONNECTOR

BREAKER LEAD BLACK-WHITE STRIPE

BLACK

RED

RED

TACHOMETER GROUND

STARTER SOLENOID

IGNITION INDICATOR LIGHT

KEY SWITCH

BLUE

COIL

AMPLIFIER

NEGATIVE BATTERY CABLE

BATTERY

POSITIVE BATTERY CABLE

GROUND

DISTRIBUTOR CAP

BREAKER BASE RETAINING SCREWS

CRANKSHAFT CAM

681150

BREAKER LEAD

BREAKER POINTS

OILER WICK

GROUND LEAD

WAVE WASHER

REVERSE CUT-OUT SPRING

ANTI-REVERSE GROUNDING STOP

ROTOR

DISTRIBUTOR

BREAKER BASE RETAINING SCREWS

BREAKER GROUND

Wiring diagram and details of the breaker points of the CD ignition system used on the 65 and 85 Hp engines since 1968.

REVERSE CUT-OUT SPRING

②

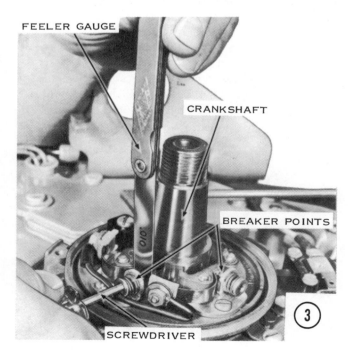

FEELER GAUGE

CRANKSHAFT

BREAKER POINTS

SCREWDRIVER

③

Replace the rotor, wave washer, and distributor cap. *CAUTION: The wave washer provides stability for the rotor and, if omitted, will cause the engine to run erratically. CAUTION: Make sure that the distributor cap is seated properly between the bearing head bosses.* Install the stator, with the screws dipped in Loctite and torqued to 48–60 in-lbs.

ADJUSTING THE IGNITION TIMING

⑤ Move the distributor to its fully advanced position. The timing mark on the distributor cap boss should be aligned with the mark on the breaker base control arm boss.

⑥ If necessary, adjust the spark advance stop screw until the marks align.

⑦ The ignition timing should not change during normal engine operation. However, if the spark advance stop screw has been disturbed, new breaker points have

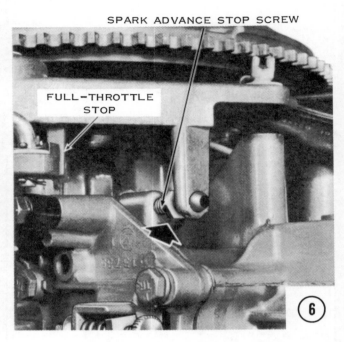

been installed, or the amplifier has been replaced, the ignition timing should be checked. Connect a timing lamp to No. 1 cylinder spark plug. Start the engine, shift into gear, and adjust the speed to 4,500 rpm. The straight timing line must fall within the square timing mark on the left bracket, as shown. *NOTE: The wedge-shaped mark can be used for timing No. 2 cylinder spark plug.*

SYNCHRONIZING THE CARBURETOR AND DISTRIBUTOR LINKAGE

⑧ Adjust the position of the throttle arm with respect to the cam follower by moving the throttle cam so that the scribe mark aligns with the center of the cam-follower roller. Loosen the adjusting screw, and then move the throttle arm to its limit so that the throttle

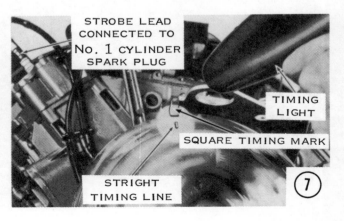

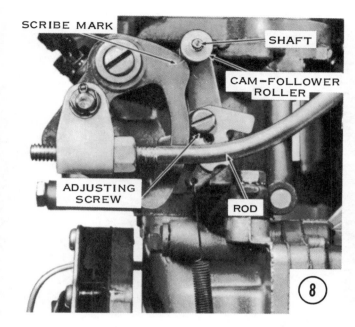

SCRIBE MARK · SHAFT · CAM-FOLLOWER ROLLER · ADJUSTING SCREW · ROD

(8)

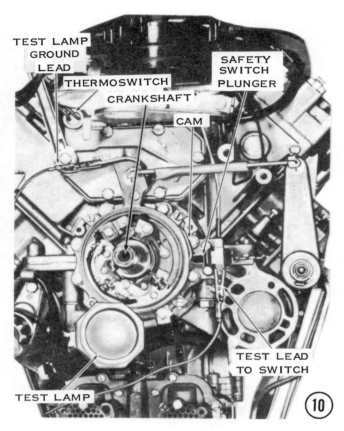

TEST LAMP GROUND LEAD · THERMOSWITCH · CRANKSHAFT · CAM · SAFETY SWITCH PLUNGER · TEST LEAD TO SWITCH · TEST LAMP

(10)

valves are closed. Make sure that the cam-follower roller is contacting the cam, and then tighten the screw.

⑨ With the control shaft at its wide-open throttle position and against its stop, the throttle shaft arm must also be against its stop. If necessary, adjust it by turning the throttle cam yoke on the throttle control rod until the throttle shaft arm is against its stop with the control shaft in the wide-open throttle position.

ADJUSTING THE SAFETY SWITCH

⑩ A safety switch, mounted on the crankcase head, engages a cam on the distributor base. It prevents the cranking motor from being actuated with the throttle advanced while the engine is in gear. To adjust this switch, loosen the retaining screws and position the safety switch to close on the flat of the cam. *NOTE: A click can be heard when the switch closes.* Tighten the screws after having made the adjustment. The switch is normally open and must close to permit starting the engine. This should be checked with a test lamp, with one test lead connected to the switch terminal and the other to a good ground.

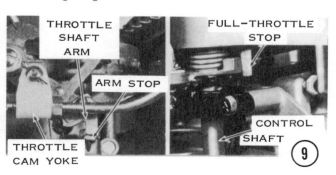

THROTTLE SHAFT ARM · FULL-THROTTLE STOP · ARM STOP · CONTROL SHAFT · THROTTLE CAM YOKE

(9)

ADJUSTING THE CARBURETOR

⑪ Remove the low-speed adjusting knobs and replace them upside down on the low-speed adjusting needles to clear the stops on the carburetor. Turn each needle gently into its seat, and then back it out 5/8 turn. *CAUTION: Don't force the needles into their seats, or you will damage the tapers, making an accurate adjustment difficult.* Start the engine and allow it to reach operating temperature. Shift into gear and retard the throttle to the fast-idle position (700–750 rpm). Slowly turn one low-speed needle clockwise (lean) until the engine hesitates or spits slightly, and then slowly turn the adjusting needle out until the engine reaches the highest rpm consistent with smooth performance. *CAUTION: Since it is almost impossible to detect minor speed changes in a V-4 engine, it is imperative to use a tachometer for making these adjustments with accuracy.* Snap open the throttle and, if the engine hesitates, enrich the low-speed adjustment slightly until the engine responds to the throttle properly. Replace the low-speed knobs in their normal positions without disturbing the positions of the adjusting needles.

⑫ Adjust the idle speed to 650 rpm while the engine is in gear.

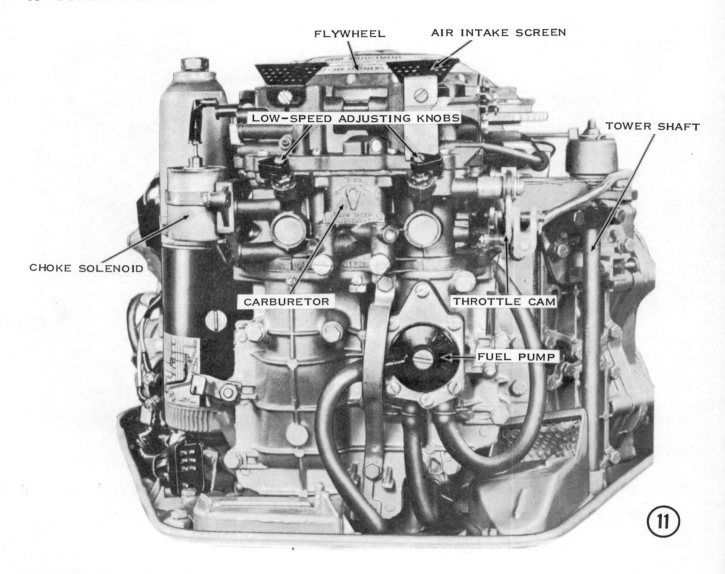

FLYWHEEL
AIR INTAKE SCREEN
LOW-SPEED ADJUSTING KNOBS
TOWER SHAFT
CHOKE SOLENOID
CARBURETOR
THROTTLE CAM
FUEL PUMP

(11)

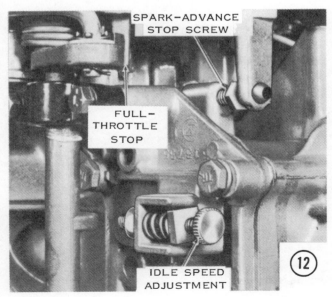

SPARK-ADVANCE
STOP SCREW
FULL-
THROTTLE
STOP
IDLE SPEED
ADJUSTMENT

(12)

FOUR-CYLINDER ENGINE TUNE-UP SERVICE PROCEDURES

100 Hp (1967) Engine with a Breakerless-Type CD Ignition System

These four-cylinder engines are equipped with a CD (Capacitor-Discharge) type of ignition system. A pulse generator (which is called a sensor) replaces the conventional breaker points. The pulse generator is located in a belt-driven distributor; it actuates a solid-state amplifier (which is called an electronic pack).

The solid-state amplifier changes the battery voltage to 300 DC volts. This voltage is stored in a capacitor for discharging through an ignition coil when the circuit is triggered by an electrical current generated by the pulse

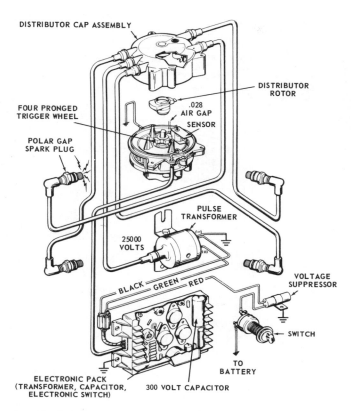

DISTRIBUTOR CAP ASSEMBLY

DISTRIBUTOR ROTOR

FOUR PRONGED TRIGGER WHEEL

.028 AIR GAP

SENSOR

POLAR GAP SPARK PLUG

PULSE TRANSFORMER

25000 VOLTS

VOLTAGE SUPPRESSOR

BLACK — GREEN — RED

SWITCH

TO BATTERY

ELECTRONIC PACK (TRANSFORMER, CAPACITOR, ELECTRONIC SWITCH)

300 VOLT CAPACITOR

Details of the Breakerless-Type CD Ignition System, which uses a pulse generator in place of the conventional breaker points.

generator. The capacitor discharges through a special ignition coil (which is called a pulse transformer) to generate a 25,000-volt charge for firing the surface-gap type spark plugs. This extremely high voltage has been dramatically successful in overcoming spark plug fouling.

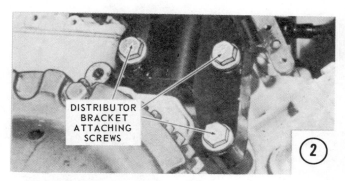

DISTRIBUTOR BRACKET ATTACHING SCREWS

2

DISASSEMBLING THE DISTRIBUTOR

① Unscrew the high-tension wires by twisting them from the spark plugs and ignition coil in a counterclockwise direction. Remove the screws holding the distributor cap to the breaker plate, and then lift off the distributor cap. *CAUTION: Don't lose the carbon rotor brush and spring from the center of the cap.* Disconnect the control shaft linkage and the safety switch wire. Lift off the rotor.

② To remove the distributor from the engine, take off the ring gear cover, remove the three bracket mounting screws, and then slide the bracket forward to release belt tension. Lift the belt off the distributor pulley. Remove the distributor and bracket assembly from the engine.

③ To remove the trigger wheel, use two screwdrivers to pry it off the shaft, as shown. Take out the distributor shaft key. Remove the two screws holding the distributor plate to the distributor housing, and then lift off the plate. Remove the hex nut, lockwasher, and flat washer holding the pulley to the distributor shaft.

④ Remove the cap from the bottom of the distributor housing and sleeve assembly. Use a pair of No. 4 Truarc pliers, Tool No. 307429, to take off the retaining

HIGH TENSION LEADS

LINKAGE

SAFETY SWITCH

1

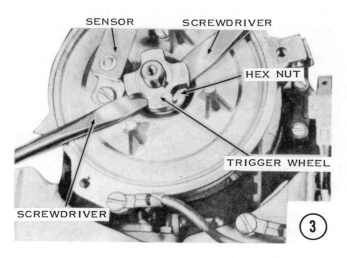

SENSOR

SCREWDRIVER

HEX NUT

TRIGGER WHEEL

SCREWDRIVER

3

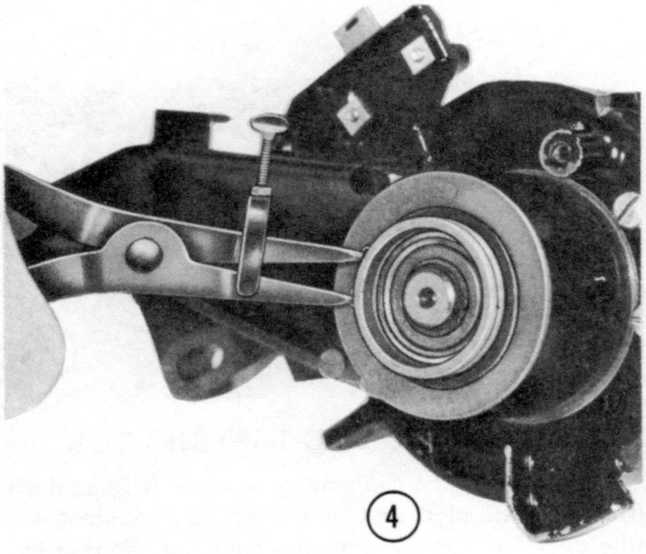

4

ring. This will separate the distributor housing from the distributor bracket and expose the large needle bearing, which is pressed into the distributor bracket. *CAUTION: The distributor shaft bearings are easily damaged if the shaft is pressed from the distributor housing because the stress must be applied to a critical area of the bearings. Don't attempt to remove the bearings unless they must be cleaned or replaced.* Check the bearings by rotating the shaft slowly to note any roughness. Move the shaft from side to side and then up and down to check for play. If it is necessary to remove the bearings, use an arbor press and a suitable support. After cleaning the bearings, repack them with a ball bearing grease having a high melting point.

ASSEMBLING

⑤ Assemble the bearings and shaft to the distributor housing. Press the top bearing onto the shaft, using an arbor press. *CAUTION: Press against the inner race only.* Press the top bearing and shaft assembly into the distributor housing, pressing against the outer race only. Press the bottom bearing into place, using a fixture so that the pressure can be applied to the inner and outer races of both bearings. Replace the pulley, washers, and nut, and then tighten the nut securely. *NOTE: Always use a new flat washer over the pulley to assure proper tightening.* Start the cam over the shaft and ball assembly. Press the key into the shaft, and then install the trigger wheel. Use a deep 9/16″ socket to drive the trigger wheel squarely onto the shaft. Assemble the distributor housing and bracket, using new felt washers. Replace the retaining rings and the housing cap. Attach the distributor to the engine with the cap screws, leaving them loose enough to allow for a belt adjustment.

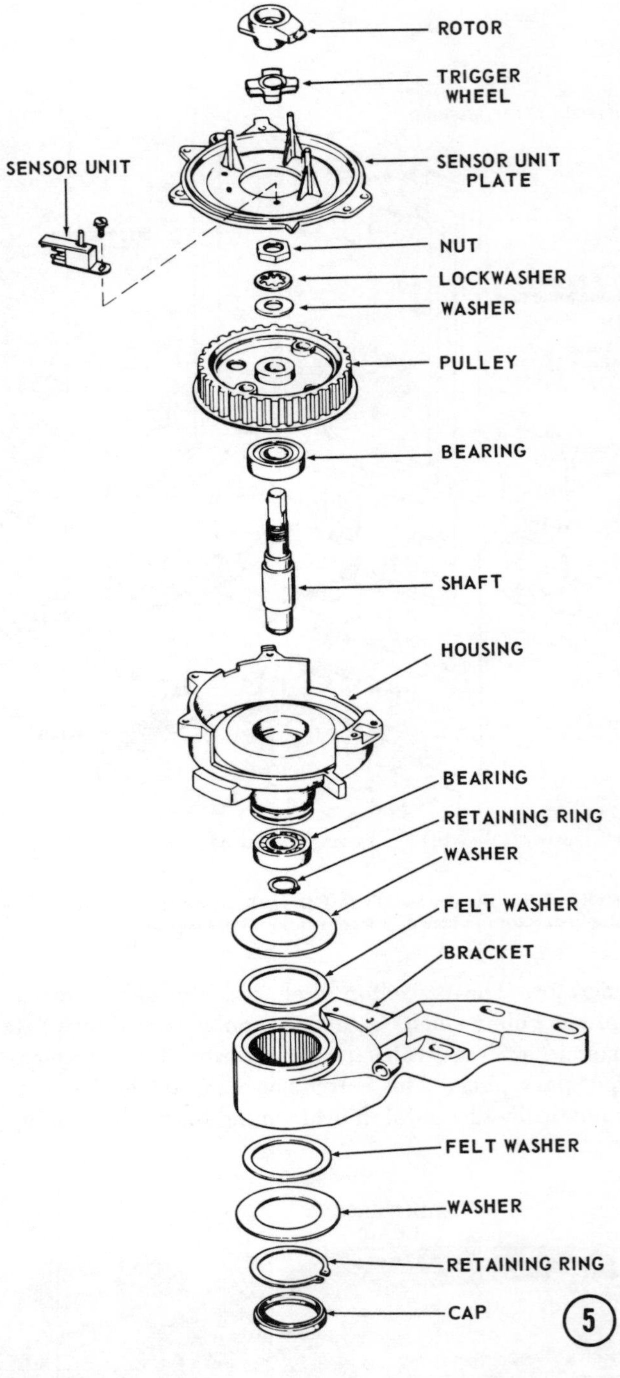
ROTOR
TRIGGER WHEEL
SENSOR UNIT
SENSOR UNIT PLATE
NUT
LOCKWASHER
WASHER
PULLEY
BEARING
SHAFT
HOUSING
BEARING
RETAINING RING
WASHER
FELT WASHER
BRACKET
FELT WASHER
WASHER
RETAINING RING
CAP

5

BELT TIMING

⑥ Rotate the flywheel so that the timing marks on the flywheel and ring gear cover are in line, as shown. *CAUTION: Always rotate the flywheel in a clockwise direction to prevent damage to the water pump impeller.*

⑦ If the ring gear cover has been removed, align the marks on the flywheel and cylinder block, as shown.

RING GEAR COVER

BELT TIMING

(6)

TIMING MARKS

(8)

Remove the spark plugs to relieve powerhead compression.

⑧ With the timing marks on the flywheel aligned, turn the distributor pulley until the timing marks on the bracket and pulley are in line. Install the drive belt.

⑨ Adjust the distributor bracket for the proper amount of tension; the tension is correct when the belt can be deflected 1/4"–3/8" under a one-pound pressure applied near the center. Tighten the distributor bracket mounting screws securely.

⑩ Replace the distributor plate assembly and check the sensor adjustment. With one trigger wheel lobe

1/4"–3/8"

(9)

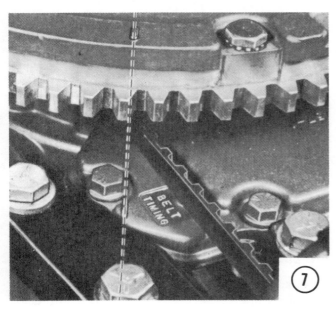

BELT TIMING

(7)

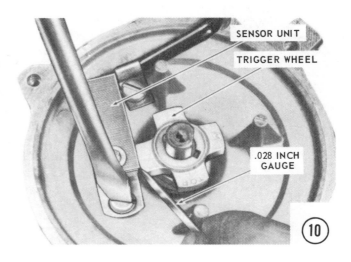

SENSOR UNIT

TRIGGER WHEEL

.028 INCH GAUGE

(10)

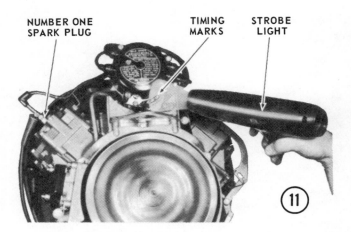

NUMBER ONE SPARK PLUG — TIMING MARKS — STROBE LIGHT

⑪

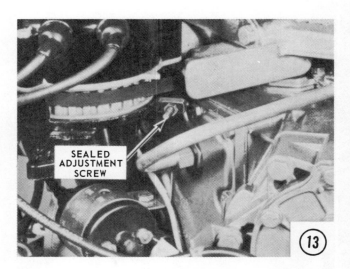

SEALED ADJUSTMENT SCREW

⑬

aligned with the sensor, the air gap should be adjusted to 0.028″, as shown. Move the sensor in or out as required, and then tighten the retaining screws securely. Replace the rotor, distributor cap, and linkage. *CAUTION: Make sure that the carbon brush and spring are properly located in the center of the distributor cap.*

CHECKING THE TIMING

⑪ The timing should not change during normal engine operation. However, if the seal is broken on the timing adjustment screw, or if the electronic pack has been replaced, the timing should be checked. Attach a timing light to No. 1 cylinder spark plug, and then start the engine. Adjust the engine speed to 500 rpm while in gear. The timing marks on the distributor housing and pulley should line up. If the marks do not align, check for a damaged or missing distributor key or a worn distributor shaft keyway, which would allow the pulley or

trigger wheel to move. *CAUTION: The belt timing must be correct before you proceed further.*

⑫ With the timing light still connected to No. 1 cylinder spark plug, open the throttle until the engine runs at 4,500 rpm while in gear. Direct the timing light to the flywheel, and the back timing mark must fall within the square timing mark on the ring gear. *NOTE: There are two ring gear timing marks on some models. The front timing mark can be used by connecting the timing light to No. 3 cylinder spark plug.*

⑬ If a timing adjustment is required, turn the sealed adjustment screw to obtain the proper setting. *CAUTION: Reseal the screw after making an adjustment to prevent anyone from changing it.*

SYNCHRONIZING THE CARBURETOR AND DISTRIBUTOR LINKAGE

⑭ Move the distributor by hand to the fully advanced position. The inside surface of the control shaft

BACK TIMING MARK

FRONT TIMING MARK

⑫

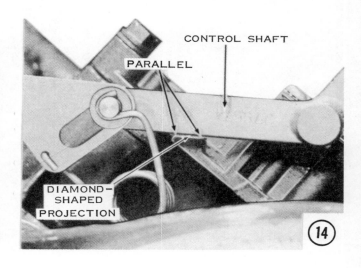

CONTROL SHAFT

PARALLEL

DIAMOND-SHAPED PROJECTION

⑭

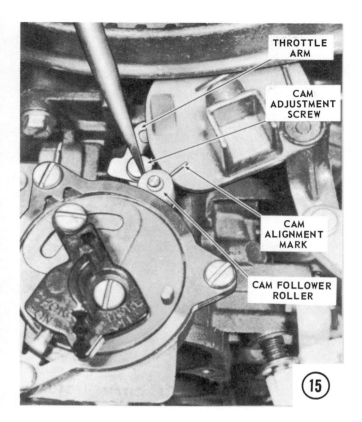

(15)

loosen the two linkage screws, and then make the necessary adjustment while holding the distributor in the fully advanced position. Tighten the screws securely.

⑮ Check the pickup position of the throttle with the cam. The roller should begin to open the throttle as the center of the roller shaft aligns with the cam alignment mark, as shown. If necessary, loosen the screw holding the cam follower to the throttle arm, and then push the throttle arm to the closed position. Hold the cam-follower roller in contact with the cam, while it is correctly aligned with the mark, and then tighten the retaining screw. Recheck the adjustment; the cam-follower roller should just begin to move as the mark on the cam passes the center line of the cam-follower roller.

⑯ Check the full-throttle stop adjustments by moving the control shaft against its full-throttle stop. At this position, the carburetor throttle must be against its full-throttle stop. If necessary, make an adjustment by removing the link pin and turning the yoke on the throttle control rod as required. *NOTE: The carburetor and distributor linkage are correctly synchronized when the throttle control shaft and the throttle arm reach their fully open positions at the same time that the distributor reaches its fully advanced position.*

arm should be parallel with the edge of the diamond-shaped projection on the control shaft bracket, as shown. If the control shaft arm is not in the correct position,

SAFETY SWITCH ADJUSTMENT

⑰ A safety switch is mounted on the distributor bracket; it prevents the starter from being actuated at full throttle. To adjust this switch, loosen the screws and move the switch so that its contacts close at the midpoint of the cam. *NOTE: A click can be heard when*

THROTTLE CONTROL ROD

(16)

(17)

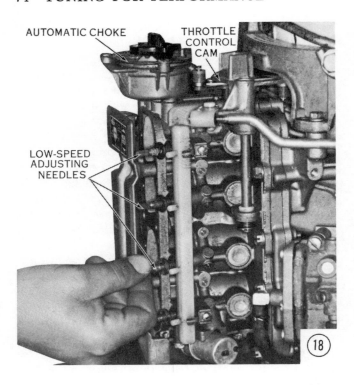

AUTOMATIC CHOKE

THROTTLE CONTROL CAM

LOW-SPEED ADJUSTING NEEDLES

⑱

IDLE SPEED ADJUSTING SCREW

⑲

the switch contacts close. Tighten the screws securely. The switch is normally open and the contacts must close to permit the starter to operate. Check the circuit with a test lamp, if available. When the switch button reaches the midpoint of the cam slope, the lamp should light.

ADJUSTING THE CARBURETOR

⑱ Remove the low-speed adjusting knobs and replace them upside down on the low-speed adjusting needles to clear the stops on the carburetor. Turn each needle gently into its seat, and then back it out 5/8 turn. *CAUTION: Don't force the needles into their seats, or you will damage the tapers, making an accurate adjustment difficult.* Start the engine and allow it to reach operating temperature. Shift into gear and retard the throttle to the fast-idle position (700–750 rpm). Slowly turn one low-speed needle clockwise (lean) until the engine hesitates or spits slightly, and then slowly turn the adjusting needle out until the engine reaches the highest rpm consistent with smooth performance. *CAUTION: Since it is almost impossible to detect minor speed changes in a V-4 engine, it is imperative to use a tachometer for making these adjustments with accuracy.* Snap open the throttle and, if the engine hesitates,

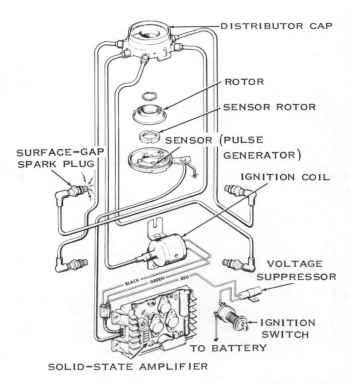

DISTRIBUTOR CAP

ROTOR

SENSOR ROTOR

SENSOR (PULSE GENERATOR)

SURFACE-GAP SPARK PLUG

IGNITION COIL

VOLTAGE SUPPRESSOR

BLACK — GREEN — RED

IGNITION SWITCH

TO BATTERY

SOLID-STATE AMPLIFIER

Details of the CD ignition system with the pulse generator located under the flywheel; it is used on the 1968-69, 100 and 115 Hp models.

enrich the low-speed adjustment slightly until the engine responds to the throttle properly. Replace the low-speed knobs in their normal positions without disturbing the positions of the adjusting needles.

⑲ Adjust the idle speed to 650 rpm while the engine is in gear.

FOUR-CYLINDER ENGINE TUNE-UP SERVICE PROCEDURES

100 & 115 Hp Engines with a Breakerless-Type CD Ignition System

These four-cylinder engines are equipped with a CD (Capacitor-Discharge) type of ignition system. A pulse generator (which is called a sensor) replaces the conventional breaker points. The pulse generator is located under the flywheel and actuates a solid-state amplifier (which is called an electronic pack).

The solid-state amplifier changes the battery voltage to 300 DC volts; this voltage is stored in a capacitor for discharging through an ignition coil when the circuit is triggered by an electrical current generated by the pulse generator. The capacitor discharges through a special ignition coil (which is called a pulse transformer) to generate a 25,000-volt charge for firing the surface-gap type spark plugs. This extremely high voltage has been dramatically successful in overcoming spark plug fouling.

DISASSEMBLING THE DISTRIBUTOR

① Remove the flywheel. Disconnect the two stator leads, and then remove the three retaining screws to lift the stator from the powerhead. Remove the high-tension lead wires by twisting them counterclockwise from the spark plugs and the ignition coil. Detach the high-tension lead grommets from the lead supports. Unscrew the leads from the distributor cap in a counterclockwise direction. Lift the distributor cap, wave washer, and rotor from the engine. *CAUTION: Don't lose the wave washer.*

② To remove the sensor rotor from the crankshaft, use two screwdrivers to pry it off. *NOTE: It is not necessary to remove the sensor unless it or the reverse cut-out spring has to be replaced.*

③ Pull the link out of the nylon ball joint. Remove the distributor plate assembly by taking out the four screws and clips holding the plate to the head. *NOTE: The reverse cut-out spring and clip grounds out the ignition should the engine attempt to run backward.*

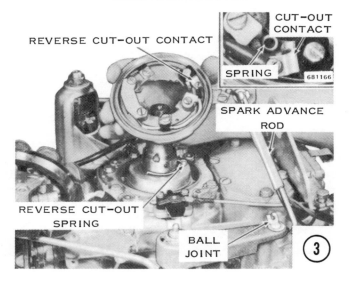

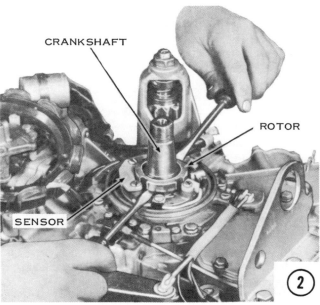

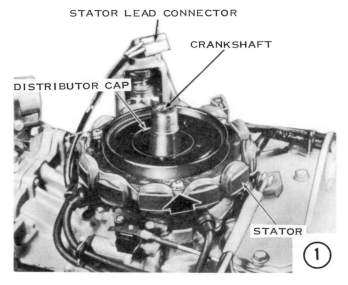

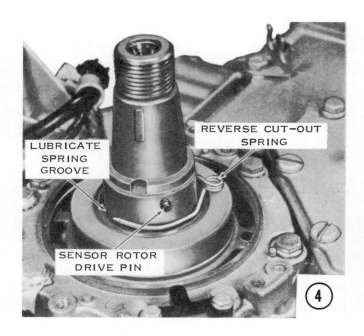

LUBRICATE SPRING GROOVE

REVERSE CUT-OUT SPRING

SENSOR ROTOR DRIVE PIN

④

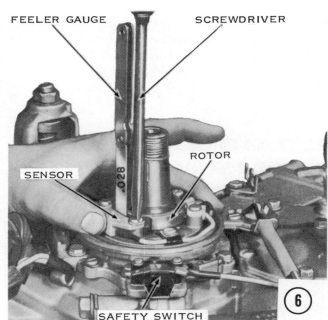

FEELER GAUGE   SCREWDRIVER

SENSOR

ROTOR

SAFETY SWITCH

⑥

ASSEMBLING

④ Install the reverse cut-out spring. Use Shell EP-2 Grease to lubricate it.

⑤ Lubricate the nylon base retainer with oil, and then install it on the distributor base assembly, with the flat side facing up. Attach the base to the crankcase bearing head with the clips and screws. Connect the link to the ball joint by pressing it into position.

⑥ Install the sensor rotor, engaging the rotor with the pin on the crankshaft. Adjust the sensor gap to a clearance of 0.028″ by inserting the feeler gauge blade between the sensor and the sensor rotor lobe, as shown. Hold the sensor against the feeler gauge blade, and then tighten the sensor retaining screws. Recheck the gap; the gauge must pass through with a slight drag.

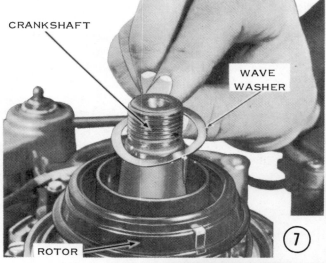

CRANKSHAFT

WAVE WASHER

ROTOR

⑦

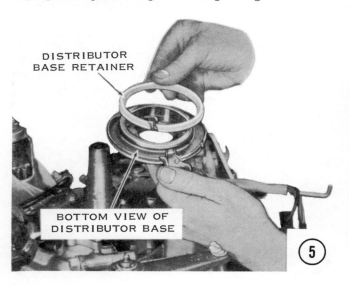

DISTRIBUTOR BASE RETAINER

BOTTOM VIEW OF DISTRIBUTOR BASE

⑤

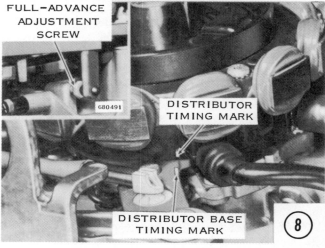

FULL-ADVANCE ADJUSTMENT SCREW

680491

DISTRIBUTOR TIMING MARK

DISTRIBUTOR BASE TIMING MARK

⑧

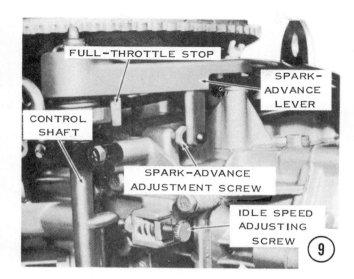

FULL-THROTTLE STOP

SPARK-ADVANCE LEVER

CONTROL SHAFT

SPARK-ADVANCE ADJUSTMENT SCREW

IDLE SPEED ADJUSTING SCREW

9

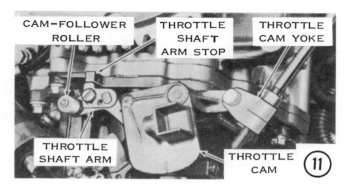

CAM-FOLLOWER ROLLER

THROTTLE SHAFT ARM STOP

THROTTLE CAM YOKE

THROTTLE SHAFT ARM

THROTTLE CAM

11

⑦ Connect the sensor lead, and then install the distributor rotor, wave washer, and distributor cap. *CAUTION: Make sure that the distributor cap is seated properly in the base, or the cap will be damaged when the stator retaining screws are tightened.* Install the stator with the screws dipped in Loctite. Torque the screws to 48–60 in-lbs.

ADJUSTING THE IGNITION TIMING

⑧ Align the timing marks on the distributor cover and the distributor base control arm. If necessary, turn

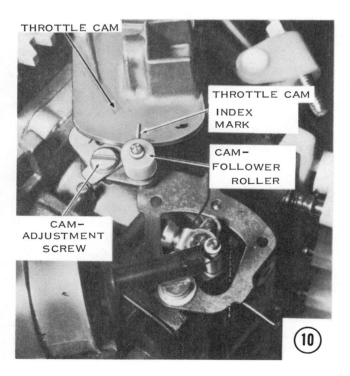

THROTTLE CAM

THROTTLE CAM INDEX MARK

CAM-FOLLOWER ROLLER

CAM-ADJUSTMENT SCREW

10

the full-advance adjustment screw (insert). Install the flywheel and tighten the nut to 70–85 ft-lbs. Install and tighten the lift bracket screws.

⑨ To check the ignition timing, connect a timing lamp to No. 1 cylinder spark plug, start the engine, and adjust the speed to 4,500 rpm with the shift lever in gear. The straight timing mark on the flywheel must fall within the timing indicator mark on the lift bracket. If an adjustment is necessary, turn the spark-advance adjustment screw.

SYNCHRONIZING THE CARBURETOR AND DISTRIBUTOR LINKAGE

⑩ Adjust the position of the throttle arm with respect to the cam-follower roller. The roller should begin to open the throttle valves when the center of the roller shaft aligns with the index mark on the throttle cam. If necessary, loosen the cam adjustment screw and push the throttle arm to the closed position while holding the cam-follower roller in contact with the throttle cam. Tighten the screw and recheck the adjustment; the cam-follower roller should just begin to move as the index mark on the cam passes the center line of the cam-follower roller.

⑪ With the control shaft at its full-throttle position, against its stop, the throttle shaft arm must also be against its stop. If an adjustment is required, turn the throttle cam yoke on the throttle control rod until the throttle shaft arm is against its stop with the control shaft in the full-throttle position.

ADJUSTING THE SAFETY SWITCH

⑫ A safety switch, mounted on the crankcase head, engages a cam on the distributor base which prevents the cranking motor from being actuated at full throttle. To adjust this switch, loosen the retaining screws, and then position the switch so that it closes on the ramp of the cam. *NOTE: A click can be heard when the switch contacts close.* The switch is normally open and must

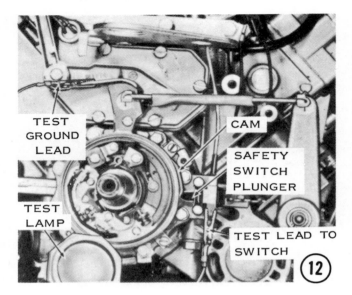

TEST GROUND LEAD

TEST LAMP

CAM

SAFETY SWITCH PLUNGER

TEST LEAD TO SWITCH

⑫

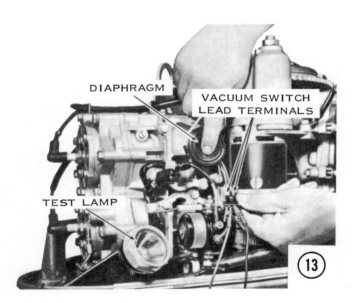

DIAPHRAGM

VACUUM SWITCH LEAD TERMINALS

TEST LAMP

⑬

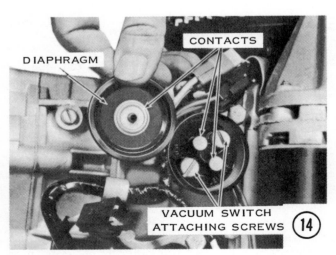

DIAPHRAGM

CONTACTS

VACUUM SWITCH ATTACHING SCREWS

⑭

close to permit using the cranking motor. The switch contacts can be checked with a self-powered test lamp. Connect one test lead to the switch contact and one to a good ground. The lamp should light when the manual starting position marks are aligned.

VACUUM SWITCH

⑬ The vacuum switch should remain open when the ignition key is turned to the ON position. The switch contacts must close when the key is turned to the START position and the cranking motor begins to crank the engine. To test the vacuum switch, disconnect the wires at the connector and connect a test lamp between the switch lead terminals. The test lamp should light only when the engine is being cranked. If the switch fails to operate properly, depress the center of the rubber diaphragm and the test lamp should light.

⑭ If the switch is defective, pull off the rubber diaphragm, and then remove the two screws and gasket from the bypass cover. Disassemble the switch components and wash them in solvent. Inspect the valve and seat for any condition that could prevent proper seating. Clean the contacts, inspect the diaphragm and diaphragm contact, and check the fit of the diaphragm over the switch housing. *CAUTION: An air leak could prevent the contacts from closing.* Assemble the check valve and test its action by alternately blowing and sucking air through the valve. The disc valve must close under pressure and open under suction. Assemble the switch to the bypass cover, using a new gasket. Tighten the screws securely. Slip the diaphragm over the rim of the switch and recheck the operation with a test lamp.

ADJUSTING THE CARBURETOR

⑮ Center the low-speed control knob link, and then remove all four knobs. Gently seat each low-speed adjusting needle by turning it clockwise, and then back each one out 5/8 turn for a preliminary adjustment. *CAUTION: Don't force the needle into its seat, or you will damage the taper, making an accurate adjustment difficult.* Start the engine and, shifting into gear, operate it at half throttle until it reaches operating temperature. Because it is impossible to detect minor speed changes in a V-4 engine, a tachometer must be used for making the following adjustments accurately. Open the throttle fully to clear the engine, and then retard the throttle to the fast-idle position (700–750 rpm). Slowly turn one low-speed adjusting needle clockwise (lean) until the engine hesitates or spits slightly, and then back the adjusting needle out until the engine reaches the highest rpm consistent with smooth performance. Snap open the throttle

CARBURETOR

CONTROL LINK

CONTROL KNOBS

15

and, if the engine hesitates, enrich the low-speed adjustment slightly until the engine responds to the throttle properly. Replace the low-speed knobs in their normal positions without disturbing the adjusting needles.

⑯ Turn the idle speed adjusting screw so that the engine idles at 650 rpm in gear.

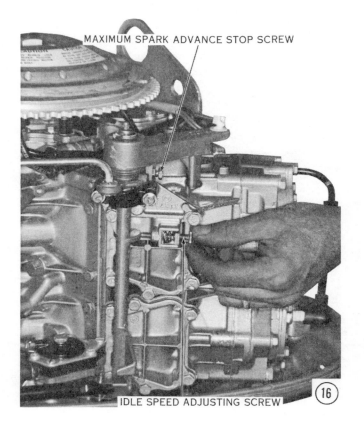

MAXIMUM SPARK ADVANCE STOP SCREW

IDLE SPEED ADJUSTING SCREW

16

4
FUEL SYSTEM SERVICE

The fuel systems of the two smaller engines are gravity fed, while the larger engines use a single-stage fuel pump to lift the fuel from a remote gas tank.

The carburetors of the two-cylinder engines are basically alike in construction details, except that some of the larger models have a fixed high-speed jet and some have an automatic choke.

Service procedures for these similar models will be grouped, using exploded views as a guide. Service procedures for the carburetors of the larger engines will be covered through step-by-step illustrated instructions.

FUEL PUMP

The fuel pump is of the single-stage, diaphragm-displacement type; it is operated by changes in crankcase pressure. Alternate suction and pressure pulses in the crankcase are transmitted to the fuel pump diaphragm through a flexible hose. Fuel is drawn through a fine-mesh filter before entering the pump.

The fuel pump is attached to the powerhead with two screws and is serviced only as an assembly. The filter screen can be serviced by taking out the cover retaining screw.

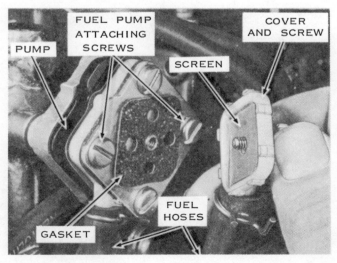

The fuel pump is serviced as an assembly. The filter screen can be cleaned or replaced by taking off the fuel pump cover.

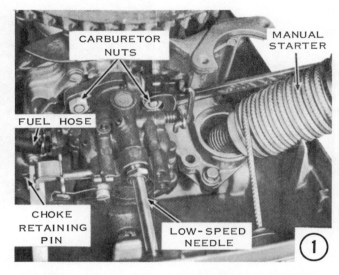

REMOVING THE CARBURETOR
1.5, 3, 4, 5, 6, 9.5, 18 & 20 Hp Engines

① Shut off the fuel supply at the shut-off valve. Remove the low-speed needle adjusting knob. Disconnect the choke retaining pin and control shaft. Disconnect the fuel hose at the carburetor. Keep the free end above the level of the carburetor to prevent fuel from leaking into the lower motor casing. Remove the two

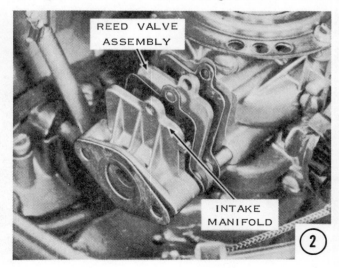

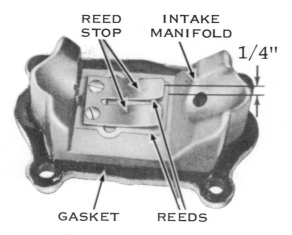

REED STOP   INTAKE MANIFOLD

1/4"

GASKET   REEDS

This picture shows the reed valves of the 1.5 Hp engine. The stop should be adjusted so that it extends 1/4" above the level of the base.

REED VALVE

STOP

Details of the reed valve assembly used on the 9.5 Hp engine.

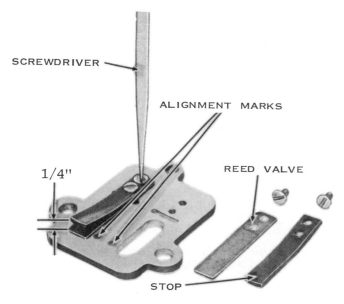

SCREWDRIVER

ALIGNMENT MARKS

1/4"

REED VALVE

STOP

Details of the reed valve assembly used on the 3.0 Hp engine.

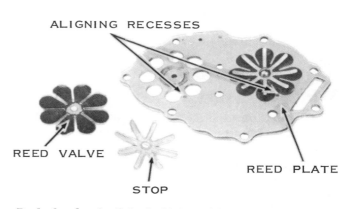

ALIGNING RECESSES

REED VALVE

STOP

REED PLATE

Reed valve plate details for the 20, 33, and 40 Hp engines.

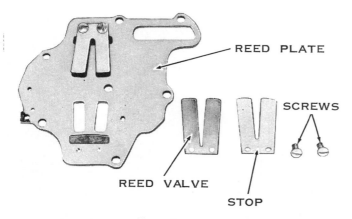

REED PLATE

SCREWS

REED VALVE

STOP

Details of the reed valve assembly used on the 5.0 and 6.0 Hp engines.

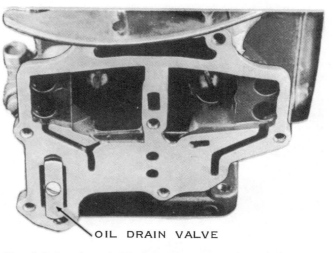

OIL DRAIN VALVE

The oil drain valve normally does not require periodic service. However, it should be cleaned whenever the engine is disassembled for service.

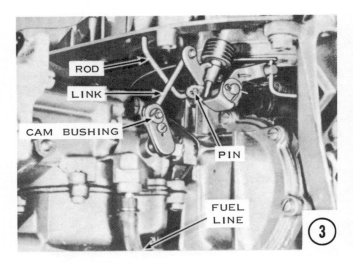

Figure 3: ROD, LINK, CAM BUSHING, PIN, FUEL LINE

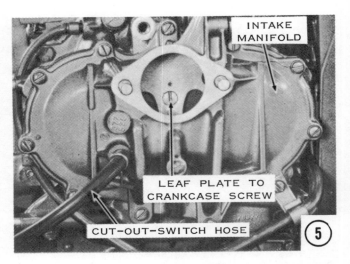

Figure 5: INTAKE MANIFOLD, LEAF PLATE TO CRANKCASE SCREW, CUT-OUT-SWITCH HOSE

screws holding the manual starter in position, and then swing the starter aside for clearance. Remove the carburetor retaining nuts and lockwashers, and then lift off the carburetor. Discard the gasket.

② To remove the reed valve assembly, take out the manifold attaching bolts, and then lift out the intake manifold and valve block as an assembly.

33 Hp Engine

③ Disconnect the fuel line at the carburetor. Remove the throttle lever link by taking out the lever pin at the throttle arm (on electric models).

④ Remove the cranking motor by disconnecting the main battery lead. Remove the three nuts and the five screws holding the starter bracket and mounting

bracket to the crankcase. Lift the starter and bracket assembly off the bracket studs. Remove the two nuts and lockwashers holding the carburetor to the intake manifold. Disconnect the choke solenoid wire at the terminal. Remove the carburetor and gasket from the intake manifold.

⑤ Remove the cotter pin from the bottom end of the starter lever lock-out rod. Disconnect the rod from the throttle lever. Remove the cut-out switch hose from the intake manifold. Take out the eleven screws holding the intake manifold to the powerhead, and then lift off the intake manifold. Remove the screw holding the reed valve plate to the crankcase, and then remove the valve and gasket assembly.

40 Hp Engine

⑥ To remove the manual starter from the powerhead, disconnect the locking lever by removing the screw

Figure 4: SCREWS, STUD NUTS, MAIN BATTERY LEAD, CARBURETOR

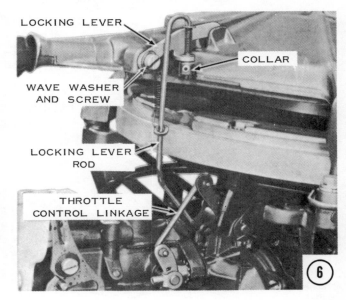

Figure 6: LOCKING LEVER, COLLAR, WAVE WASHER AND SCREW, LOCKING LEVER ROD, THROTTLE CONTROL LINKAGE

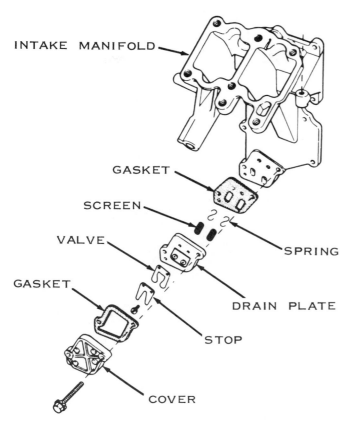

INTAKE MANIFOLD

GASKET

SCREEN

VALVE

GASKET

SPRING

DRAIN PLATE

STOP

COVER

This is the oil drain valve used on the larger two-cylinder engines.

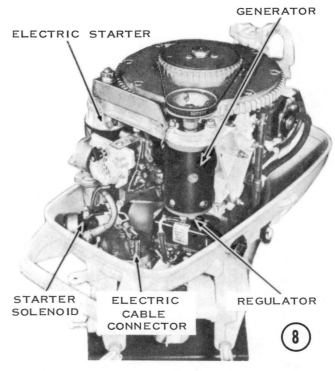

ELECTRIC STARTER

GENERATOR

STARTER SOLENOID

ELECTRIC CABLE CONNECTOR

REGULATOR

⑧

and wave washer which holds the locking lever to the starter housing. Remove the three screws, and then lift the starter assembly from the powerhead.

⑦ Remove the heat tube shield and heat exchanger tubing (automatic choke models).

⑧ Disconnect the wires from the starter, generator,

and choke solenoid. Remove the generator by taking off the pulley flange nut and lockwasher. Loosen the through-bolt nuts to permit releasing the drive belt tension. Lift off the drive belt. Remove the nuts from the generator bracket studs. Remove the screw holding the ring guard to the generator bracket. Lift the bracket and generator from the powerhead as an assembly. Remove the starter by taking out the three nuts and five screws holding the starter motor bracket and mounting bracket to the crankcase. Lift the starter and brackets off the studs.

⑨ Disconnect the fuel hose at the carburetor and

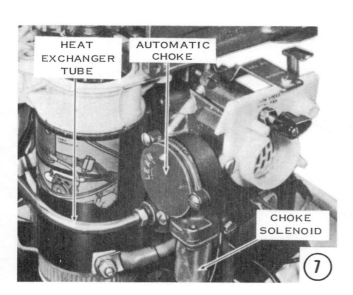

HEAT EXCHANGER TUBE

AUTOMATIC CHOKE

CHOKE SOLENOID

⑦

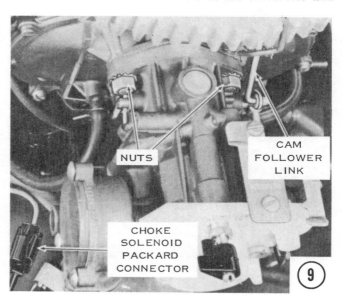

NUTS

CAM FOLLOWER LINK

CHOKE SOLENOID PACKARD CONNECTOR

⑨

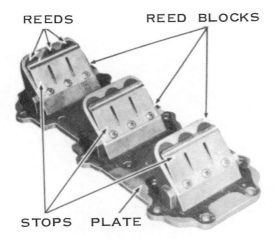

REEDS   REED BLOCKS

STOPS   PLATE

Details of the reed valve plate used on the 55 Hp engine.

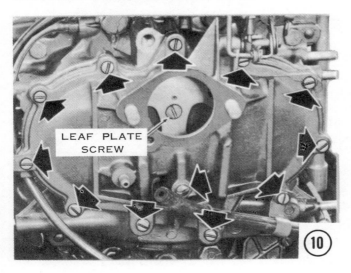

LEAF PLATE SCREW

(10)

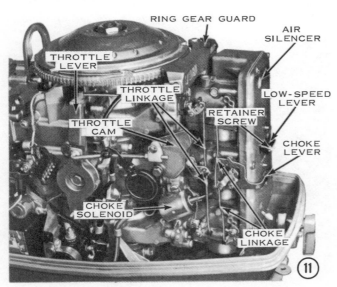

RING GEAR GUARD

AIR SILENCER

THROTTLE LEVER

THROTTLE LINKAGE

RETAINER SCREW

LOW-SPEED LEVER

THROTTLE CAM

CHOKE LEVER

CHOKE SOLENOID

CHOKE LINKAGE

(11)

WASHER

COTTER PIN

ROD

(12)

the cam follower link at the throttle arm. Remove the two nuts and lockwashers holding the carburetor to the intake manifold. Remove the carburetor and discard the gasket.

⑩ Remove the intake manifold from the powerhead and discard the gasket. Remove the screw holding the reed valve plate assembly to the powerhead, lift out the plate, and discard the gasket.

55 Hp Engine

⑪ Disconnect the three fuel hoses at the fuel pump. Remove the screw holding the low-speed adjustment

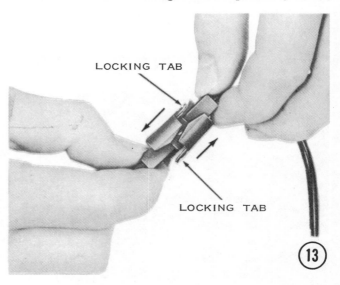

LOCKING TAB

LOCKING TAB

(13)

lever, and then pull off the lever. Remove the screws holding the air silencer cover, remove the cover, and then disconnect the drain hose. Disconnect the choke, throttle, and low-speed adjusting needle valve linkages by pulling them out of the top and bottom carburetor lever retainers. Remove the six screws holding the air silencer, and then take off the air silencer and fuel pump as an assembly. Disconnect the choke solenoid spring, remove the three screws holding the ring gear guard, and then lift off the guard. Disconnect the fuel hoses from the carburetors. Remove the nuts, lock-washers, and carburetors. Discard the gaskets.

65 & 85 Hp Engines

⑫ Remove the cotter pin and washer to disconnect the throttle control rod from the throttle cam yoke.

⑬ Disconnect the solenoid wires at the Packard connector on the starboard side of the engine. Lift up on

the locking tabs, and then slide the halves of the connector apart.

⑭ Disconnect the fuel pump hoses, marking them to assure correct assembly. Disconnect the heat exchanger tube. Remove the carburetor from the manifold by taking out the three retaining screws. Discard the gasket. Remove the fuel pump from the intake manifold, and then take off the manifold and reed valve plate assembly, being careful not to damage the reed valve plate.

100 & 115 Hp Engines

⑮ Disconnect the throttle linkage by removing the anchor yoke pin. Remove the throttle cam and bushings from the carburetor body. Remove the air inlet shield.

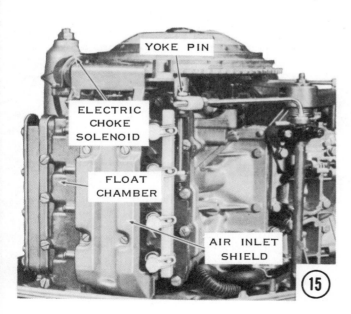

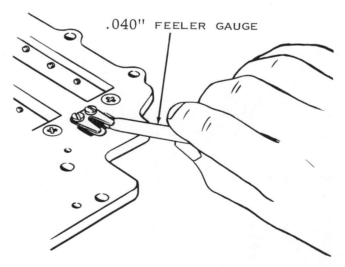

The oil drain valve used on the V-4 engines must have a clearance of 0.040″ between the plate and stop. If necessary, bend the stop for an adjustment.

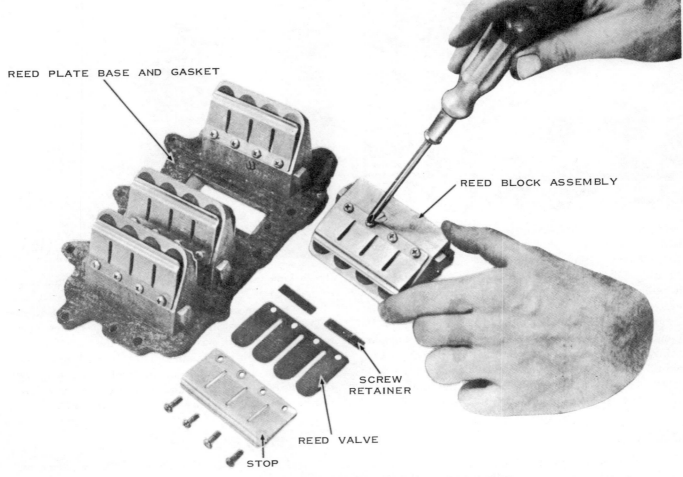

REED PLATE BASE AND GASKET

REED BLOCK ASSEMBLY

SCREW RETAINER

REED VALVE

STOP

Details of the reed valve plate assembly used on most of the V-4 engines.

⑯ Drain the carburetor by removing the plugs from the four float chambers.

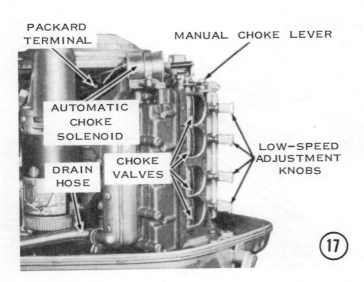

PACKARD TERMINAL

MANUAL CHOKE LEVER

AUTOMATIC CHOKE SOLENOID

DRAIN HOSE

CHOKE VALVES

LOW-SPEED ADJUSTMENT KNOBS

⑰

⑰ Disconnect the fuel line and the vent drain hose at the carburetor. Disconnect the solenoid wires at the Packard terminal by lifting up on the locking tabs and sliding the halves of the connector apart. Remove the ten screws holding the carburetor and reed valve plate to the manifold. Remove the carburetor and reed valve plate assembly, taking care not to damage the reeds.

OVERHAULING A SMALL-ENGINE CARBURETOR

All Small Engines Through 20 Hp

DISASSEMBLING

① Drain the carburetor bowl by removing the high-speed metering needle or the drain plug. Remove the packing nut. Remove the low-speed adjusting needle nut, and then take out the adjusting needle. Remove the

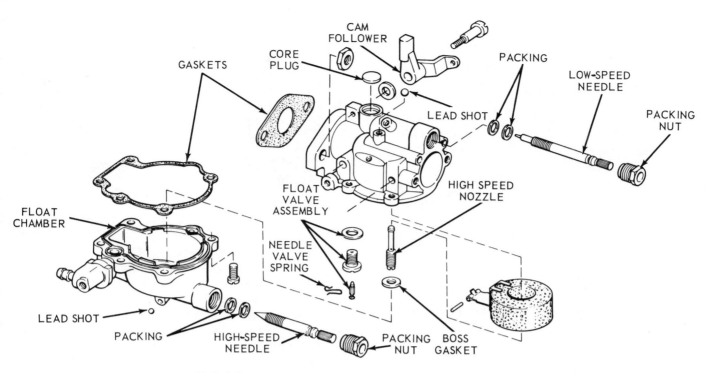

GASKETS

CORE PLUG

CAM FOLLOWER

PACKING

LOW-SPEED NEEDLE

PACKING NUT

LEAD SHOT

FLOAT VALVE ASSEMBLY

HIGH SPEED NOZZLE

FLOAT CHAMBER

NEEDLE VALVE SPRING

LEAD SHOT

PACKING

HIGH-SPEED NEEDLE

PACKING NUT

BOSS GASKET

Exploded view of the carburetor used on the 1.5 and 3.0 Hp engines.

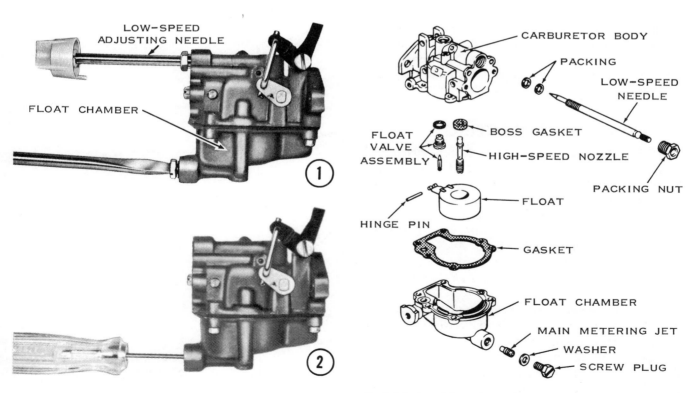

LOW-SPEED ADJUSTING NEEDLE

FLOAT CHAMBER

①

②

CARBURETOR BODY

PACKING

LOW-SPEED NEEDLE

FLOAT VALVE ASSEMBLY

BOSS GASKET

HIGH-SPEED NOZZLE

PACKING NUT

HINGE PIN

FLOAT

GASKET

FLOAT CHAMBER

MAIN METERING JET

WASHER

SCREW PLUG

Exploded view of the carburetor used on the 5, 6, and 20 Hp engines. It is similar to the other carburetors, except that it has a fixed main metering jet.

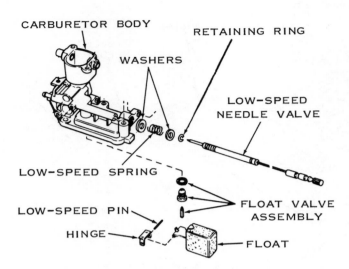

CARBURETOR BODY

RETAINING RING

WASHERS

LOW-SPEED
NEEDLE VALVE

LOW-SPEED SPRING

LOW-SPEED PIN

HINGE

FLOAT VALVE
ASSEMBLY

FLOAT

Exploded view of the carburetor body used on the 9.5 Hp engine. Note the washers at each end of the low-speed adjusting needle spring.

packing from the carburetor body and the float chamber; be careful not to damage the threads in the carburetor body.

② On models with a fixed high-speed jet, take out the main metering jet, using the illustrated tool to keep from damaging the threads. Take out the screws holding the float chamber to the carburetor body, and then separate the two castings. Discard the gasket. Remove the float hinge pin, float, and float valve. Unscrew the inlet needle valve seat and discard the gasket. Remove the high-speed nozzle.

CLEANING AND INSPECTING

Clean all parts, except the cork float, in solvent and blow dry. *CAUTION: Don't use cloth to dry the parts because of the danger of leaving lint in one of the jets or passageways.* Be sure that all particles of gasket material are removed. Flush out all passageways in the carburetor body and float chamber with solvent. Remove any gummy deposits with OMC Accessory Engine Cleaner. *NOTE: Solvent will not remove the gum which accumulates in the float chamber and on the inlet needle valve and seat.*

Check all gasket surfaces for nicks, scratches, or distortion. Slight irregularities can be corrected by using a surface plate and emery cloth.

Check the throttle shaft for excessive play. Check the operation of the choke and throttle valves to make sure that they shut off fully, yet move freely without binding. Replace the carburetor body if the valves or shafts are worn.

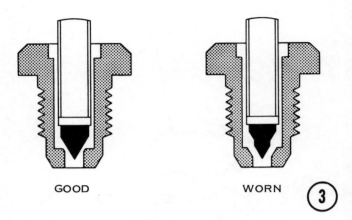

GOOD

WORN

③

Inspect the float and arm for wear or damage. If the float is oil-soaked or leaks, replace it. Check the float arm for wear in the hinge pin hole and the needle valve contact area. Replace the float if it is heavy or damaged. Inspect the hinge pin for wear, which generally results from vibration. Replace the pin if it is grooved.

③ Always replace the needle valve and seat assembly as this is the part of the carburetor which wears the most. If this valve leaks, the fuel level will become too high and the fuel may leak. Always replace all O-ring seals and gaskets to prevent leaks.

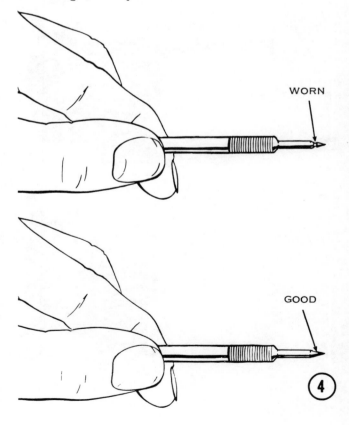

WORN

GOOD

④

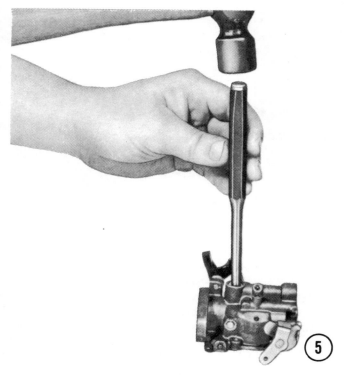

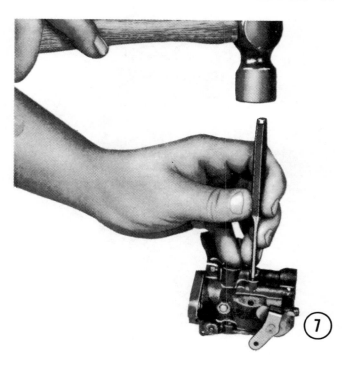

④ Inspect the tapered part of the adjusting needle valves to make sure that there are no grooves, nicks, or scratches, which would make an accurate adjustment difficult.

⑤ If necessary, remove the core plug to clean out the low-speed orifices. If leakage occurs at the core plug area, a smart tap with a hammer and a flat punch in

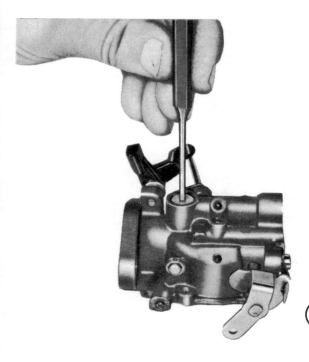

the center of the core plug will correct the condition.

⑥ If leakage persists, drill a 1/8″ hole through the center of the core plug to a depth of not more than 1/16″ below the surface. Use a punch to pry out the core plug. Inspect and clean the casting contact area carefully. If nicks, scratches, or an out-of-round condition exists, the casting will have to be replaced. If the hole in the casting is normal, apply a bead of Sealer 1000 to the outer edge of a new core plug, and then place the plug in the casting, convex side facing up. Flatten the plug with a flat punch, and then recheck for leakage.

⑦ If leakage occurs around a lead shot area, tap the center of the lead shot with a hammer to correct the condition.

⑧ If necessary, remove the lead shot with a sharp-edged tool. Clean and inspect the casting opening. If it is normal, install a new lead shot and flatten it out with a light hammer tap. Recheck for leakage.

ASSEMBLING

⑨ Replace the high-speed nozzle. Install a new needle valve seat, using a new gasket. Replace the needle valve, and then install the float and hinge pin in the carburetor body. Check the float level by turning the carburetor casting upside down so that the weight of

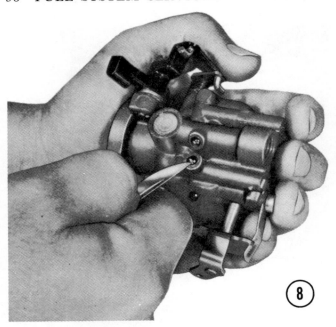

8

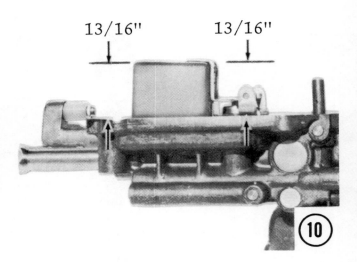

13/16"   13/16"

10

the float closes the needle valve. The float must be parallel and flush with the edge of the casting. Install a new float chamber gasket, and then secure the float chamber to the carburetor body, tightening the screws securely.

⑩ On the 9.5 Hp engine carburetor, turn the carburetor casting upside down so that the weight of the float closes the needle valve. The float should be parallel with the face of the casting and 13/16″ from the flange.

⑪ To measure the float drop on the 9.5 model, turn the body upright, as shown, and the float should drop 1 7/16″ from the flange of the body.

⑫ Replace the packing on the low-speed adjusting needle gland, and then install the needle and packing nut, but do not tighten it. *NOTE: There are washers at each end of the spring on the 9.5 model, as shown.* Replace the high-speed metering jet or adjusting needle, tightening the packing gland nut finger-tight. Turn each of the adjusting needles down until it seats lightly. *CAUTION: Don't turn the adjusting needle in tightly, or you will damage the taper, making an accurate adjustment difficult.* Back out the low-speed adjusting needle for a preliminary adjustment as follows: 1/2 turn for the 6 Hp engine; 3/4 turn for the 9.5; 1 1/4 turns for the 1.5, 3.0, and 5.0; and 2 turns for the 18/20 Hp models. Back out the high-speed adjusting needle 3/4 turn for all models. Tighten the packing gland nuts until the adjusting needle can just be turned with your fingers.

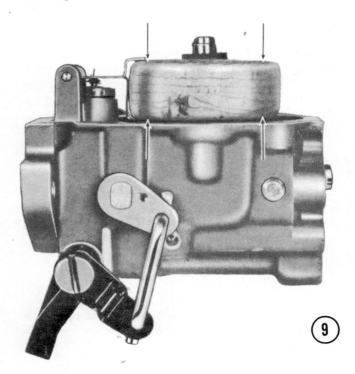

9

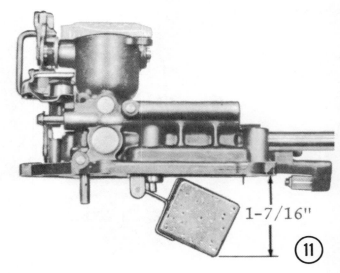

1-7/16"

11

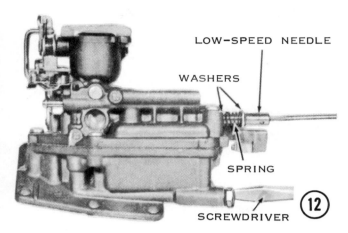

LOW-SPEED NEEDLE

WASHERS

SPRING

SCREWDRIVER

⑫

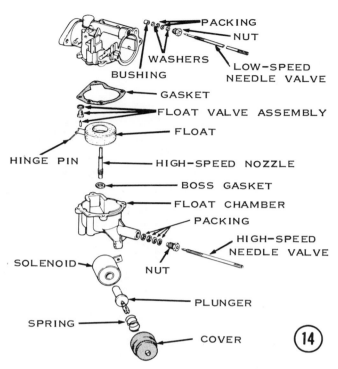

PACKING

NUT

WASHERS

BUSHING

LOW-SPEED NEEDLE VALVE

GASKET

FLOAT VALVE ASSEMBLY

FLOAT

HINGE PIN

HIGH-SPEED NOZZLE

BOSS GASKET

FLOAT CHAMBER

PACKING

SOLENOID

NUT

HIGH-SPEED NEEDLE VALVE

PLUNGER

SPRING

COVER

⑭

33 Hp Engine

⑬ This is the same basic carburetor used on the previous models with the addition of an automatic choke which is operated by a solenoid. To disassemble this carburetor, remove the screw in the end of the low-speed adjusting needle so that you can take off the adjusting knob. Remove the two screws to take off the control panel.

⑭ This exploded view shows that the parts are installed in the same relative positions as on the carburetor just covered.

⑮ After assembling the carburetor, check the choke valve for free operation, and then attach the choke arm to the choke shaft. Install the choke solenoid and spring. Pull out the manual choke lever to the fully choked

position. Adjust the position of the choke solenoid in the bracket until the solenoid plunger has approximately 1/16″ free play. The closed end of the solenoid should be approximately flush with the edge of the boss, as shown. For a preliminary adjustment, the low-speed adjusting needle should be backed out 1 1/4 turns and the high-speed needle 3/8 turn.

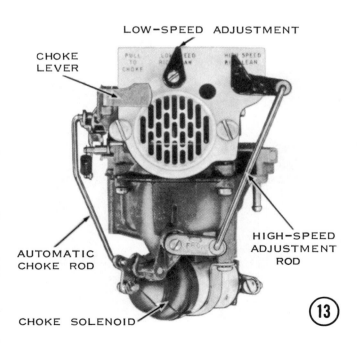

CHOKE LEVER

LOW-SPEED ADJUSTMENT

AUTOMATIC CHOKE ROD

HIGH-SPEED ADJUSTMENT ROD

CHOKE SOLENOID

⑬

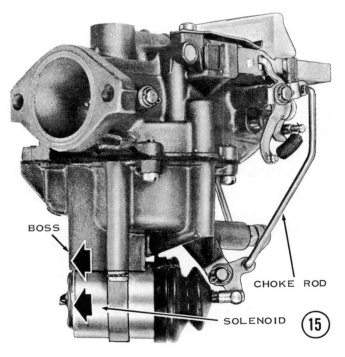

BOSS

CHOKE ROD

SOLENOID

⑮

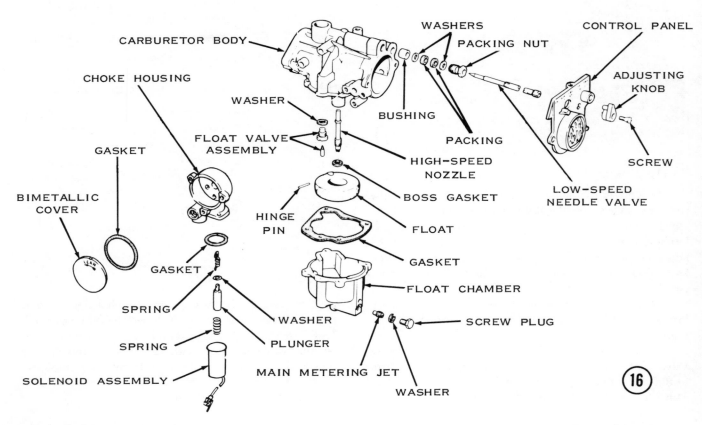

CARBURETOR BODY

WASHERS

PACKING NUT

CONTROL PANEL

CHOKE HOUSING

ADJUSTING KNOB

WASHER

BUSHING

FLOAT VALVE ASSEMBLY

PACKING

GASKET

HIGH-SPEED NOZZLE

SCREW

BIMETALLIC COVER

HINGE PIN

BOSS GASKET

LOW-SPEED NEEDLE VALVE

FLOAT

GASKET

GASKET

FLOAT CHAMBER

SPRING

WASHER

SPRING

PLUNGER

SCREW PLUG

SOLENOID ASSEMBLY

MAIN METERING JET

WASHER

⑯

40 Hp Engine

⑯ The carburetor used on the 40 Hp engine is basically the same as the previous models; it has a fixed high-speed jet and an automatic choke, which is attached to the side of the carburetor casting. The high-speed jet is not adjustable. For a preliminary adjustment, back off the low-speed adjusting needle 7/8 turn.

55 Hp Engine

⑰ This engine uses three carburetors of similar design. As seen by the exploded view, the servicing instructions are similar to those for the previous models. The top of the float should be parallel with the rim of the casting. The low-speed adjusting needle should be backed out 5/8 turn for a preliminary adjustment.

⑱ If the spring was removed from the solenoid plunger, install it by twisting it onto the plunger 2 1/2 to 3 1/2 turns. Attach the solenoid to the intake manifold with the clamp and two screws. The solenoid should be positioned so that the shoulder of the rod extends out 1/4", as shown.

1/4"

⑱

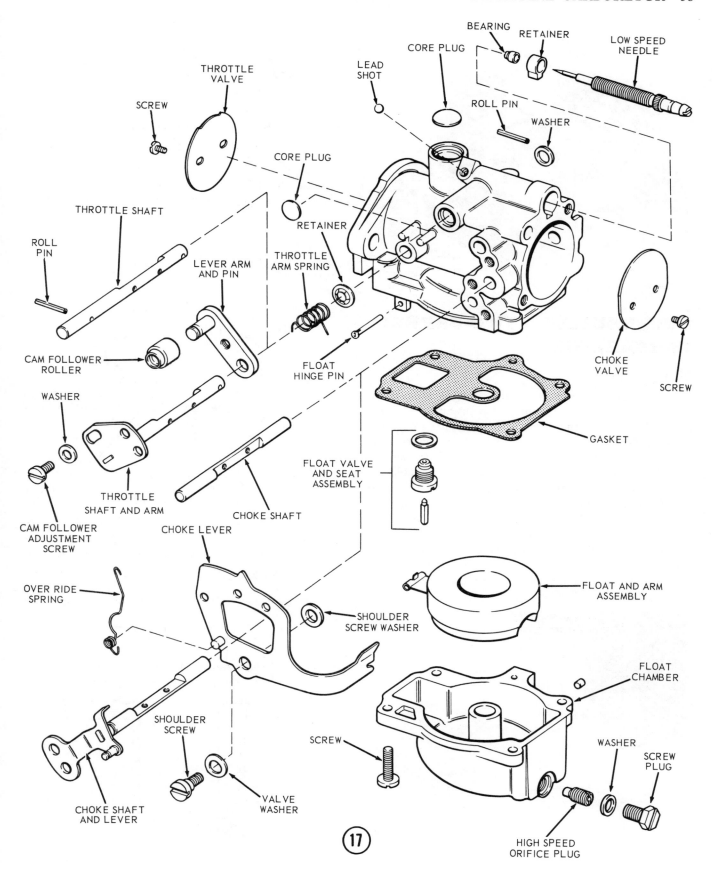

SCREW

THROTTLE VALVE

LEAD SHOT

CORE PLUG

BEARING

RETAINER

LOW SPEED NEEDLE

ROLL PIN

WASHER

CORE PLUG

THROTTLE SHAFT

RETAINER

THROTTLE ARM SPRING

ROLL PIN

LEVER ARM AND PIN

CHOKE VALVE

SCREW

CAM FOLLOWER ROLLER

FLOAT HINGE PIN

WASHER

GASKET

CAM FOLLOWER ADJUSTMENT SCREW

THROTTLE SHAFT AND ARM

CHOKE SHAFT

FLOAT VALVE AND SEAT ASSEMBLY

CHOKE LEVER

OVER RIDE SPRING

SHOULDER SCREW WASHER

FLOAT AND ARM ASSEMBLY

FLOAT CHAMBER

SHOULDER SCREW

SCREW

WASHER

SCREW PLUG

CHOKE SHAFT AND LEVER

VALVE WASHER

HIGH SPEED ORIFICE PLUG

17

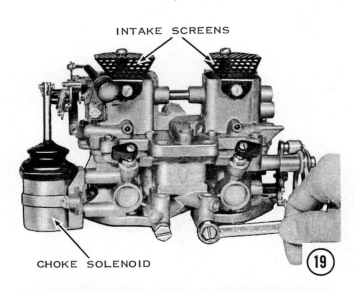

INTAKE SCREENS

CHOKE SOLENOID

⑲

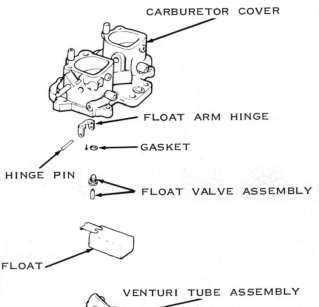

CARBURETOR COVER

FLOAT ARM HINGE

GASKET

HINGE PIN

FLOAT VALVE ASSEMBLY

FLOAT

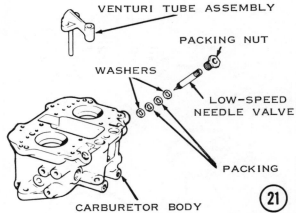

VENTURI TUBE ASSEMBLY

PACKING NUT

WASHERS

LOW-SPEED NEEDLE VALVE

PACKING

CARBURETOR BODY

㉑

OVERHAULING A TWO-BARREL CARBURETOR

65 Hp Engine

⑲ Drain the carburetor by removing the plugs from the body. Take off the air intake screens and the choke solenoid. Remove the lever and bellcrank from the cover. *NOTE: The threaded ends of the choke and throttle valve attaching screws are staked during assembly.* Under normal conditions, it is not desirable to remove the choke and throttle valves.

⑳ Remove the main metering jets, using a special screwdriver, Tool No. 379664, to keep from damaging the threads in the carburetor body.

㉑ Remove the eight screws holding the carburetor cover to the body, and then separate the two castings. Remove the nylon hinge pin to permit removal of the

float. Remove the float valve, seat, and gasket from the carburetor. Remove the low-speed needle packing nuts, and then unscrew the low-speed needle valves. Remove the packing and washers, being careful not to damage the threads.

㉒ Replace the float valve and seat, using a new

⑳

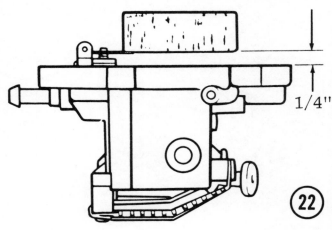

1/4"

㉒

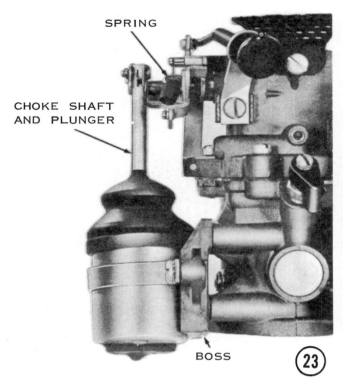

choke arm to the shaft, and then install the choke solenoid and spring. Adjust the position of the choke solenoid so that the choke valves close when the plunger bottoms in the solenoid. The closed end of the solenoid should be approximately flush with the boss, as shown. With the choke knob pulled out all the way, the choke shaft should have 1/16" free play. The low-speed adjusting needle valves should be backed out 5/8 turn for a preliminary adjustment.

gasket. Install the float and hinge pin. Turn the carburetor cover upside down so that the weight of the float closes the needle valve. The float should be parallel with the face of the casting and be approximately 1/4" from the flange, as shown.

㉓ Check the choke for free operation. Attach the

85 Hp Engine

㉔ The 85 Hp engine carburetor is basically like the two-barrel unit used on the 65 Hp engine, except that the high-speed nozzles and venturis are different.

㉕ To assure the correct positioning of the high-speed venturis, it is necessary to use a venturi-locating

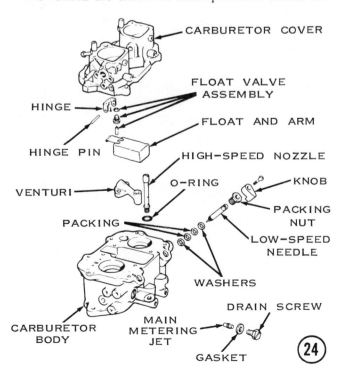

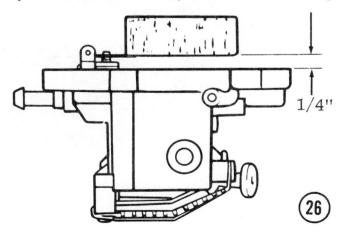

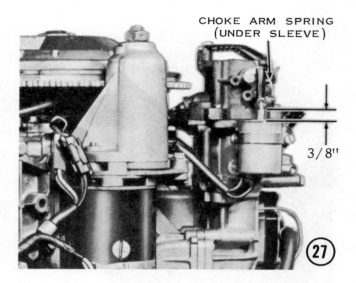

CHOKE ARM SPRING
(UNDER SLEEVE)

3/8"

(27)

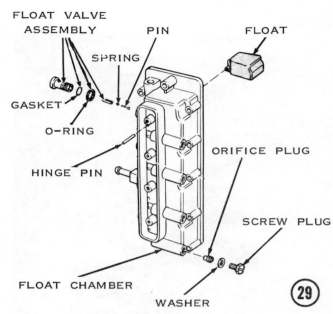

FLOAT VALVE
ASSEMBLY   PIN   FLOAT

SPRING

GASKET

O-RING

HINGE PIN   ORIFICE PLUG

SCREW PLUG

FLOAT CHAMBER   WASHER   (29)

gauge, Tool No. 379242, so that the engine will run efficiently.

㉖ Replace the float valve seat and gasket. Install the needle valve, float, and hinge pin. Turn the cover upside down so that the weight of the float closes the needle valve. The float should be parallel to the face of the casting and approximately 1/4" from the flange, as shown. Install the low-speed needle valves, and then back each out one full turn for a preliminary adjustment.

㉗ Check the choke valves for free operation. Install the choke solenoid. Attach the choke arm spring, and twist it 2 1/2 to 3 1/2 turns before attaching it to the solenoid plunger. The distance from the edge of the solenoid to the end of the plunger should be 3/8", as shown. Adjust the position of the solenoid in its bracket, if necessary.

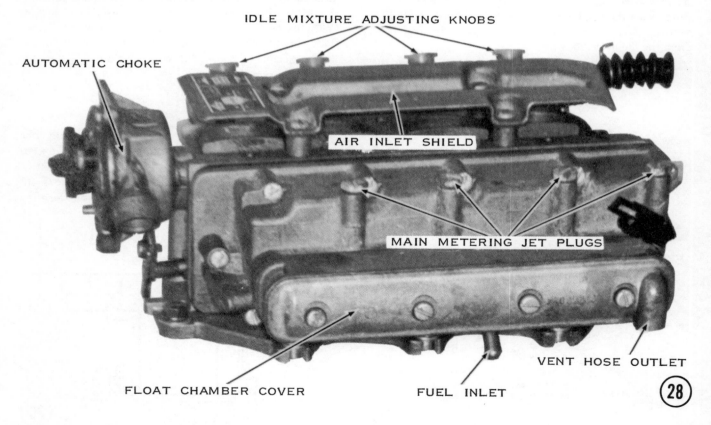

IDLE MIXTURE ADJUSTING KNOBS

AUTOMATIC CHOKE

AIR INLET SHIELD

MAIN METERING JET PLUGS

FLOAT CHAMBER COVER   FUEL INLET   VENT HOSE OUTLET

(28)

(30)

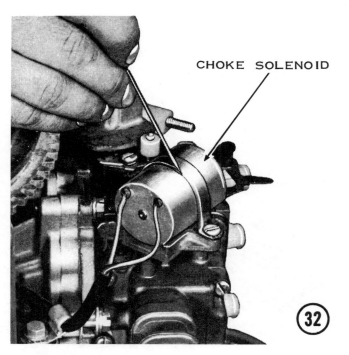

CHOKE SOLENOID

(32)

OVERHAULING A FOUR-BARREL CARBURETOR

100 & 115 Hp Engines

㉘ Remove the float chamber by taking out the 12 retaining screws. *CAUTION: Hold the float chamber upright to prevent the floats from dropping out.*

㉙ Lift out the floats, needle valves, pins, and springs. Unscrew the needle valve seats. *CAUTION: Keep each set together, as they are matched parts.*

㉚ Remove the main metering (high-speed) jet plugs, and then unscrew the jets, using a special screwdriver, Tool No. 379664, to keep from damaging the threads in the body.

㉛ Remove the high-speed tube assemblies and the float chamber-to-carburetor body gaskets and plate.

㉜ Before removing the choke solenoid, scribe a mark on the solenoid case alongside of its retaining strap as a reference line for assembly. Disconnect the choke solenoid spring from the choke arm. Remove the solenoid by loosening the two retaining strap screws. Loosen the screw, and then lift the choke arm from the choke shaft. *NOTE: The threaded ends of the throttle and choke valve attaching screws are staked during manufacture to prevent loss. Under normal conditions, it is not desirable to remove the choke or throttle valves.*

㉝ To remove the low-speed adjusting needle valves, pry off the control knobs. *CAUTION: Don't lose the springs and washers.* Remove the control knob adjusting link. With the aid of the knobs, turn the low-speed adjusting needle valves counterclockwise to remove them.

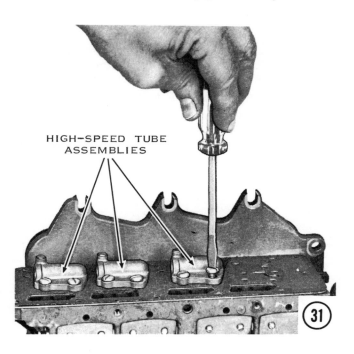

HIGH-SPEED TUBE ASSEMBLIES

(31)

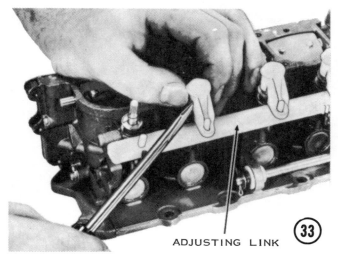

ADJUSTING LINK

(33)

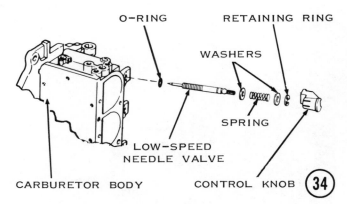

O-RING RETAINING RING
WASHERS
LOW-SPEED
NEEDLE VALVE
SPRING
CARBURETOR BODY CONTROL KNOB (34)

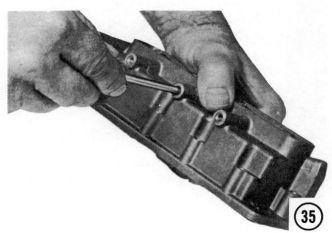

(35)

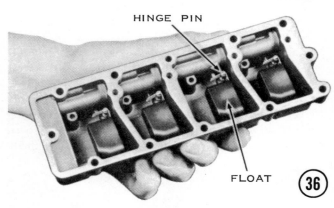

HINGE PIN
FLOAT (36)

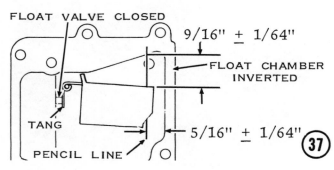

FLOAT VALVE CLOSED
9/16" ± 1/64"
FLOAT CHAMBER INVERTED
TANG
5/16" ± 1/64" (37)
PENCIL LINE

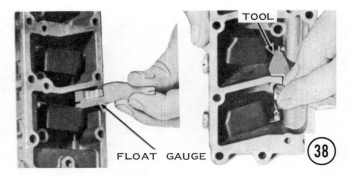

TOOL
FLOAT GAUGE (38)

㉞ Replace the O-ring seals in the carburetor body. Install the springs, washers, and retaining rings on the low-speed adjusting needle valves. Screw the needles in with your fingers, using an adjusting knob to assist, until the needle valves seat lightly, and then back each out 5/8 turn for a preliminary adjustment. *CAUTION: Don't force the needle valves into the seats, or you will damage the taper, making an adjustment difficult. NOTE: The rest of the linkage will be installed after the low-speed adjustments have been made on a running engine.*

㉟ Replace the main metering jets, plugs, and washers. Use the special tool to keep from damaging the threads. Correctly locate a new carburetor-to-float chamber gasket, and then attach the high-speed tube assemblies to the carburetor body.

㊱ Install the inlet needle valve seats in the float chamber. Position the inlet needles, with springs and pins in place, and then slide the floats onto the hinge pins. Make sure that the floats do not bind on the hinge pins. *CAUTION: The needles valves and seats must be installed in matched sets.*

㊲ To make a float level adjustment, turn the float chamber upside down so that the weight of the float closes the needle valve. Scribe a pencil line parallel to the gasket surface, 5/16" down the entire length of the float chamber. Where this line touches the top gasket surface, measure down 9/16" to obtain the correct float level setting.

㊳ A special float gauge, Tool No. 380546, is available to check the float setting. Insert the gauge into the float chamber, as shown at the left. Hold the gauge so

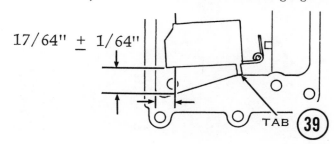

17/64" ± 1/64"

TAB (39)

that the tang rests on the machined surface; the edge of the gauge should be flush against the top of the float and the float chamber. *CAUTION: Don't compress the spring; only the weight of the float should be against the needle valve.* To change the float setting, insert the

slotted end of the gauge (tool) over the tang to bend it, as shown at the right. *CAUTION: Bend the tang as close to the hinge pin as possible.*

㊴ To measure the float drop, turn the float chamber right side up. The float should drop 17/64″ along the 5/16″ line measured from the bottom of the float chamber to the bottom of the float. Bend the float tab to make an adjustment. Fasten the float chamber to the carburetor body with 12 screws.

㊵ Check the operation of the choke to be sure that the choke valves shut off the air flow fully. Air leakage will cause hard starting. Assemble the automatic choke arm, making sure that the choke spring is properly installed. The choke spring must hold the choke valves closed when the choke knob is in the ON position and must hold the choke valves open when the choke knob is in the OFF position. *CAUTION: The choke valves must be free to open under spring tension at all times, regardless of the choke knob position.* Install the choke solenoid and spring, aligning the scribe mark on the case with the edge of the retaining strap. Adjust the position of the solenoid in the strap so that the end of the plunger measures 3/8″ from the front of the solenoid case.

The carburetor must be functioning properly and the engine tuned for best performance.

5
ENGINE SERVICE

Most outboard motors operate on the two-cycle principle. That is, they fire each time that the piston comes up. Most two-cycle motors have reed-type valves in place of the poppet-type used in a four-stroke cycle engine. Also, the oil must be pre-mixed with the fuel as both have to pass through the crankcase on the way to the combustion chamber.

PRINCIPLES OF OPERATION

The piston in a two-cycle motor acts as an inlet and exhaust valve. In starting a two-cycle motor, the crankshaft turns and the piston rises. Starting with the piston at its highest point of travel (and with the combustion chamber filled with a compressed mixture of air and fuel), a spark from the spark plug ignites the compressed mixture. The resulting explosion within the cylinder forces the piston down, delivering its energy to the crank shaft. During the upward stroke, the piston draws a fresh charge of fuel and air through the intake reed valve and into the crankcase. The crankcase, which is airtight, contains the crankshaft and connecting rods. On the downward stroke, the charge of fuel and air, previously drawn in, is compressed in the crankcase and, when the piston approaches the bottom of the stroke, an exhaust port is uncovered on the side of the cylinder wall. The unburned gases escape through this port, and the combustion chamber pressure falls. An instant later, the piston uncovers an inlet port on the opposite side, and the fresh charge forces its way up from the crankcase to drive out the remainder of the exhaust gases. A projection on the top of the piston, on the intake side, deflects the fresh charge and prevents it from passing directly across the cylinder and out of the exhaust port.

Recently, a new system of loop scavenging the combustion chamber has come into use. This engine has an almost flat piston dome, with a slightly curved contour. Two intake ports are slanted upward and face each other. This has a directional effect on the two incoming charges so that they impinge on each other and flow upward and around the smooth dome-shape of the combustion chamber, and then down and out of the exhaust ports on the adjacent side of the cylinder wall. The flow pattern of the fresh incoming fuel-laden gases very effectively drives out the burned gases.

On alternate-firing, twin-cylinder outboard motors, the pistons are connected to the crankshaft at a 180° angle, and a power stroke is delivered every 180°, producing the reciprocating motion which is transferred to the shaft to create the rotary motion. The firing order is governed by the magneto, which is connected to one end

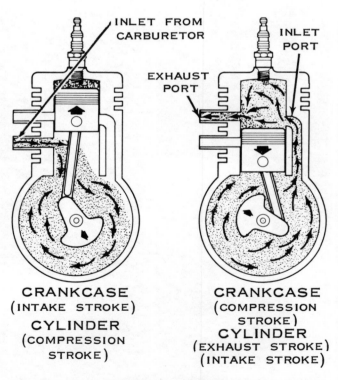

INLET FROM CARBURETOR

INLET PORT

EXHAUST PORT

CRANKCASE
(INTAKE STROKE)
CYLINDER
(COMPRESSION STROKE)

CRANKCASE
(COMPRESSION STROKE)
CYLINDER
(EXHAUST STROKE)
(INTAKE STROKE)

The two-stroke cycle engine fires each time that the piston comes up. Because the crankcase acts as a transfer pump for the air-fuel mixture, lubrication of the engine depends on the addition of lubricating oil to the gasoline.

of the crankshaft. At each 180° of rotation of the crankshaft, electrical sparks are generated and transmitted to the spark plugs to fire the charges alternately. A cam, mounted on the crankshaft within the magneto, opens and closes the breaker points to produce these sparks.

Most two-cycle motors use reed-type inlet valves. They operate automatically, opening when the pressure in the crankcase is low enough so that the outside pressure can overcome the reed tension. The rate of speed at which the engine is operating varies the crankcase pressure and regulates the degree of opening of the reeds. This allows a satisfactory performance level throughout the entire speed range of the engine because the reeds open to the varying demands created by the different speeds.

DETAILS OF THE ENGINE

All of the two-cylinder outboard motors manufactured by the Outboard Marine Corporation are basically alike in construction details, and all of the four-cylinder engines are similarly based on a common design. Therefore, detailed repair instructions for the 18/20 Hp (two-cylinder) and the 100 Hp (four-cylinder) engines are covered through step-by-step illustrated sequences. The engineering design of the one-cylinder engine is similar to that of the two-cylinder engine, and the small differences are covered by an exploded view and essential service notes. The three-cylinder engine uses a unique

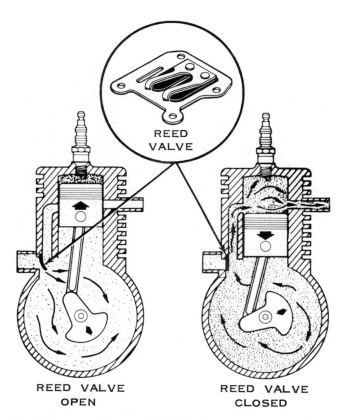

REED VALVE
OPEN

REED VALVE
CLOSED

Reed valves are used to control the flow of fuel to the crankcase. As the piston moves upward in the cylinder, the resulting crankcase suction overcomes the spring tension of the reed, pulling the free end from its seat so that the air-fuel mixture can be sucked into the crankcase.

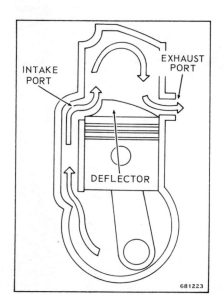

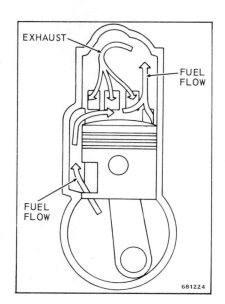

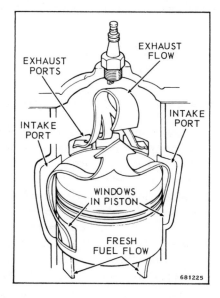

These drawings show the difference between a cross-flow type of combustion chamber (left) and the new loop-scavenged chamber (right two drawings). In the loop-scavenged system, the piston dome is rather flat. The incoming gases are deflected across the piston by the angular direction of the ports and drive out the exhaust gases, as shown at the right.

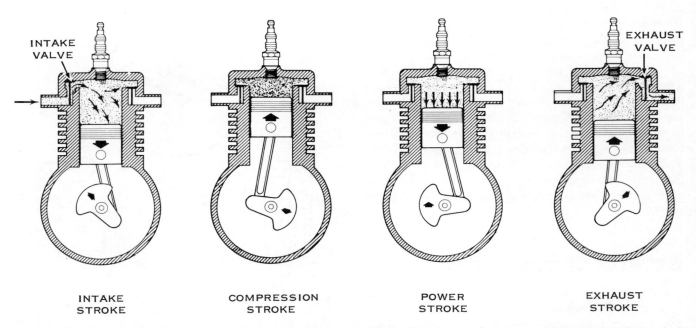

INTAKE VALVE

EXHAUST VALVE

INTAKE STROKE

COMPRESSION STROKE

POWER STROKE

EXHAUST STROKE

This diagram shows the four-stroke cycle gasoline engine, which fires every second time the piston reaches the top of its stroke. In other words, it takes four strokes of the piston to complete one entire cycle.

loop-scavenging principle to move the gases into and out of the combustion chambers. Details of this engine are covered through an exploded view and essential service notes.

Before attempting to repair one of these engines, it is absolutely essential to invest in some special tools and equipment to do the job properly. Without the proper tools, some of the processes are exceedingly difficult, and the danger of damaging parts becomes greater.

GENERAL INSTRUCTIONS

Make sure that the work bench and surrounding areas are clean before starting to work. Use clean containers to hold the parts to keep them from being lost; biscuit tins do very nicely for screws, washers, nuts, and the other small parts. Use bread tins or coffee cans for the larger parts. Always keep replacement parts in their cartons or wrappers until ready for use. If parts are unwrapped, they are apt to get dirty, to be lost, or to be mixed with other parts which are similar.

When an engine comes into the shop for repair or overhaul, clean the exterior thoroughly. As the engine is disassembled, clean the parts in solvent and dry them with low-pressure compressed air.

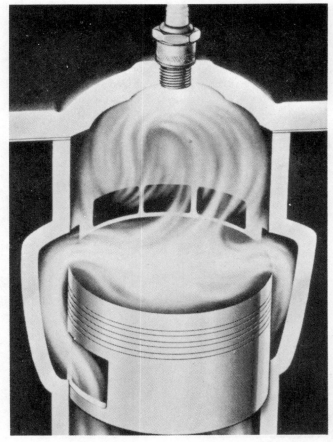

In the loop-scavenged engine, the intake gases are deflected across the top of the piston by the angle of the intake ports. No deflector is used.

ONE-CYLINDER ENGINE SERVICE NOTES

To disassemble the engine, remove the cover, carburetor, manifold, and fuel tank. Take off the flywheel, magneto cam, and magneto armature plate. Remove the spark plug. Remove the six screws holding the powerhead to the exhaust housing, and then lift the powerhead to the bench for further work.

Use the exploded view to assist in disassembling the engine, making sure to note the special instructions which follow:

To remove the connecting rod screws, it is necessary first to bend back the lock plate tabs. If a tab is broken off, it is essential to find the piece so that it cannot remain in the engine to cause damage. Thirty (30) needle bearings are used in the connecting rod and cap. Be careful not to lose any needle bearings or the two connecting rod-to-cap dowels.

Measure the cylinder bore for wear, which must not exceed 0.002″, or the cylinders should be rebored. A 0.020″ oversize piston and ring set is available for service.

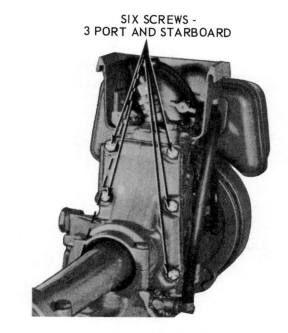

SIX SCREWS - 3 PORT AND STARBOARD

To remove the powerhead from the one-cylinder engine, take out the six screws from underneath, as shown.

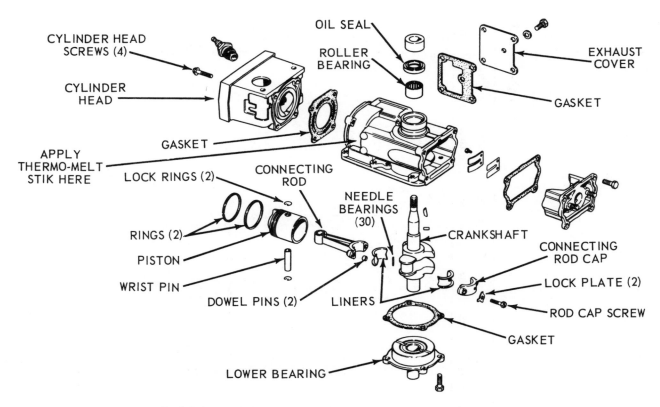

Exploded view of the parts of the powerhead of the one-cylinder engine.

MECHANICAL ENGINE SPECIFICATIONS

Models (Hp)	Cyl.	Year	Bore (Inches)	Stroke (Inches)	Displacement (Cu. In.)	Crankpin	Top Main	Center Main	Bottom Main
							Crankshaft Sizes		
1.5	1	1968–69	1-9/16	1-3/8	2.64	.6685–.6690	.7497–.7502	—	.7497–.7502
3.0	2	1952–68	1-9/16	1-3/8	5.28	.6250–.6255	.6849–.6854	.6849–.6854	.6849–.6854
4.0	2	1969	1-9/16	1-3/8	5.28	.6250–.6255	.7515–.7520	.6849–.6854	.6849–.6854
5.0	2	1965–68	1-15/16	1-1/2	8.84	.6685–.6690	.8075–.8080	.8075–.8080	.8075–.8080
5.5	2	1956–64	1-15/16	1-1/2	8.84	.6685–.6690	.8075–.8080	.8075–.8080	.8075–.8080
6.0	2	1965–69	1-15/16	1-1/2	8.84	.6685–.6690	.8075–.8080	.8075–.8080	.8075–.8080
9.5	2	1964–69	2-5/16	1-13/16	15.2	.8127–.8132	.8120–.8125	.8127–.8132	.8120–.8125
18/20	2	1957–69	2-1/2	2-1/4	22.0	1.0000–1.0005	.9995–1.0000	.9995–1.0000	.9995–1.0000
25	2	1969	2-1/2	2-1/4	22.0	1.0000–1.0005	.9995–1.0000	.9995–1.0000	.9995–1.0000
28	2	1962–64	2-7/8	2-3/4	35.7	1.1823–1.1828	1.2495–1.2500	.9995–1.0000	.9995–1.0000
33	2	1965–69	3-1/16	2-3/4	40.5	1.1823–1.1828	1.2495–1.2500	.9995–1.0000	.9995–1.0000
40	2	1960–69	3-3/16	2-3/4	43.9	1.1823–1.1828	1.2495–1.2500	.9995–1.0000	.9995–1.0000
55	3	1968–69	3.0	2-11/32	49.7	1.1823–1.1828	1.4974–1.4979	1.3748–1.3752	1.1810–1.1815
60	4	1964–67	3.0	2-1/2	70.7	1.1812–1.1819	1.2653–1.2658	1.3748–1.3752	1.1810–1.1815
65	4	1968	3.0	2-1/2	70.7	1.1823–1.1828	1.4975–1.4980	1.3748–1.3752	1.1810–1.1815
75	4	1960–65	3-3/8	2-1/2	89.5	1.1823–1.1828	1.2653–1.2658	1.3748–1.3752	1.1810–1.1815
80	4	1966–67	3-3/8	2-1/2	89.5	1.1823–1.1828	1.2653–1.2658	1.3748–1.3752	1.1810–1.1815
85	4	1968	3-3/8	2-1/2	89.5	1.1823–1.1828	1.2653–1.2658	1.3748–1.3752	1.1810–1.1815
85	4	1969	3-3/8	2.588	92.6	1.1823–1.1828	1.2653–1.2658	1.3748–1.3752	1.1810–1.1815
90	4	1964–65	3-3/8	2-1/2	89.5	1.1823–1.1828	1.2653–1.2658	1.3748–1.3752	1.1810–1.1815
100	4	1966–68	3-3/8	2-1/2	89.5	1.1823–1.1828	1.2653–1.2658	1.3748–1.3752	1.1810–1.1815
115	4	1969	3-7/16	2.588	96.1	1.1823–1.1828	1.2653–1.2658	1.3748–1.3752	1.1810–1.1815

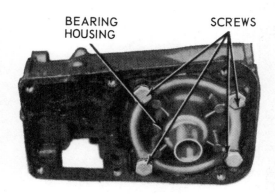

The crankshaft lower bearing is supported by four screws.

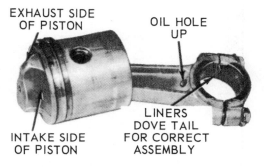

This picture shows how the piston should be assembled to the connecting rod.

When installing a new wrist pin, it must be inserted through the slip-fit side of the piston (marked "L," for loose). The exhaust deflector side of the piston should be on the same side as the boss markings on the connecting rod and cap. When installed in the engine, the oil hole in the big end of the connecting rod must be facing

The slip-fit side of the piston is marked with an "L." The wrist pin must be installed from this side.

up, and the exhaust deflector side of the piston should be facing the port side of the engine.

When replacing the needle bearing inserts, make sure that the dovetail ends match when the connecting rod and cap are matched. When installing the connecting rod, position 14 needle bearings in the connecting rod, holding them in place with OMC Needle Bearing Grease. Move the piston up so that the connecting rod bearings are against the crankpin. Apply some Needle Bearing Grease to the crankpin, and then install 16 needle bearings. Attach the cap, making sure that the dowel pins are in place. To check whether all of the needle bearings are in place, insert a small rod or piece

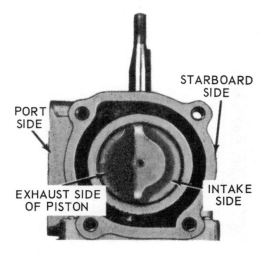

When installing the piston in the cylinder, make sure that the exhaust side of the piston is facing the port side of the engine.

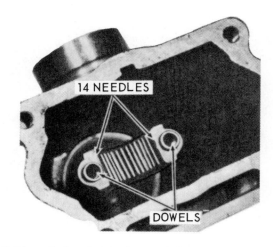

Install 14 needle bearings in the rod, holding them in place with OMC Needle Bearing Grease.

ENGINE CLEARANCE CHART

Models (Hp)	Piston			Crankshaft				Connecting Rod	
	Ring End Gap	Ring Side Clearance	Bore Clearance	Upper Main	Center Main	Lower Main	End Play	Piston End	Crankshaft End
1.5	.005-.015	.0010-.0035	.0043-.0055	②	—	②	.001-.024	.0004-.0011	②
3.0	.005-.015	.0010-.0035	.0013-.0025	.0013-.0023	.0013-.0023	.0013-.0023	.002-.010	.0004-.0011	.0007-.0017
4.0	.005-.015	.0010-.0035	.0008-.0020	②	.0013-.0023	.0013-.0023	.002-.007	.0004-.0011	.0007-.0017
5.0	.005-.015	.0010-.0035	.0018-.0030	.0015-.0025	.0015-.0025	.0015-.0025	.002-.010	.0003-.0010	②
5.5	.005-.015	.0010-.0035	.0018-.0030	.0015-.0025	.0015-.0025	.0015-.0025	.002-.010	.0003-.0010	②
6.0	.005-.015	.0010-.0035	.0018-.0030	.0015-.0025	.0015-.0025	.0015-.0025	.002-.010	.0003-.0010	②
9.5	.007-.017	.0010-.0035	.0035-.0050	①	②	①	.002-.012	②	②
18/20	.007-.017	.0020-.0040	.0032-.0047	①	①	①	.004-.023	②	①
25	.007-.017	.0020-.0040	.0033-.0048	①	①	①	.004-.023	②	①
28	.007-.017	.0045-.0070	.0030-.0045	①	①	①	.003-.011	②	①
33	.007-.017	.0045-.0070	.0030-.0045	①	①	①	.003-.011	②	①
40	.007-.017	.0020-.0045	.0030-.0045	①	①	①	.003-.011	②	①
55	.007-.017	.0015-.0046	.0040-.0055	①	①	③	.00055-.01635	②	①
60	.007-.017	.0045-.0070	.0035-.0050	①	①	③	.0006-.0336	②	①
65	.007-.017	.0045-.0070	.0035-.0050	①	①	③	.0006-.0336	②	①
75	.007-.017	.0045-.0070	.0025-.0045	①	①	③	.0006-.0345	②	①
80	.007-.017	.0045-.0070	.0025-.0040	①	①	③	.0006-.0345	②	①
85	.007-.017	.0045-.0070	.0025-.0040	①	①	③	.0006-.0345	②	①
90	.007-.017	.0045-.0070	.0015-.0030	①	①	③	.0006-.0345	②	①
100	.007-.017	.0045-.0070	.0015-.0030	①	①	③	.0006-.0345	②	①
115	.007-.017	.0020-.0040	.0025-.0045	①	①	③	.0006-.0345	②	①

① Roller bearing.
② Needle bearing.
③ Ball bearing.

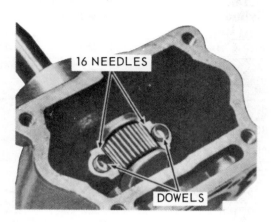

Position 16 needle bearings on the crankpin, as shown.

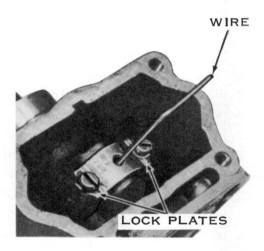

If the correct number of needle bearings has been installed, you should not be able to touch the crankpin with a piece of wire inserted through the oil hole.

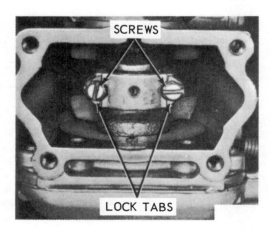

The locking tabs must be made to conform to the flat on the screw. *CAUTION: Don't back off the screw to align the flat with the tab.*

of wire through the oil hole in the cap, as shown. It should not be possible to touch the crankpin with the wire, unless one of the needle bearings has been left out. Tighten the connecting rod screws to 60–66 in-lbs. of torque, and then bend up the locks. *CAUTION: Don't back off the screw if the locking tab does not fit against the flat on the screw. It is essential, instead, that the tab be made to conform to the flat on the screw.* Check the rod for binding; it must float freely over the full length of the crankpin.

When installing the magneto cam, make sure that the side marked TOP faces up.

Complete tuning instructions for the one-cylinder engine are covered in Chapter 3.

OVERHAULING A TWO-CYLINDER ENGINE

The following instructions specifically cover the 18/20 Hp engine, but they apply equally well to all two-cylinder engines. Specifications and tuning instructions may vary somewhat from the other engines; therefore, detailed specification charts for all engines are provided in this chapter. Tuning instructions for the other engines are covered in detail in Chapter 3.

REMOVING THE POWERHEAD

① Remove the hood by depressing the latch and then lifting the hood from the front.

② Remove the low-speed mixture adjusting knob by prying it off with a screwdriver. Remove the arm from the low-speed adjusting needle valve. Lift up on the rear of the choke arm to disconnect the choke control shaft from the carburetor.

③ Remove the manual starter by taking out the

ENGINE TORQUE CHART

Models (Hp)	Spark Plugs (Ft-lbs.)	Flywheel Nut (Ft-lbs.)	Connecting Rod Screws (In-lbs.)	Cylinder Head Screws (In-lbs.)	Crankcase-to-Cylinder Screws (In-lbs.)			Crankcase Head (Bearing Housing) Screws	
					Upper	Center	Lower	Upper (In-lbs.)	Lower (In-lbs.)
1.5	17.5–20.5	22–25	60–66	60–80	—	—	—	—	60–80
3.0	17.5–20.5	30–40	60–66	60–80	60–80	60–80	60–80	—	—
4.0	17.5–20.5	30–40	60–66	60–80	60–80	60–80	60–80	—	—
5.0	17.5–20.5	40–45	60–66	60–80	60–80	60–80	60–80	—	—
5.5	17.5–20.5	40–45	60–66	60–80	60–80	60–80	60–80	—	—
6.0	17.5–20.5	40–45	60–66	60–80	60–80	60–80	60–80	—	—
9.5	17.5–20.5	40–45	90–100	96–120	120–145	120–145	120–145	—	—
18/20	17.5–20.5	40–45	180–186	96–120	110–130	120–130	110–130	—	—
25	17.5–20.5	40–45	180–186	96–120	110–130	120–130	110–130	—	—
28	17.5–20.5	100–105	348–372	168–192	150–170	162–168	150–170	—	—
33	17.5–20.5	100–105	348–372	168–192	150–170	162–168	150–170	—	—
40	17.5–20.5	100–105	348–372	168–192	150–170	162–168	150–170	—	—
55	17.5–20.5	70–85	348–372	168–192 ①	144–168	144–168	144–168	96–120	96–120
60	17.5–20.5	70–85	348–372	168–192 ②	144–168	162–168	144–168	96–120	96–120
65	17.5–20.5	70–85	348–372	168–192 ②	144–168	162–168	144–168	96–120	96–120
75	17.5–20.5	70–85	348–372	168–192 ②	144–168	162–168	144–168	96–120	96–120
80	17.5–20.5	70–85	348–372	168–192 ②	144–168	162–168	144–168	96–120	96–120
85	17.5–20.5	70–85	348–372	168–192 ②	144–168	162–168	144–168	96–120	96–120
90	17.5–20.5	70–85	348–372	168–192 ②	144–168	162–168	144–168	96–120	96–120
100	17.5–20.5	70–85	348–372	168–192 ②	144–168	162–168	144–168	96–120	96–120
115	17.5–20.5	70–85	348–372	168–192 ②	144–168	162–168	144–168	96–120	96–120

STANDARD SCREWS:

	Inch-Pounds	Foot-Pounds
No. 6	7–10	
No. 8	15–22	
No. 10	25–35	2–3
No. 12	35–40	3–4
1/4"	60–80	5–7
5/16"	120–140	10–12
3/8"	220–240	18–20

① Retorque the cylinder head screws to 192–216 in-lbs. after the engine has been tested and tuned.
② Retorque the cylinder head screws to 216–240 in-lbs. after the engine has been tested and tuned.

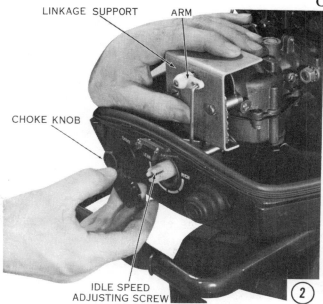

LINKAGE SUPPORT — ARM

CHOKE KNOB

IDLE SPEED
ADJUSTING SCREW

②

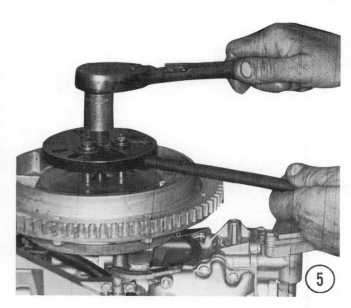

⑤

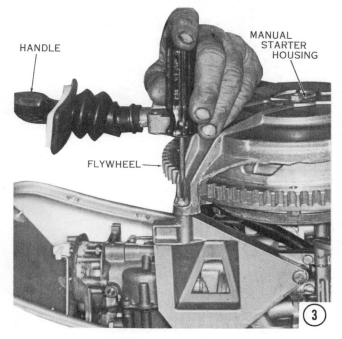

HANDLE

MANUAL
STARTER
HOUSING

FLYWHEEL

③

three housing retaining screws and then lifting off the assembly.

④ Remove the flywheel nut. Keep the flywheel from turning with the special holding tool shown.

⑤ Attach a flywheel puller, Tool No. 378103, and then turn the center screw down until the flywheel is loosened. *CAUTION: Make sure that the screws holding the puller to the flywheel are tight, or you may pull out the threads. NOTE: It may be necessary to strike the*

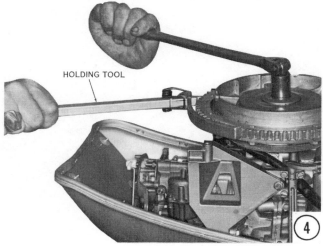

HOLDING TOOL

④

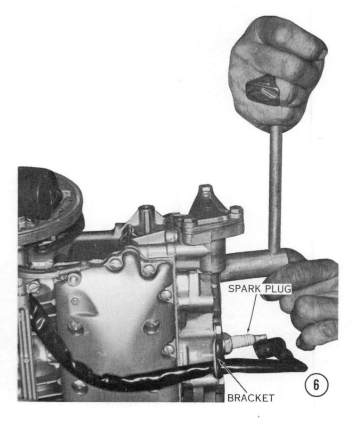

SPARK PLUG

BRACKET

⑥

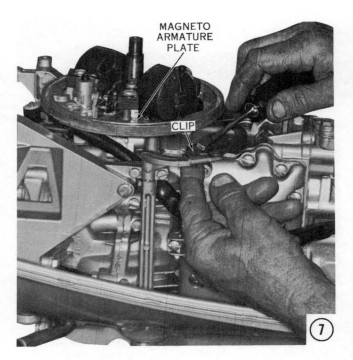

MAGNETO ARMATURE PLATE

CLIP

⑦

center screw sharply with a medium weight hammer to break the taper fit, if it is tight. Lift off the flywheel.

⑥ Twist the high-tension leads clockwise off the spark plugs. Remove the high-tension wire bracket on

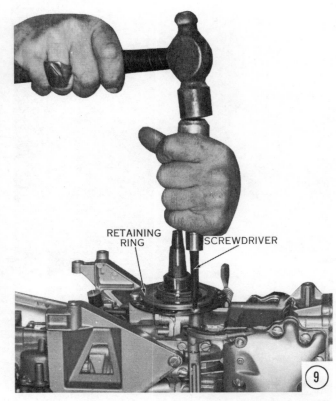

RETAINING RING   SCREWDRIVER

⑨

the cylinder head. Remove the spark plugs, supporting the end of the socket to keep it from tilting. *CAUTION: Unless the socket is properly supported, it may tilt and crack the porcelain.*

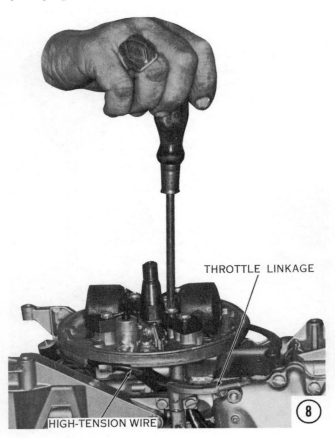

THROTTLE LINKAGE

HIGH-TENSION WIRE

⑧

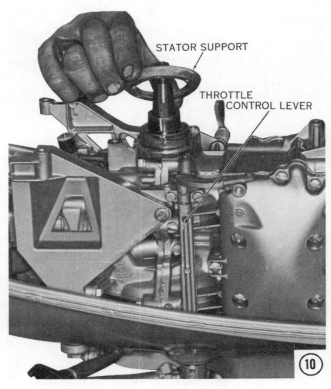

STATOR SUPPORT

THROTTLE CONTROL LEVER

⑩

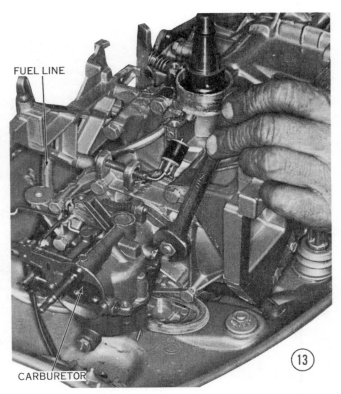

⑦ Remove the magneto armature plate link spring clip in order to disconnect the throttle linkage.

⑧ Take out the four Phillips-headed screws which hold the magneto armature plate to the powerhead. *NOTE: These screws have special split threads and it is necessary to lift them in order to engage a second set of threads after the first set of threads disengages. Lift*

the magneto armature plate assembly from the powerhead by threading the wiring harness through the opening between the throttle linkage and the powerhead.

⑨ Remove the magneto armature plate support and the retaining ring. *CAUTION: It is necessary to use the special impact screwdriver shown in order to loosen the screws without damaging them.*

⑩ Take off the armature plate support. Note the way that the angled surface faces down. This is important when installing this plate because if it is installed in reverse, it is impossible to assemble the magneto armature plate properly.

⑪ Push the cam-follower roller forward so that you can remove the screw holding the throttle linkage to the cross-shaft. Disconnect the cam-follower spring which holds the roller in the retracted position.

⑫ Remove the two screws holding the linkage support to the carburetor, disconnect the linkage, and then lift out the support.

⑬ Remove the two nuts holding the carburetor to the powerhead, lift off the carburetor, and discard the gasket. Disconnect the fuel line at the carburetor. *CAUTION: Keep the free end of the line above the level of the carburetor to prevent fuel from spilling into the lower cover.*

⑭ Remove the shifter lock spring. Disconnect the two fuel lines to the fuel pump, and then remove the

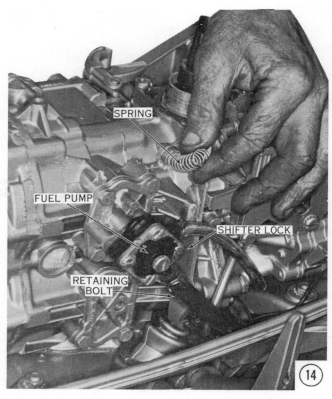

SPRING

FUEL PUMP

SHIFTER LOCK

RETAINING BOLT

(14)

fuel pump in order to gain access to the shifter lock retaining bolt.

⑮ Remove the shifter lock retaining bolt. *NOTE:*

STARTER HOUSING MOUNTING BRACKETS

(15)

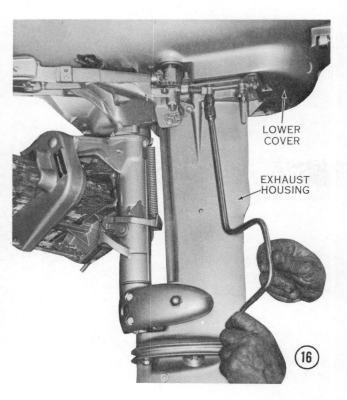

LOWER COVER

EXHAUST HOUSING

(16)

It is not necessary to detach the shifter lock from the rubber grommet. Remove the screws holding the port and starboard starter housing mounting brackets. The throttle control lever comes off with the port side starter

(17)

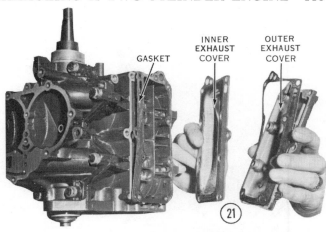

housing mounting bracket.

⑯ Remove the six hex-headed screws and one Phillips-headed screw which hold the powerhead to the exhaust housing. *NOTE: The Phillips-headed screw is located between the exhaust housing and the swivel bracket.*

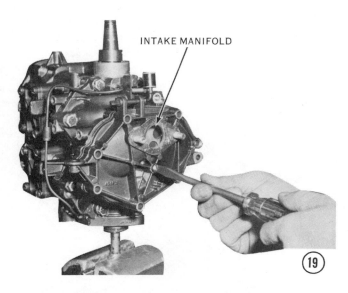

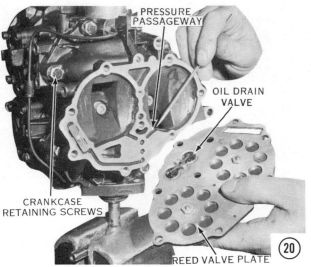

⑰ Lift the powerhead up to disengage the crankshaft from the driveshaft splines, and then place the powerhead on a bench for disassembly.

DISASSEMBLING THE POWERHEAD

⑱ Take out the bolts holding the cylinder head, remove the head, and discard the gasket.

⑲ Remove the eight screws holding the intake manifold to the powerhead, and then lift off the manifold.

⑳ Take out the retaining screw, and then lift off the reed-valve plate assembly. Discard the gasket. Remove the drain valve.

㉑ Remove the bolts holding the exhaust cover, and then take off the outer and inner exhaust covers. Discard the gaskets. *NOTE: If pitting exists on the inner exhaust plate, install a new one.*

㉒ Remove the bolts holding the two bypass covers to the powerhead. Take off the covers and discard the gaskets.

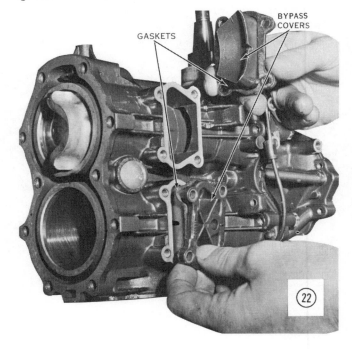

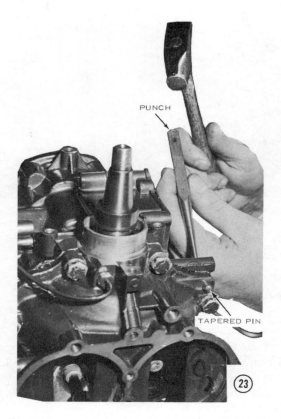

PUNCH

TAPERED PIN

(23)

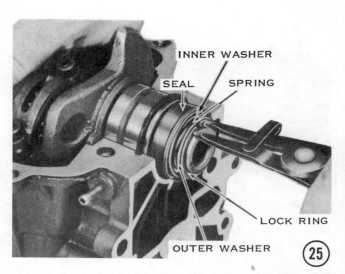

INNER WASHER

SEAL   SPRING

LOCK RING

OUTER WASHER

(25)

pair of No. 2 Truarc pliers, Tool No. 303858. Remove the outer washer, spring, inner washer, and seal.

㉖ Remove the connecting rod cap screws. Take off the caps and roller bearings. *NOTE: 15 rollers are used in each bearing. CAUTION: The pistons, connecting rods, caps, and bearing retainers are matched parts and seat with the operation of the engine. Because of this,*

㉓ Drive out the two tapered pins which align the crankcase halves. *CAUTION: Drive the pins out from the back of the crankcase.*

㉔ Remove the two Allen-headed screws and the eight hex-headed screws holding the crankcase to the cylinder block. Tap the top side of the crankshaft with a rawhide mallet to break the seal between the crankcase and the cylinder block. Lift off the crankcase.

㉕ Remove the carbon seal from the lower end of the crankshaft by taking off the retaining ring with a

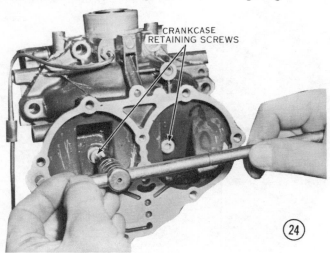

CRANKCASE RETAINING SCREWS

(24)

CONNECTING ROD CAPS

(26)

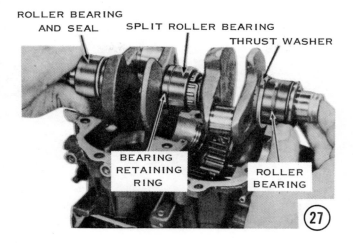

ROLLER BEARING AND SEAL   SPLIT ROLLER BEARING   THRUST WASHER   BEARING RETAINING RING   ROLLER BEARING

27

29

it is essential to maintain their original positions during disassembly. Mark each connecting rod, cap, piston, and bearing component to assure correct mating when they are assembled. Also mark the cylinders from which the parts are removed.

㉗ Lift the crankshaft from the cylinder block. Remove the crankshaft main bearings. Slide the center bearing retaining ring aside in order to be able to separate the center main bearing halves. Replace the matching caps on the proper connecting rods.

㉘ Push the piston assemblies out of the bores.

Remove the piston rings by prying the ends loose enough to grip them with pliers. Break the rings away from the pistons. *CAUTION: Don't try to save the old rings. Always install a complete set of new piston rings during every powerhead overhaul.*

㉙ To detach the connecting rods from the pistons, use a pair of Truarc pliers, Tool No. 277152, to take out the retaining rings.

㉚ Drive the wrist pin through the piston from the "loose" side (arrow). *CAUTION: When removing a wrist pin, the "loose" side of the piston must be facing up, and the driving tool must be applied through the "loose" side hole.*

CLEANING AND INSPECTING

Cylinder Block and Crankcase

Check the cylinder walls for excessive wear and the cylinder ports for carbon accumulation. The cylinder walls wear in varying degrees depending on lubrication

PISTON RINGS

28

LOOSE

30

To remove the glaze, use a flexible hone. A few up-and-down strokes should provide the cross-hatched pattern so necessary for good ring break-in.

and the conditions under which the engine is operated. Most wear is in the port area and the ring travel area. Check the cylinder for size and wall straightness by using an inside micrometer. If the wear is greater than 0.003″, replace the cylinder block or rebore it for oversize pistons. Piston and ring sets are available in 0.020″ and 0.040″ oversizes.

Carbon accumulations in the exhaust ports restrict the flow of exhaust gases and have a considerable effect on the performance of the engine. Carefully scrape the carbon from the cylinder heads and exhaust ports with a blunt instrument. The exhaust ports and all exhaust passages must be freed of carbon deposits to insure maximum performance. *CAUTION: Avoid getting carbon particles in the water jackets. CAUTION: Don't scratch the gasket surfaces, or you will cause leaks.*

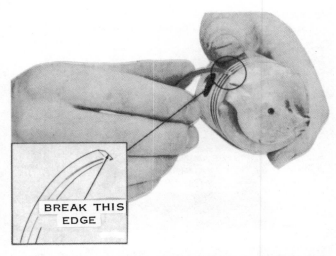

A piece of broken piston ring can be used as a scraper to remove the carbon from the ring grooves.

With continued engine operation, the cylinder walls take on a glaze which reduces the effectiveness of the seal between the piston rings and the cylinder walls. The result is reduced compression and a decrease in engine performance. Break the glaze by using a fine cylinder hone to refinish the walls. A few up-and-down motions of the tool should be sufficient to remove all cylinder wall glaze. Blow out all oil passages and drains.

Gasket Surfaces

Remove all traces of dried cement from the gasket surfaces, using lacquer thinner or trichloroethylene. Check all gasket faces for flatness. Under certain conditions, the faces may warp or spring, particularly where thin sections or flanges are employed and are subject to numerous temperature changes. To check for flatness, lay a sheet of No. 120 grit emery cloth on a surface plate or a piece of plate glass. Place the part to be surfaced on

To dress the gasket surface of a cylinder head, move it over a piece of emery cloth on a surface plate.

To measure the ring end gap, push the ring down into the cylinder bore with a piston to square it up.

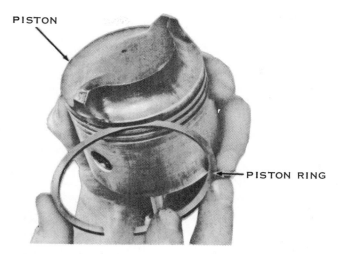

PISTON

PISTON RING

Make sure that the ring is free in the groove by rotating it around, as shown. Remove any burrs which restrict free movement of the ring.

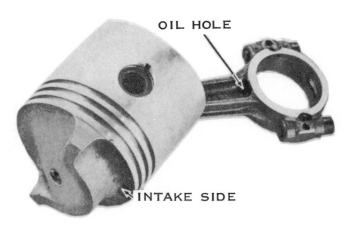

OIL HOLE

INTAKE SIDE

When assembling the piston to the connecting rod, make sure that the intake side of the piston is facing the direction shown when the oil hole in the rod is facing up.

the emery cloth, and then move it slowly back and forth several times in a figure 8 motion, exerting evenly distributed but light pressure. If the surface is warped or sprung, the high spots making contact with the surface plate will take on a dull polish, while the low areas will retain their original state. To insure flatness, continue surfacing until the entire gasket surface is polished to a dull luster. Finish surfacing with 180 grit emery cloth.

Bearings

All areas where bearings are to be serviced should be kept free from accumulations of oil and dirt to avoid

Measure the side clearance of each new piston ring and check the measurement against specifications.

contaminating the bearings. Place the bearings in a wire basket and immerse them in a solvent such as Solvasol. The tank should have a screened false bottom to prevent settlings from being stirred up. Agitate the basket frequently until the grease, oil, and sludge are thoroughly loosened and can be flushed out. Bearings that contain especially heavy carbon deposits or hardened grease should be soaked in a separate container of solvent.

Use a spray gun with an air filter to apply the cleaning solvent. Use clean solvent to flush each bearing until all dirt and residue are removed. Since dry bearings rust rapidly, lubricate them at once with light, clean oil. After draining the excess oil, place them in a covered container until ready for assembly.

Discard bearings which show any of the following: (1) Rusted rollers or raceways. (2) A fractured ring. This may be caused by forcing a cocked bearing off a shaft or by too heavy a press-fit. (3) Worn, galled, or abraded surfaces. These may be caused by too loose a fit or a bearing locked by dirt and turning on the shaft or in the housing. (4) Badly discolored rollers and races. This is usually due to an inadequate supply of lubricant. Moderate discoloration is not a cause for rejection.

Pistons

Check the pistons for roundness, excessive skirt wear, and scoring. The piston skirts must be perfectly round and unscratched to prevent the entrance of exhaust gases into the crankcase compression chambers.

Carefully remove all carbon deposits from inside of the piston head. Inspect the ring grooves for carbon accumulation, excessive wear, or damage to the groove walls. Carefully scrape all carbon from the ring grooves, making certain that the carbon clinging to the bottom and sides of the grooves has been thoroughly removed.

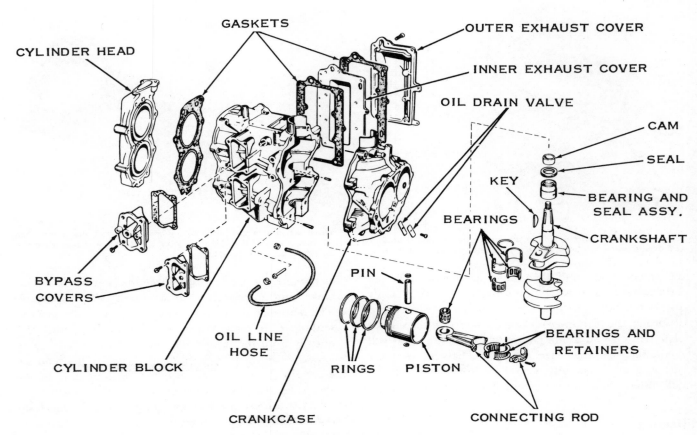

Exploded view of the parts of the 18/20 Hp engine.

CAUTION: Don't scratch the grooves. A tool for cleaning the ring grooves can be made by breaking an old ring, grinding an angle on the edge, and then breaking

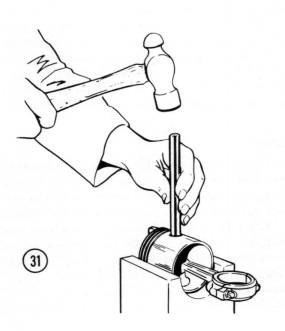

the lower sharp edge to prevent damaging the lower ring land. *CAUTION: Care must be taken not to damage the lower ring lands, which are the ring sealing surfaces.*

Before installing new piston rings, check the gap between the ends of each ring by placing it in its cylinder bore and then pushing the ring down in the bore slightly with the bottom of a piston, which will square it up.

Check each ring and groove for side clearance with a feeler gauge.

Always replace all gaskets and O-ring seals.

ASSEMBLING

㉛ To assemble the connecting rod to its piston, lubricate the wrist pin, making sure that the surfaces are clean. Place a drop of oil in each pin hole. Position the needle bearings in the small end of the connecting rod, and then insert the wrist pin through the "loose" side of the piston. Use a fixture to support the piston to guard against distortion or damage. Drive the pin through the hole. *NOTE: This can be accomplished easier if the piston is heated slightly to expand it.*

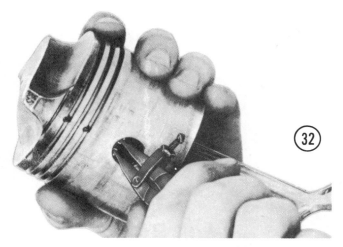

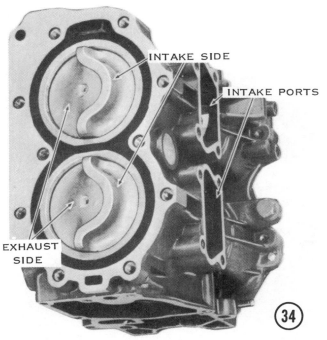

③② Replace the lock rings, making sure that they seat securely in the grooves.

③③ Check each piston with a micrometer to determine whether it has been distorted during assembly of the wrist pin. If necessary, tap the high side with a light mallet to restore the original roundness. *CAUTION: Don't use a steel hammer.*

③④ Install new piston rings on each piston. Spread each ring with a ring expander tool just enough to slip it over the head of the piston and down into place. Make sure that the rings fit freely in the ring grooves. *NOTE: The ring grooves are pinned to keep the rings from turning. This is done primarily to prevent the ends of the rings from catching on the edges of the ports in the cylinders; it also assures staggered ring gaps.* Coat the pistons and cylinder bores with oil, and then install each piston and connecting rod assembly, making sure to match each assembly to the cylinder from which it was removed. The deflector on the intake side of the piston must be facing toward the intake port, as shown. The piston rings must be compressed before the piston can be installed in the cylinder. *CAUTION: Make sure that the rings are correctly positioned with their gaps over the pins. CAUTION: Proceed slowly and don't force the piston into the cylinder. Also, make sure that the parts are free from dirt and grit.* Perfectly good cylinder walls, pistons, and rings can be ruined in a few minutes

of engine operation when care is not exercised in keeping the parts clean. Work in clean surroundings and with reasonably clean hands. Coat all bearing surfaces, cylinder walls, and other parts with clean oil before assembling them.

③⑤ Install the center main bearing retainer halves, with the retaining ring groove toward the top end of the crankshaft. Secure the bearing halves with the retaining ring. Position the other main bearings on the crankshaft, and then install a new O-ring seal on the lower bearing.

③⑥ Apply a coat of OMC Needle Bearing Grease to both halves of the retainers to hold them in place, and then install the retainers in the connecting rods. *CAUTION: The bearing retainer halves are matched. Don't*

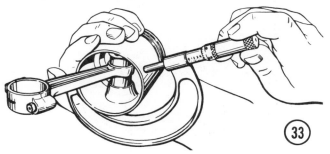

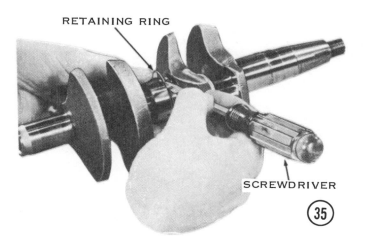

BEARING RETAINER   ROLLERS

(36)

(38)

embossings are provided on the matching sides of each rod and cap. Draw a pencil over the chamfered corners on both sides to make sure that the cap and rod are aligned at the parting joint. If they are not properly matched, the extended edges can be felt with the pencil point. *CAUTION: Misalignment will affect the normal free action of the roller bearings, resulting in damage to the parts.*

interchange the retainer halves or turn them end for end. The notched ends must be facing each other. Lower the crankshaft onto the cylinder block, aligning the connecting rods with the journals and the upper and lower bearings with the dowel pins in the block.

㊲ Position the smaller retainers, with roller bearings, over the crankshaft, and then install the connecting rod caps. *CAUTION: The rod caps are not interchangeable with those of other rods, nor should the caps be turned end for end.* To assist in correct assembly, small

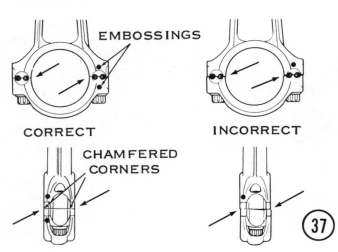

EMBOSSINGS

CORRECT   INCORRECT

CHAMFERED CORNERS

(37)

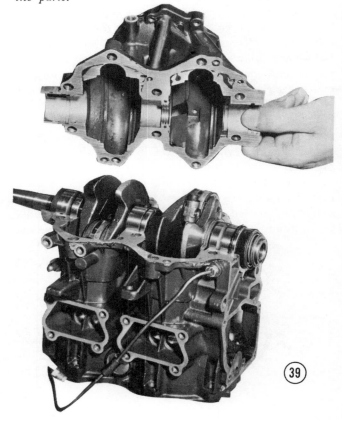

(39)

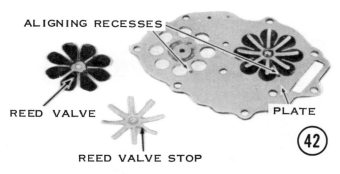

ALIGNING RECESSES

REED VALVE

REED VALVE STOP

PLATE

42

38 Tighten the connecting rod cap screws to 180–186 in-lbs. of torque. *CAUTION: The bearing retainers must rotate freely on the crankpins.*

39 Apply a thin line of Sealer 1000 to the faces of the crankcase. *CAUTION: Don't use too much, or the excess will squeeze out and foul the oil channels.* Install the crankcase and tighten the screws finger-tight. Replace the taper pins, driving them in carefully with a hammer. Torque the upper and lower retaining screws to 110–130 in-lbs. and the center screws to 120–130 in-lbs. Check for binding by rotating the crankshaft clockwise from the flywheel end.

40 Install a new carbon seal at the lower end of the crankshaft. Replace the inner washer, spring, and outer washer, securing the assembly with a new Truarc ring.

41 Replace the oil drain valve, making sure that the valve seats properly and that the space between it and the stop is 0.040″. If necessary, bend the stop as required.

42 The proper operation of the reed valves is essential to good engine performance. The importance of keeping the reeds free from distortion cannot be overemphasized. Replace any reed or stop which shows evidence of distortion or damage. The reeds must maintain contact with the plate until a predetermined pressure is

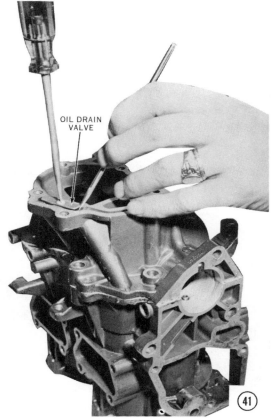

OIL DRAIN VALVE

40

41

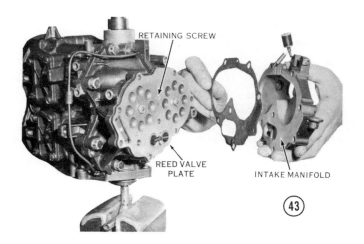

RETAINING SCREW

REED VALVE PLATE

INTAKE MANIFOLD

43

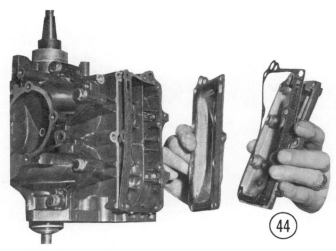

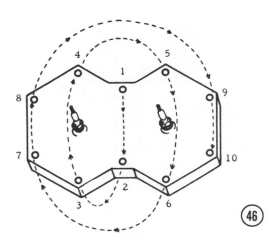

exerted by the vacuum in the crankcase. Reed travel is limited by the reed stop. When crankcase vacuum drops, spring action holds the reeds against the plate. Center the valves over the recesses in the plate. Tighten the screws evenly to avoid distortion, and then examine each reed carefully to make sure that it lies flat against the plate with no edges turned up or away from the plate. *CAUTION: Don't lift or bend reed segments by hand, or you will damage them.*

⑬ Install the assembled reed-valve plate to the crankcase, using a new gasket. Tighten the retaining screw securely. Position a new intake manifold gasket on the reed-valve plate, and then install the intake manifold. Tighten the eight screws securely.

⑭ Replace the inner and outer exhaust covers, using new gaskets. Install all screws finger-tight before tightening any of them.

⑮ Replace the bypass covers, using new gaskets. Tighten the retaining screws securely.

⑯ Install the cylinder head, using a new gasket. Tighten the head bolts to 96–120 in-lbs. of torque, following the sequence shown. *NOTE: The cylinder head screws must be torqued to the same specifications after the engine has been tested and has cooled off.*

INSTALLING THE POWERHEAD

⑰ Make sure that the gasket surfaces of the power-

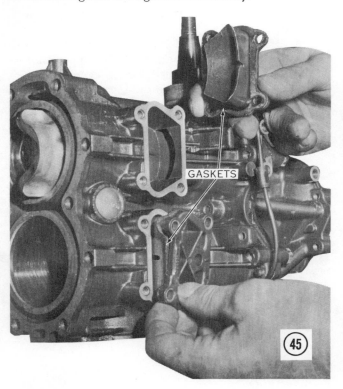

GASKETS

(48)

head and the exhaust housing are clean. Position a new gasket on the exhaust housing, and then lower the powerhead onto the exhaust housing, taking care to avoid damaging the splined ends of the crankshaft and driveshaft. *NOTE: The splines can be engaged with ease if the crankshaft is rotated in a clockwise direction as the powerhead is lowered into position. CAUTION: Don't rotate the crankshaft counterclockwise, or you will damage the water pump impeller.*

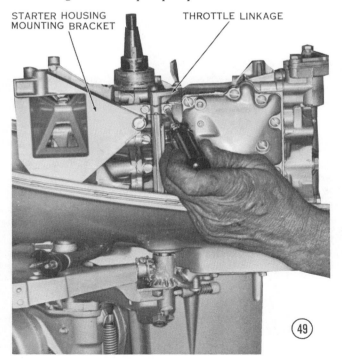

STARTER HOUSING MOUNTING BRACKET   THROTTLE LINKAGE

(49)

SHIFTER LOCK   SPRING

FUEL PUMP   RETAINING BOLT

(50)

㊽ Install the seven screws holding the powerhead to the exhaust housing. *NOTE: The Phillips-headed screw should be installed between the exhaust housing and the swivel bracket.*

㊾ Install the starter housing mounting brackets and the throttle linkage.

㊿ Install the shifter lock retaining bolt, and then replace the spring. Install the fuel pump, using a new gasket. Attach both fuel lines.

51 Attach the fuel line to the inlet fitting at the base of the carburetor, and then position a new gasket

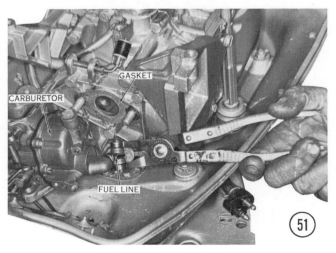

GASKET

CARBURETOR

FUEL LINE

(51)

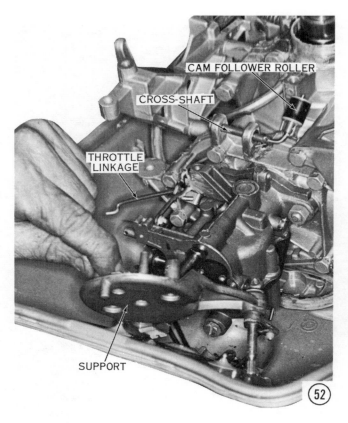

CAM FOLLOWER ROLLER
CROSS-SHAFT
THROTTLE LINKAGE
SUPPORT

(52)

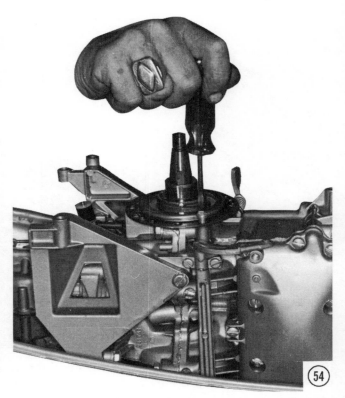

(54)

on the intake manifold flange. Install the carburetor, tightening the two nuts evenly. *CAUTION: Uneven tightening of these nuts can crack the casting.*

52 Install the carburetor linkage support bracket,

tightening the two retaining screws securely. Attach the throttle linkage to the cross-shaft.

53 Attach the cam-follower roller spring. Position the magneto plate support, with the tapered side facing

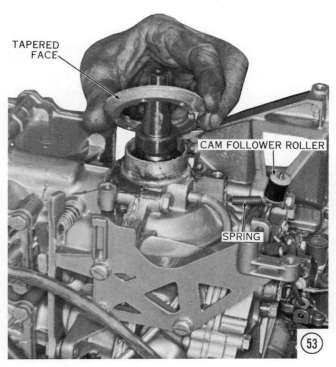

TAPERED FACE
CAM FOLLOWER ROLLER
SPRING

(53)

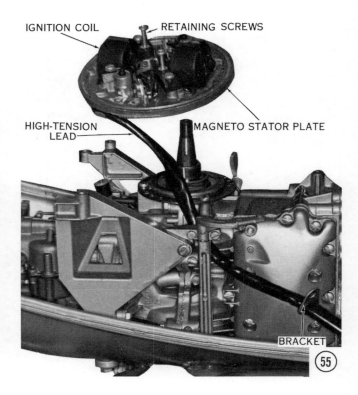

IGNITION COIL
RETAINING SCREWS
HIGH-TENSION LEAD
MAGNETO STATOR PLATE
BRACKET

(55)

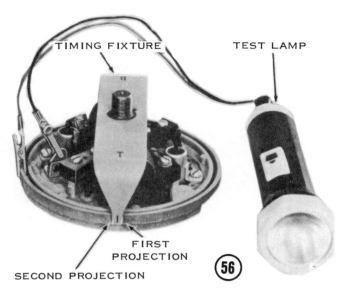

TIMING FIXTURE   TEST LAMP

FIRST
PROJECTION

SECOND PROJECTION

(56)

a good ground and the forward breaker point screw terminal. Position a timing fixture, Tool No. 304667, on the crankshaft. Rotate the crankshaft so that the side of the fixture marked "T" (top) is aligned with the first projection on the armature plate. *CAUTION: Always rotate the crankshaft in a clockwise direction to avoid damaging the water pump impeller.* The breaker points must just open when the timing fixture is midway between the two projections on the magneto armature plate. *NOTE: If new breaker points are installed, they must open as the timing fixture passes the first timing mark. This allows for seating of the breaker fiber block.* If a test lamp is not available, adjust both sets of breaker points to open exactly 0.020″ (0.022″ for new points) with the breaker arm on the high part of the cam lobe.

57⃝ Rotate the crankshaft 180° clockwise until the timing fixture is opposite the second set of timing marks on the magneto armature plate, and then repeat the timing procedure for the second set of breaker points. Disconnect the test lamp, and then reconnect the wires to the breaker point terminals.

down, as shown. *CAUTION: If installed upside down, it will be impossible to assemble the magneto armature plate properly.*

54⃝ Install the retaining ring, securing it with the three screws. Use an impact screwdriver to tighten them securely.

55⃝ Thread the high-tension wires through the opening between the powerhead and the throttle control linkage, and then lower the magneto armature plate over the crankshaft. Tighten the retaining screws securely. Install the throttle linkage clip. Replace the high-tension wire support bracket.

THROTTLE CAM SYNCHRONIZATION

58⃝ Advance the throttle control to the position where the cam-follower roller is centered between the two marks on the throttle cam. The throttle valve must be closed at this point. If necessary, loosen the two hex-headed screws holding the cam to the magneto armature plate, and then push the cam toward the rear of the engine. Now, pull the cam forward until it just contacts the cam-follower roller. The throttle valve must just begin to open after the edge of the roller passes the second mark on the cam. *CAUTION: The choke knob must be all the way in.*

ADJUSTING THE IGNITION TIMING

56⃝ Disconnect all wires from the breaker point assemblies. Connect a self-powered test lamp between

(57)

MARKS
ON CAM

CAM

CAM FOLLOWER
ROLLER

(58)

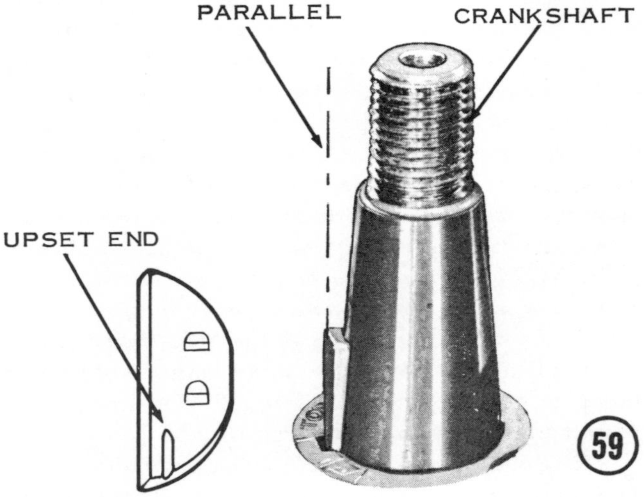
PARALLEL
CRANKSHAFT
UPSET END
(59)

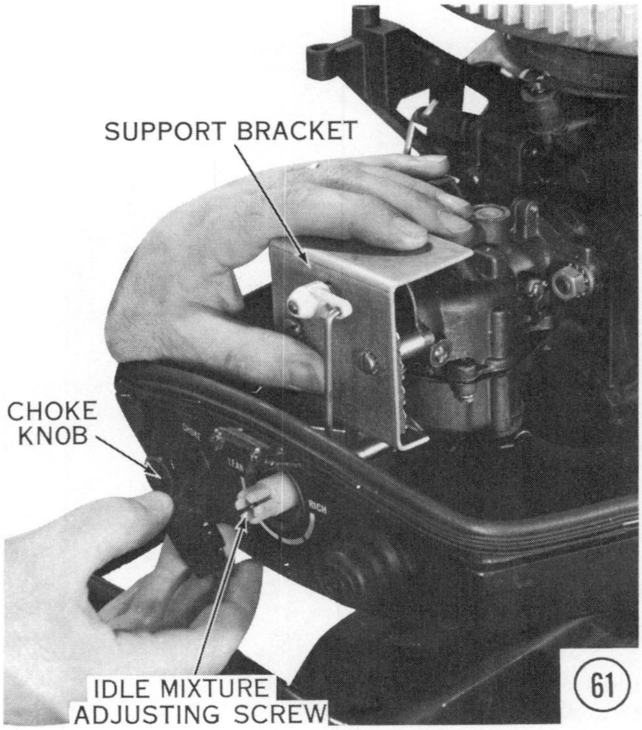
SUPPORT BRACKET
CHOKE
KNOB
IDLE MIXTURE
ADJUSTING SCREW
(61)

(59) If the flywheel key has been removed, assemble it to the crankshaft with the outer edge vertical. Make sure that the single upset mark on the side of the key is facing down. *CAUTION: Incorrect installation of the key will so affect the cam position as to result in a retarded ignition timing.*

(60) Check the crankshaft and flywheel tapers for any traces of oil, which must be removed with solvent. *CAUTION: The assembly must be perfectly dry. CAUTION: Don't allow solvent to wash the oil out of the oiler wick.* Replace the flywheel and the nut, tightening it to 40–45 ft-lbs. of torque.

(61) Install the linkage support on the rear of the carburetor, tightening the two screws securely. Replace the low-speed adjusting valve arm. Lift up on the choke arm to install the choke control rod at the carburetor.

(62) Install new spark plugs, gapping them to 0.030″. Torque the spark plugs to 17–20 ft-lbs. Connect the high-tension wires. Install the manual starter housing, tightening the three screws evenly.

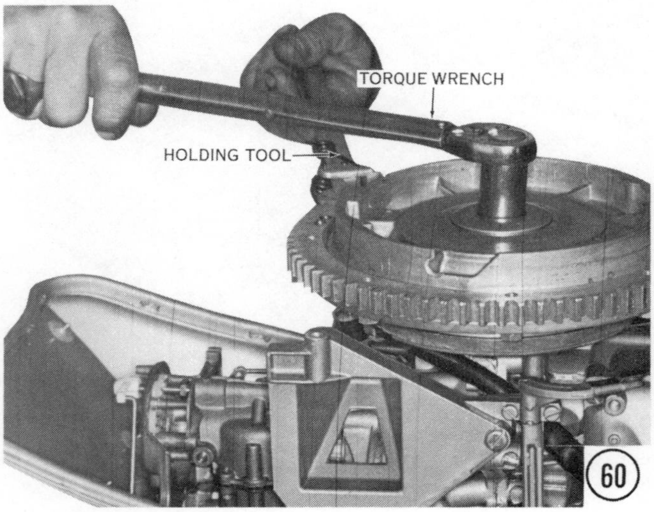
TORQUE WRENCH
HOLDING TOOL
(60)

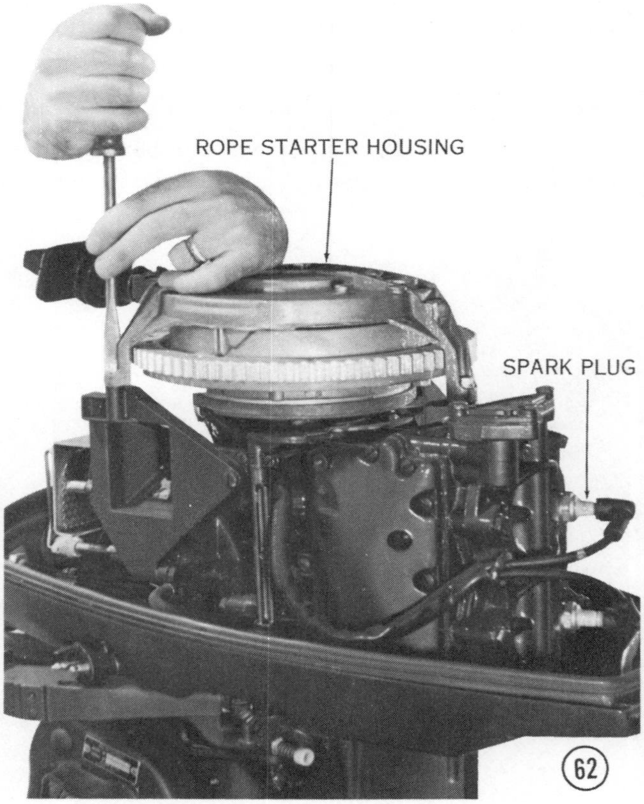
ROPE STARTER HOUSING
SPARK PLUG
(62)

63 Install the hood, hooking it under the rear catch and then dropping it into position. Hook the front latch to secure the hood.

Additional tuning adjustments can be found in Chapter 3.

THREE-CYLINDER ENGINE SERVICE NOTES

The three-cylinder engine was introduced in 1968 as a 55 Hp version. The engine was the first to use a loop-scavenging principle for two-cycle engine operation.

Windows in the pistons allow the fresh fuel mixture to enter the combustion chamber from the crankcase through a smooth, unbroken transfer passage, which is designed for the best efficiency. The two intake ports

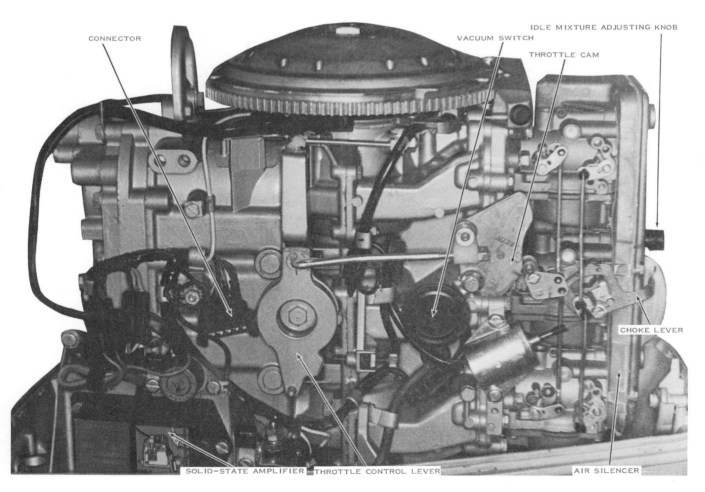

Details of the starboard side of the three-cylinder engine.

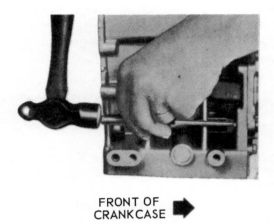

FRONT OF CRANKCASE ➡

Two tapered pins keep the crankcase aligned with the cylinder block. They must be removed by driving them out from the back to the front of the crankcase.

The piston is stamped UP to indicate the side that should be facing the top of the engine.

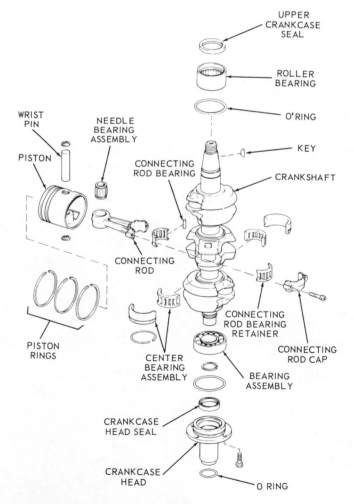

Exploded view of the parts of the crankshaft and piston assembly used on the three-cylinder engine.

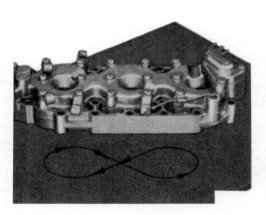

The cylinder head can be trued by moving it over a piece of emery cloth placed on a surface plate.

The glaze on the cylinder walls should be removed with a flexible hone.

The full-floating wrist pin used on the three-cylinder engine is held in the piston by means of two lock rings.

are slanted upward and face each other, providing a directional effect to force the two incoming air-fuel charges to impinge on each other. This directs the flow upward and around the smooth, dome-shaped combustion chamber to drive the burned gases out of the exhaust ports on the other side of the cylinder wall.

REMOVING THE ENGINE

Remove the carburetor, reed-valve plate assembly, fuel pump and filter, and fuel hoses. Take off the flywheel, stator, distributor, and safety switch. Remove the electric starter by disconnecting the red cable and the three screws. Push the cable and grommet through the crankcase web. Disconnect the wiring. Remove the amplifier with the wiring intact.

Remove the throttle control lever and the throttle cam. Take out the crankcase front bracket-to-engine cover screws. Remove the front and rear exhaust cover screws and the aft nut and washer from the stud in the powerhead. Remove the six screws holding the powerhead to the exhaust housing, and then lift the powerhead from the adaptor.

DISASSEMBLING

Remove the lower main bearing seal housing. Take off the cylinder head. Before attempting to remove the crankcase, drive out the two taper pins from the back to the front of the crankcase. Remove the eight small and four large hex-headed screws and nuts holding the crankcase to the cylinder block. Tap the crankshaft with a rawhide mallet to break the seal.

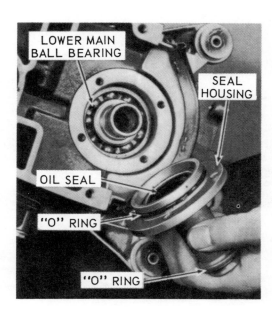

The lower main bearing seal housing should be removed before disassembling the main parts of the engine.

SERVICE NOTES

The connecting rod screws can be removed by using a 5/16", 12-point socket. Sixteen rollers are used in each connecting rod bearing.

The top main bearing, with its O-ring seal, slides

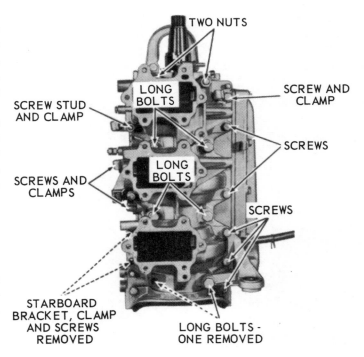

This shows the screws and clamps holding the crankcase to the cylinder block.

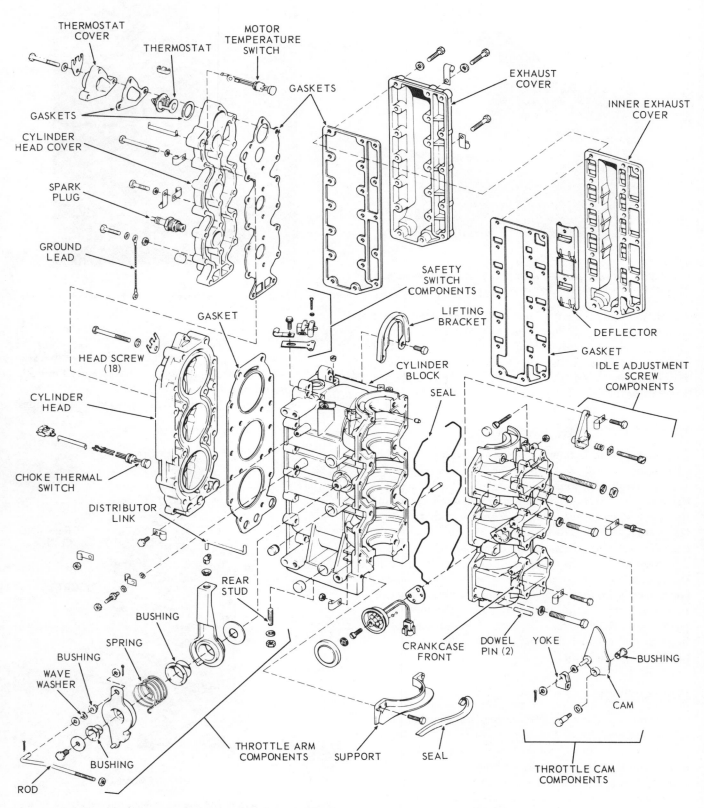

THERMOSTAT COVER

THERMOSTAT

MOTOR TEMPERATURE SWITCH

GASKETS

EXHAUST COVER

INNER EXHAUST COVER

GASKETS

CYLINDER HEAD COVER

SPARK PLUG

GROUND LEAD

SAFETY SWITCH COMPONENTS

GASKET

DEFLECTOR

GASKET

HEAD SCREW (18)

LIFTING BRACKET

IDLE ADJUSTMENT SCREW COMPONENTS

CYLINDER HEAD

CYLINDER BLOCK

SEAL

CHOKE THERMAL SWITCH

DISTRIBUTOR LINK

REAR STUD

BUSHING

SPRING

BUSHING

WAVE WASHER

ROD

BUSHING

CRANKCASE FRONT

DOWEL PIN (2)

YOKE

BUSHING

CAM

THROTTLE ARM COMPONENTS

SUPPORT

SEAL

THROTTLE CAM COMPONENTS

Exploded view of the parts of the powerhead of the three-cylinder engine.

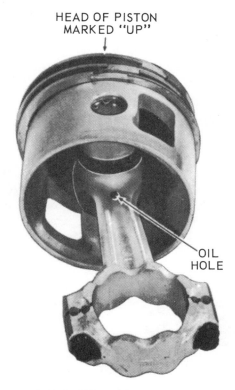

HEAD OF PISTON
MARKED "UP"

OIL
HOLE

The connecting rod should be assembled to the piston so that the oil hole and the marking on the top of the piston face the top of the engine.

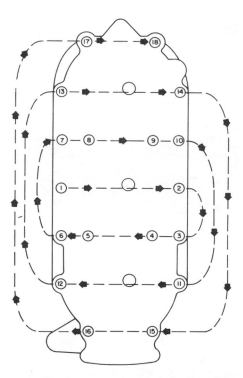

Cylinder head bolt tightening sequence for the three-cylinder engine.

off the crankshaft journal. The bottom main bearing is held in place with a Truarc retaining ring. The two halves of each center main bearing are held together with retaining rings.

The wrist pin is full-floating, with both piston pin holes the same size. There is no need to observe the precaution of starting the wrist pin from the loose side, as in the other engines. When assembling the piston and connecting rod, the side of the piston marked UP and the oil hole in the connecting rod must be facing the top of the engine. The bearing in the small end of the connecting rod contains ten needle bearings.

When installing the crankshaft in the cylinder block, make sure to align the top main and the two center main bearings with the dowel pins in the cylinder block.

The crankcase face is grooved for a rubber seal. Run a fine bead of Sealer 1000 in the groove to hold the seal. Trim the ends of the seal to allow 1/32" to extend beyond the edge of the machined surfaces for a good terminal seal. Apply a thin line of Sealer 1000 to each crankcase face. *CAUTION: Don't use too much sealer or the excess will squeeze out and foul the oil channels.*

Complete tuning instructions are covered in Chapter 3.

BREAK-IN

Operate the engine at a fast-idle speed for the first 10 minutes. Check the operation of the water pump. For the remainder of the first hour, run the engine at half throttle (not over 3,000 rpm).

For easy planing boats, it is desirable to bring the boat into planing position with full power and then reduce the throttle setting to one-half. Make sure that the boat maintains a planing attitude at this throttle setting.

During the second hour, bring the boat into a planing attitude, and then reduce power to three-quarter throttle (approximately 4,000 rpm). During the second hour, periodically apply full throttle for periods of one to two minutes, and then return the throttle to its original setting of 4,000 rpm. Avoid continuous full-throttle operation for extended periods for the next few hours.

OVERHAULING A FOUR-CYLINDER ENGINE

The following instructions specifically cover the 1966, 100 Hp, V-4 engine, but they apply equally well

to all four-cylinder engines. Specifications and tuning instructions may vary somewhat from the other engines; therefore, detailed specification charts for all engines are provided in this chapter. Tuning instructions for the other four-cylinder engines are covered in detail in Chapter 3.

REMOVING THE POWERHEAD

① Turn the hood latch a half turn, and then lift off the hood.

② Disconnect the low-tension wiring from the ignition coil and the cranking motor solenoid. Release the wiring harness by detaching the alternator connector, releasing the terminal block, and removing the fuse

DISTRIBUTOR

IGNITION COIL

ALTERNATOR CONNECTOR

CARBURETOR

FUSE BLOCK

CRANKING MOTOR SOLENOID

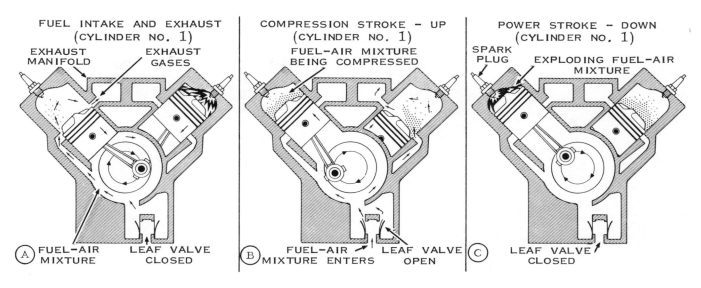

Diagram of the operation of a V-4, two-stroke-cycle engine.

block retaining nuts. Remove the cranking motor solenoid.

③ Remove the three capscrews holding the rope starter plate to the flywheel. Lift off the plate.

④ Disconnect the high-tension wiring at the spark plugs, and then remove the spark plugs. *CAUTION: Support the rear of the socket to keep it from tilting, which would crack the porcelain.* Remove the two retaining screws, and then take off the solid-state amplifier case. Disconnect the two hoses leading to the water thermostat housing, remove the retaining screws, and then lift off the assembly.

⑤ Disconnect the throttle control rod at the throttle control shaft and the distributor linkage at the sliding joint where the two screws hold the shafts together.

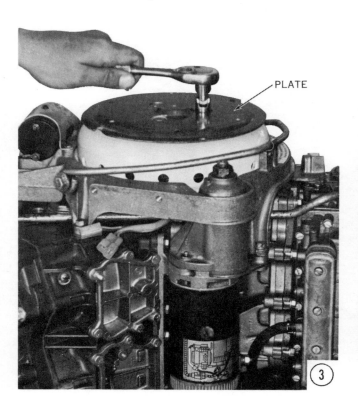

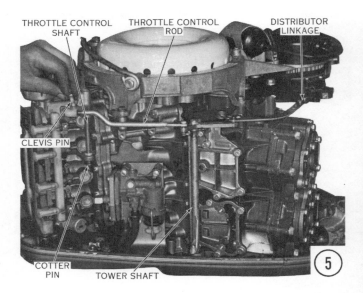

THROTTLE CONTROL SHAFT
THROTTLE CONTROL ROD
DISTRIBUTOR LINKAGE
CLEVIS PIN
COTTER PIN
TOWER SHAFT

(5)

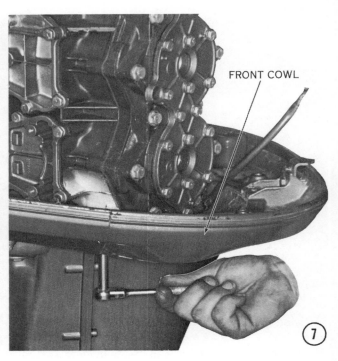

FRONT COWL

(7)

Remove the bolts at the base of the tower shaft bearings, and then lift off the tower shaft. Remove the cotter pin at the base of the throttle control shaft, and then lift off the shaft. Catch the plastic bearing and washer from the bottom of the shaft.

⑥ Disconnect the fuel lines and the pressure line between the fuel pump and the crankcase. Remove the retaining bolts, and then lift off the fuel pump.

⑦ Remove the front lower cowl retaining bolts, and then take off the front cowl.

⑧ Take out the six motor leg cover plate retaining screws, and then lift off the cover plate.

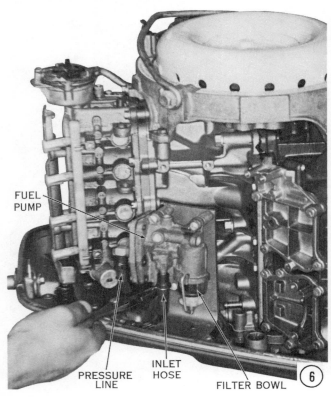

FUEL PUMP
PRESSURE LINE
INLET HOSE
FILTER BOWL

(6)

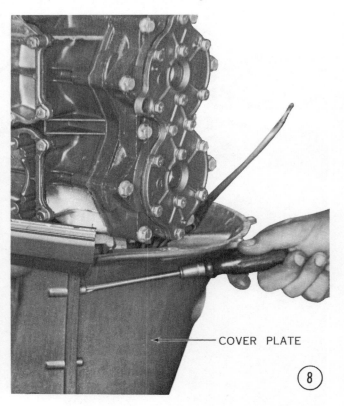

COVER PLATE

(8)

⑨ Remove the rear cowl retaining bolts, and then take off the rear cowl.

⑩ Remove the bolts holding the powerhead to the adaptor plate.

⑪ Attach a chain hoist, and then lift the powerhead from the motor leg.

DISASSEMBLING THE POWERHEAD

⑫ Remove the automatic choke heat tube and the ignition coil.

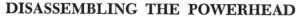

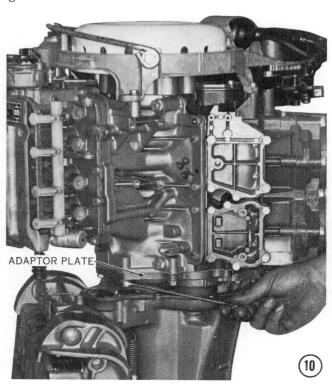

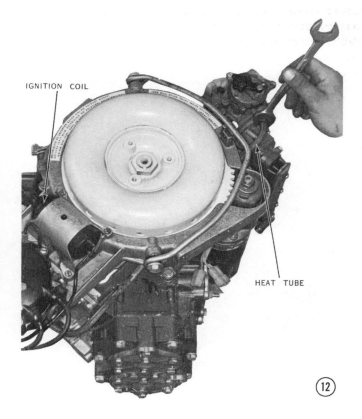

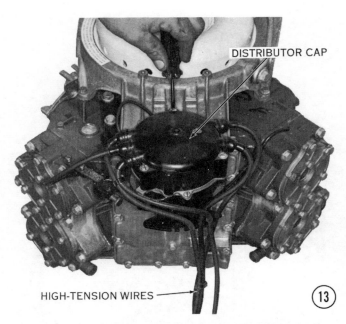

DISTRIBUTOR CAP

HIGH-TENSION WIRES

⑬

⑬ Take out the three screws holding the distributor cap, and then remove the cap and high-tension wiring as an assembly.

⑭ Remove the rotor and the two distributor plate retaining screws. Lift out the distributor plate as an assembly.

⑮ Remove the bolts and lockwashers holding the ring gear cover in place, and then lift off the cover. Take out the three bolts holding the distributor bracket,

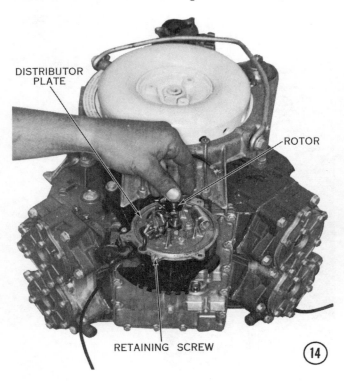

DISTRIBUTOR PLATE

ROTOR

RETAINING SCREW

⑭

RING GEAR COVER

TIMING BELT

DISTRIBUTOR BRACKET

⑮

slide it back to release the timing belt, and then lift off the bracket.

⑯ Loosen the two cranking motor through-bolts, and then disengage the cranking motor from the drive-end casting by sliding it down and away.

DRIVE-END CASTING

CRANKING MOTOR

⑯

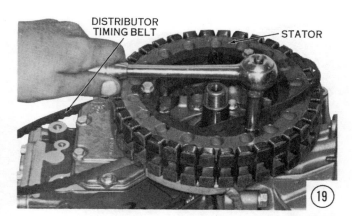

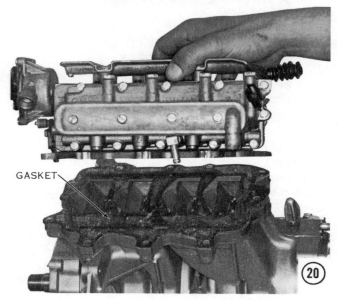

⑰ Remove the bolt and lockwasher holding the drive-end assembly to the crankcase. Don't disassemble the drive-end casting unless it requires service.

⑱ Remove the flywheel retaining nut and lockwasher, and then lift off the flywheel. If it is tight, it may be necessary to use a puller, Tool No. 378103.

⑲ Remove the three stator winding retaining bolts. Lift off the stator and the distributor timing belt.

⑳ Remove the ten retaining bolts, and then lift off the carburetor assembly. Discard the flange gasket.

㉑ Lift out the reed-valve block as an assembly. Discard the gasket.

㉒ Remove the four intake port bypass covers. Discard the gaskets.

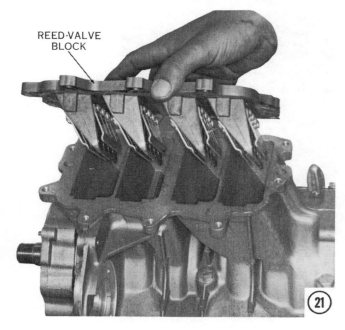

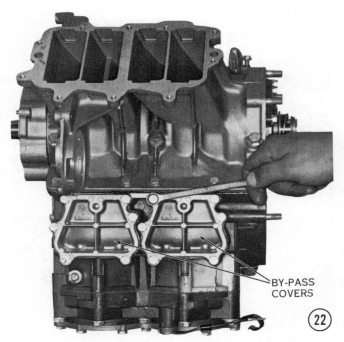

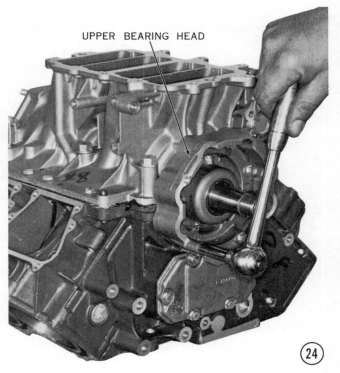

UPPER BEARING HEAD

㉒

㉓ Invert the cylinder block, and then remove the cylinder head retaining bolts. Lift off each cylinder head and discard the gaskets. Remove the exhaust cover plate retaining bolts, and then lift off the cover. Discard the gasket.

BY-PASS COVERS

㉔

㉔ Take out the upper bearing head retaining bolts, and then pry out the upper bearing head. Discard the gasket and O-ring seals.

㉕ Remove the lock ring, and then take off the carbon seal parts as follows: lock ring, washer, spring, washer, and carbon seal. Take out the eight outer bolts and lockwashers which hold the lower bearing head to the crankcase and cylinder block.

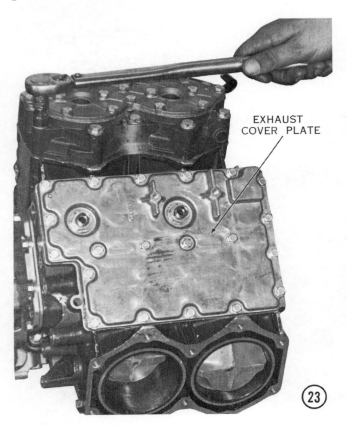

EXHAUST COVER PLATE

㉓

LOWER BEARING HEAD

SPRING

LOCK RING

CARBON SEAL

㉕

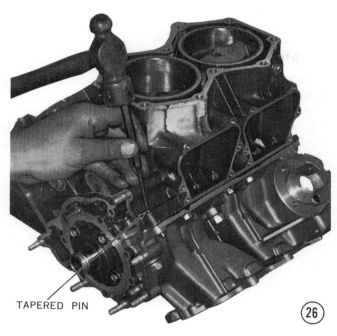

TAPERED PIN

26

26 Drive out the two tapered pins, one at each corner of the cylinder block.

27 Remove the six main bearing bolts, and then take out the crankcase-to-cylinder block retaining bolts. Tap the crankshaft with a rawhide mallet to break the seal between the crankcase and the cylinder block. Lift the crankcase from the block. *CAUTION: Don't pry between the block and crankcase, or you will damage the sealing surfaces.*

28 Remove the four bolts, seals, and lockwashers holding the lower head plate to the bearing retainer plate. Remove the lower bearing head plate and discard the O-ring seals and the gasket.

29 If the ball bearing is rough or has excessive side play, it must be replaced. To remove the ball bearing from the crankshaft, first take out the lock ring.

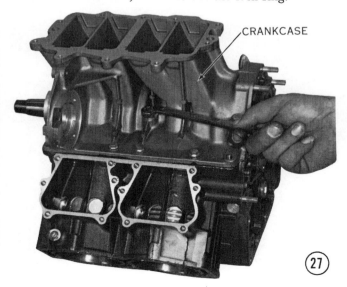

CRANKCASE

27

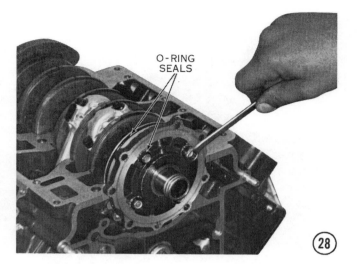

O-RING
SEALS

28

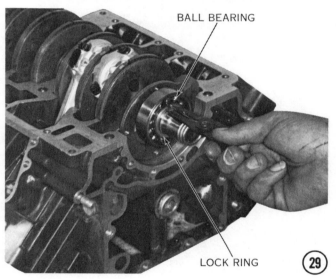

BALL BEARING

LOCK RING

29

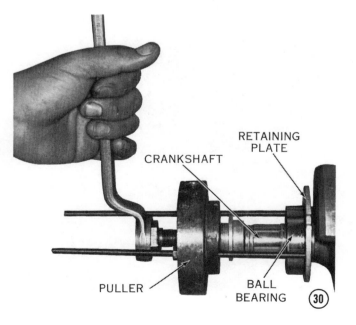

CRANKSHAFT

RETAINING
PLATE

PULLER

BALL
BEARING

30

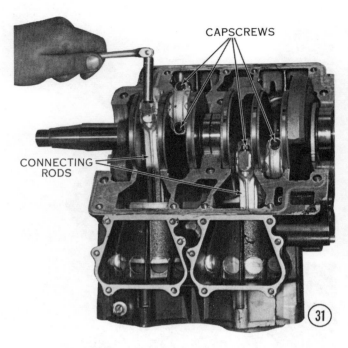

CAPSCREWS

CONNECTING RODS

③①

③③

㉚ Use the special bearing puller, Tool No. 378103, to remove a defective ball bearing.

㉛ Remove the connecting rod cap screws. Use a 5/16", 12-point deep socket to fit the special screw heads. *CAUTION: The pistons, connecting rods, rod bearings,*

and bearing retainers are wearing parts which seat with the operation of the engine. Therefore, it is essential to maintain their original positions for proper assembly. When the parts are removed, mark each connecting rod, cap, bearing component, and piston to assure correct mating. Also, keep the needle bearings for each cylinder together with its rod. The best way to do this is to assemble the rod, needle bearing parts, and cap just as soon as a piston assembly is removed from the cylinder bore.

㉜ Lift off the bearing cap, and then remove the bearing retainer. *CAUTION: Don't drop any roller bearings.*

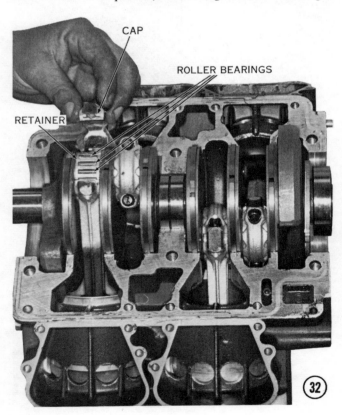

CAP

ROLLER BEARINGS

RETAINER

㉜

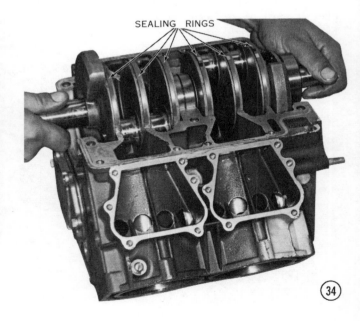

SEALING RINGS

㉞

MAIN BEARING RACE

LOCK RING ㉟

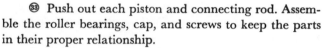

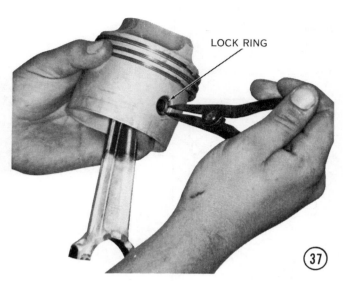

LOCK RING

㊲

㊱

㉝ Push out each piston and connecting rod. Assemble the roller bearings, cap, and screws to keep the parts in their proper relationship.

㉞ Lift out the crankshaft and sealing rings as an assembly.

㉟ Pry out the lock ring holding the two races of the main bearing together.

㊱ Separate the race halves, and then remove the roller bearings and retainers. Remove the sealing rings, if they are to be replaced.

㊲ Remove the lock rings from each end of the piston pin, and then drive out the pin. *CAUTION: One side of the piston skirt is marked LOOSE, and this side*

must be facing UP. Apply the driving tool to the loose side. Remove the piston rings by prying the ends loose enough to grip them with pliers and then breaking them away from the piston. *CAUTION: Don't attempt to save the old piston rings. Always install a new set of piston rings on each powerhead overhaul.*

CLEANING AND INSPECTING

Clean all parts in solvent and blow dry with compressed air. Don't use rags to dry the parts because of the danger of leaving lint on the parts.

Store all cleaned parts in containers to keep from losing or soiling them. Keep all mating parts together. Use several containers to keep the parts separated.

Cylinder Block and Crankcase

Carbon accumulation on the walls of the exhaust ports restricts the flow of exhaust gases, and it has a considerable effect on the performance of the engine. Carefully scrape the carbon from the cylinder heads and the exhaust ports with a blunt instrument to avoid scratching the walls. *CAUTION: Avoid getting carbon particles in the water jackets.*

Check the cylinder walls for wear. The major portion of wear will be in the port area and the ring travel area. Use an inside micrometer or a dial indicator to determine the amount of wear. If the wear is more than 0.003″, the cylinder can be bored to an oversize of 0.020″ or 0.030″. Oversize pistons and rings are available for service.

Worn cylinder walls are always glazed, and this surface must be removed by using a fine cylinder hone. A few up-and-down strokes of the hone should be

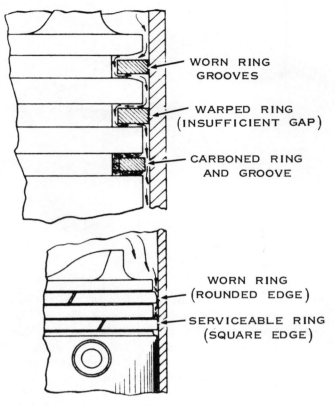

WORN RING GROOVES

WARPED RING (INSUFFICIENT GAP)

CARBONED RING AND GROOVE

WORN RING (ROUNDED EDGE)

SERVICEABLE RING (SQUARE EDGE)

Worn piston rings allow the exhaust gases to pass into the crankcase, where they contaminate the fresh fuel charge. It pays to replace the piston rings at each overhaul.

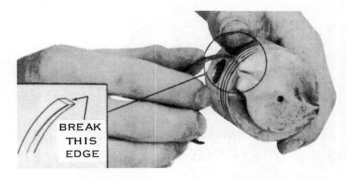

BREAK THIS EDGE

Break one of the old piston rings and use the sharp edge of the broken ring as a scraper to remove the carbon. *CAUTION: Be careful not to nick the ring groove side walls, which are the sealing surfaces.*

enough to remove the glaze. *CAUTION: Wash out the abrasives thoroughly.* Use light motor oil and clean rags until the rag shows no discoloration. *CAUTION: Cleaning solvents will not remove the abrasives thoroughly and, if allowed to remain, will shorten engine life dramatically.*

Gasket Surfaces

Remove all traces of dried cement, using lacquer

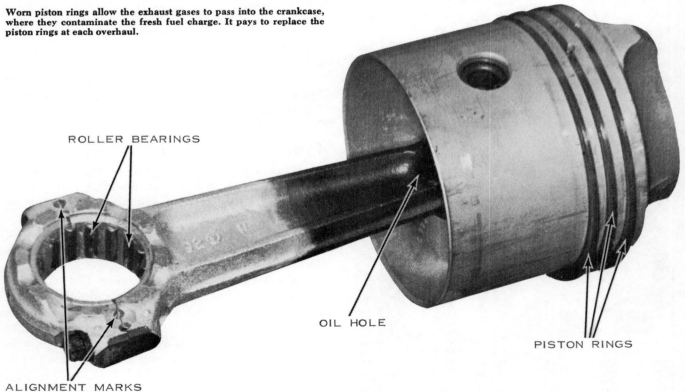

ROLLER BEARINGS

ALIGNMENT MARKS

OIL HOLE

PISTON RINGS

Details of the piston and rod assembly. The alignment marks must line up and the oil hole must be facing the top of the engine when the rod is installed in the cylinder.

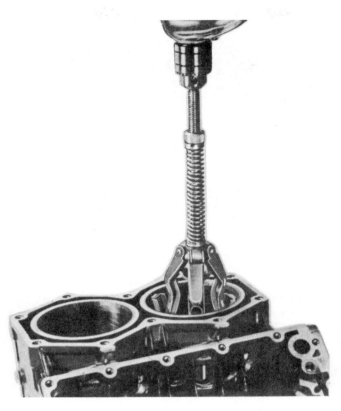

The end gap of each new piston ring should be checked by inserting it into the cylinder bore, and then measuring the end gap.

The cylinder walls should be honed to remove the glaze. If there are deep scores, the cylinder walls can be rebored. Oversize pistons and rings are available for service.

thinner or trichloroethylene. Check all gasket surfaces for flatness by laying a sheet of No. 120 emery cloth on a surface plate or a piece of plate glass. Move the part slowly back and forth several times in a figure 8 motion, exerting light pressure. If the surface has high spots, they will appear dull while the low areas will retain their original finish. Continue surfacing the part until the entire sealing surface is dull. Finish surfacing the part using a piece of No. 180 emery cloth. *CAUTION: Clean the parts thoroughly as discussed above in order to remove all traces of the abrasive.*

Crankshaft

Check the crankshaft journals for worn, galled, or abraded surfaces. Check the sealing rings for excessive

Piston rings must have side clearance in the grooves, or they will stick and cause a loss of engine power.

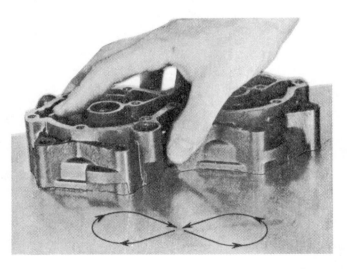

Dress sealing surfaces on a flat plate covered with a piece of emery cloth, as discussed in the text.

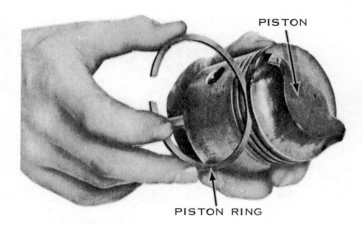

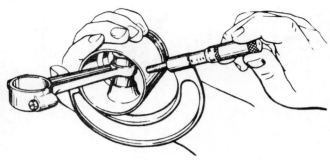

Mike the piston skirt in several places after installing a new wrist pin to make sure that you have not distorted the piston.

Always roll new piston rings around the ring grooves to see that there are no burrs, which would cause a new ring to stick.

wear. The sealing rings must fit snugly in the cylinder block and crankcase and must form a tight seal around the crankshaft webs. *NOTE: The sealing rings are marked with different numbers of stripes to indicate the size for a perfect fit. Always use a sealing ring with the same number of stripes as a replacement.*

Bearings

Inspect the roller bearings for galled or abraded surfaces. Check the bearing races for evidence of galling. Replace any roller bearing and its mating races if there is any evidence of damage.

Inspect ball bearings for looseness or evidence of rough operation. Check the outer and inner races for evidence of galled or abraded surfaces.

Oil the cleaned bearings to keep the highly finished parts from rusting. *CAUTION: Don't spin bearings with compressed air, or you will cause irreparable damage.*

Each piston is stamped with the word LOOSE inside of the skirt to indicate the side in which the piston pin should be installed first.

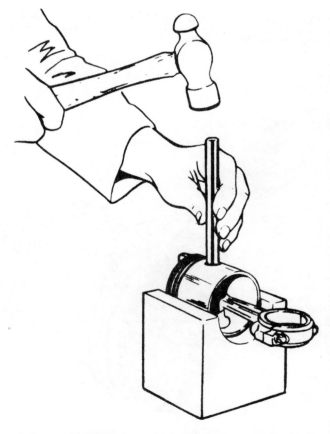

Always remove or install a piston pin by inserting the tool into the LOOSE side first.

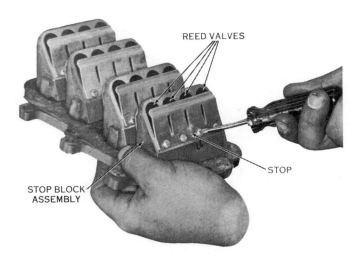

The reed valves must seat perfectly against the block, or engine operation will be erratic. Replace any defective reeds, and dress down the reed-valve block if it has nicks or burrs.

The heat switch can be tested by inserting it into a jar of heated water and noting whether or not the switch operates. Connect a self-powered test lamp to the contacts to check the operation.

Pistons

Check the pistons for wear, scores, and roundness. The piston skirts must be perfectly round and unscored to keep the exhaust gases from passing into the crankcase. Carefully scrape the carbon from inside of the

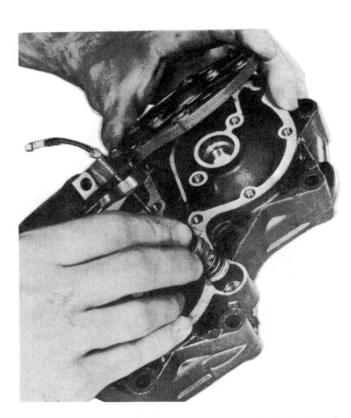

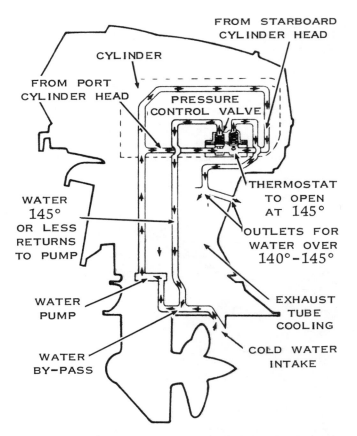

The heat switch is located in the starboard side cylinder head, and it can be removed for cleaning and testing by taking off the cylinder head cover.

The cooling system is a pressurized, recirculating, temperature-controlled system, which maintains consistent operating temperature throughout the range of engine operation, regardless of air and water temperature.

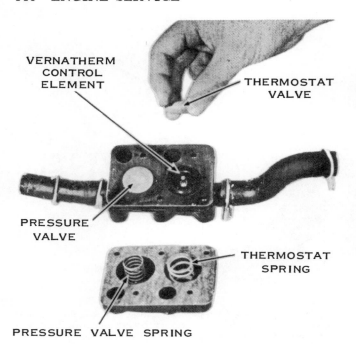

VERNATHERM CONTROL ELEMENT

THERMOSTAT VALVE

PRESSURE VALVE

THERMOSTAT SPRING

PRESSURE VALVE SPRING

The thermostat housing contains a pressure valve and spring, a Vernatherm control element, and a thermostat valve and spring. These elements control the flow of coolant as discussed in the text.

piston head and from the ring grooves. Use a broken ring to scrape the ring grooves. Be careful not to nick the ring groove sides, which are the sealing surfaces.

Rings

Always use a new set of piston rings for each overhaul. Check the end gap of each ring by placing it in its respective cylinder bore and then pushing it down slightly with the bottom of a piston to square it up.

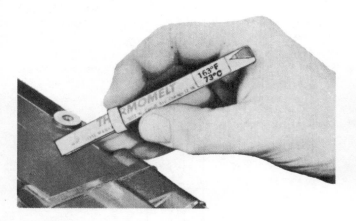

The operating temperature of an engine can be checked by using one of these Markal Thermomelt Stiks, which melt at a specific temperature. When used on a cool surface, the mark will appear dull and chalky. But when the surface temperature reaches the temperature rating of the Stik, the mark will melt, becoming liquid and glossy in appearance. Used on an engine, a 125° Thermomelt Stik mark should melt, but a 163° Thermomelt Stik mark should not.

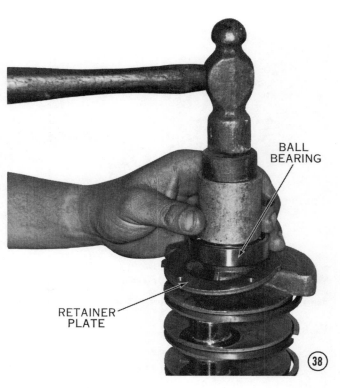

BALL BEARING

RETAINER PLATE

(38)

Check the ring side clearance with a feeler gauge. Check all measurements against specifications.

Gaskets and Seals

Always use new gaskets and O-ring seals each time that the engine is taken apart.

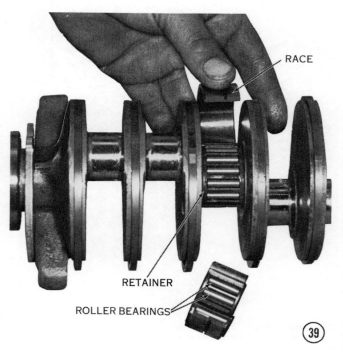

RACE

RETAINER

ROLLER BEARINGS

(39)

(40)

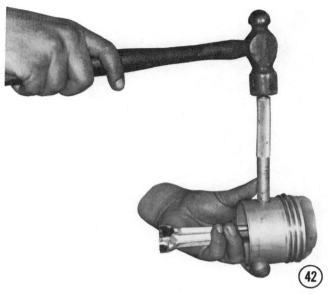

(42)

ASSEMBLING

③⑧ Place the retainer plate over the lower end of the crankshaft. Use an arbor press or a driver which fits the ball bearing inner race to press the ball bearing onto the lower journal. Oil the ball bearing, and then install the locking ring.

③⑨ Make sure that the sealing rings, which isolate the crankcase chambers from each other, are free in their grooves. Lubricate and install the center main bearing retainers, rollers, and bearing races. The narrow side of the bearing race must face the top of the engine (tapered end of the crankshaft). Replace the lock ring to secure the two halves of the bearing race.

④⓪ Position the crankshaft on the cylinder block, aligning the main bearing race with the dowel pin in the cylinder block and making sure that the sealing rings are seated properly in the webs of the block bores.

④① Install three new piston rings on each piston, using a ring expander tool to keep from giving the rings a permanent set. Spread each ring with the expander tool just enough to slip it over the head of the piston and into its groove. The ring grooves are pinned to

keep the rings from rotating to prevent the ends from catching on the edges of the ports and also to assure that the ring gaps are staggered. Make sure that the rings fit freely in the grooves.

④② The pistons must be installed with the intake side of the deflector facing the intake port. The oil hole in the wrist pin end of the connecting rod must face the top of the engine. Make sure that the wrist pin is clean, and then oil it lightly. Place a drop or two of oil in each wrist pin hole. Insert the wrist pin through the slip-fit side of the piston. *NOTE: One side of the piston is stamped LOOSE, and the wrist pin must be inserted through this hole first. CAUTION: Always drive from the loose side to the tight side; otherwise, you will distort the piston.* Wrist pin insertion can be accomplished more easily if the piston is heated slightly to expand it.

④③ Replace the lock rings, making sure that they

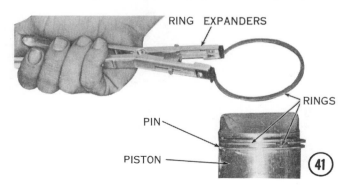

RING EXPANDERS

RINGS

PIN

PISTON

(41)

(43)

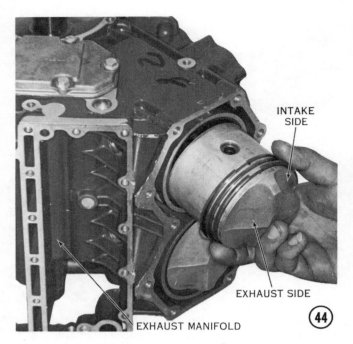

INTAKE SIDE

EXHAUST SIDE

EXHAUST MANIFOLD

44

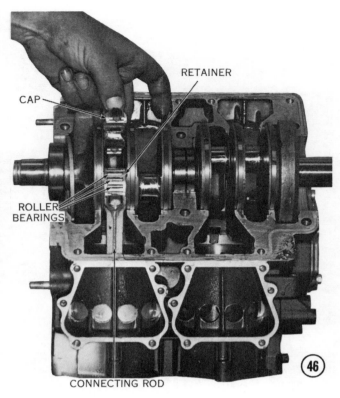

CAP

RETAINER

ROLLER BEARINGS

CONNECTING ROD

46

seat securely in the grooves provided in the piston bosses for this purpose. Check the piston with a micrometer to determine if the piston has been distorted during installation of the wrist pin. If necessary, tap the high side of the piston skirt with a light mallet in order to restore the original roundness. *CAUTION: Don't use a hammer, or you will distort the metal.* Proceed carefully and mike the piston skirt frequently until the piston is round.

④ Coat the cylinder bore and the piston with oil, and then install each piston and connecting rod assembly, being sure to match each assembly with the cylinder from which it was removed. *CAUTION: The intake side of the piston deflector must be facing the intake*

port, as shown. CAUTION: The pistons must be reversed for the other bank because the intake ports face the outside of the block on the other side.

④ Oil the piston rings, and then position a piston ring compressor, Tool No. 308867, over the cylinder bore. Insert the piston through the compressor and into the bore. Use one hand to push the piston into the cylinder bore and the other to guide the connecting rod into place and to align the rod with respect to the crankshaft.

④ Apply a coating of OMC Needle Bearing Grease,

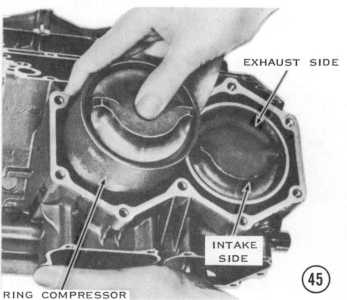

EXHAUST SIDE

INTAKE SIDE

RING COMPRESSOR

45

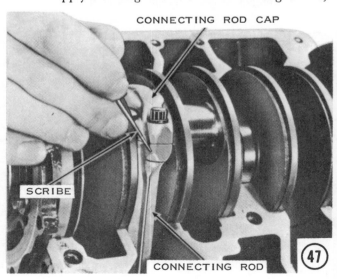

CONNECTING ROD CAP

SCRIBE

CONNECTING ROD

47

INTAKE PORTS

PISTON RINGS

(48)

shaft to see that nothing is binding, and then assemble each of the other pistons and rods in a similar manner.

④⑦ The connecting rod caps are not interchangeable, nor may the cap of the same rod be turned end for end. To assist in the correct assembly, small raised dots are provided on the matching sides of each rod and cap. Draw a pencil over the chamfered corners on both sides of the rod to make sure that the cap and rod are aligned at this point. If not, the chamfered corners can be felt as the pencil point moves over the joint. *CAU-TION: Misalignment will result in major damage to the engine.*

④⑧ Turn the crankshaft and stop when each piston is aligned with its port holes; then depress each piston ring with a screwdriver to see if it springs back. A broken ring will have no tension. *CAUTION: Remove any piston with a broken ring in order to replace the ring; otherwise, the sharp edges will score the cylinder walls.*

④⑨ Torque the connecting rod cap screws to 348–372 in-lbs. Turn the crankshaft to see that everything is free. *CAUTION: The rods and bearings must float on the crankpins.*

⑤⓪ Install new O-ring seals on the lower crankcase head and position the head with the cavity aligned with the lug on the bearing retainer plate. Insert the retainer plate screws, using new O-ring seals and screws. Draw the screws up tight, and then back them off two turns to provide a slight degree of end movement.

⑤① The crankcase face is grooved for a rubber sealing strip. Run a fine bead of Sealer 1000 in the grooves to hold the strip in place.

Part No. 378642, to the connecting rod bearing area. Position one retainer half and 7 roller bearings on each rod. Pull the piston and rod up to meet the crankpin. Apply a coating of OMC Needle Bearing Grease to the crankpin, and then install two additional roller bearings and the other retainer half on the crankpin. Place the remaining 7 roller bearings in the retainer. Attach the cap and tighten the screws finger-tight. Turn the crank-

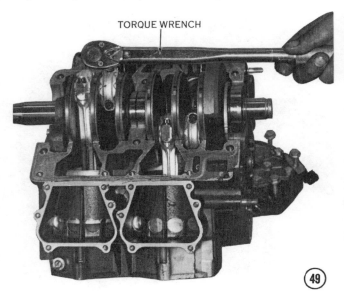

TORQUE WRENCH

(49)

O-RING SEALS

(50)

GROOVES

(51)

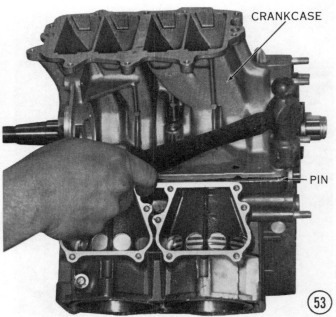

CRANKCASE

PIN

(53)

52 Thread new sealing strips into the grooves and trim the ends, allowing 1/32″ of each strip to extend beyond the edge of the machined surface. Apply a thin line of Sealer 1000 to the crankcase faces. *CAUTION: Don't apply too much, or the excess will be squeezed out and foul the oil passageways.*

53 Place the crankcase on the cylinder block, using care to avoid damaging the crankcase head O-ring seals. Replace the two crankcase taper pins. Install the lower crankcase head screws finger-tight. *NOTE: One of the eight smaller screws is shorter than the rest; it fastens the starter mounting bracket to the crankcase and should be left loose for installing the starter.* Tap in the taper pins.

54 Install the crankcase screws finger-tight, and

then rotate the crankshaft to check for binding. Tighten the center main bearing retaining bolts to 162–168 in-lbs. of torque, and then tighten the upper and lower main bearing bolts to 144–168 in-lbs. of torque. Tighten securely the screws holding the crankcase to the cylinder block.

55 Torque the lower bearing retainer plate bolts to 96–120 in-lbs. Install a new carbon seal, using a new O-ring seal in the groove inside of the carbon seal. Install the retainer and then the spring, with the small end facing out. Replace the outer retainer and the lock ring.

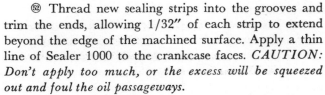

SEALING STRIPS

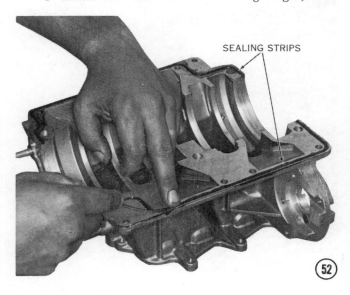

(52)

(54)

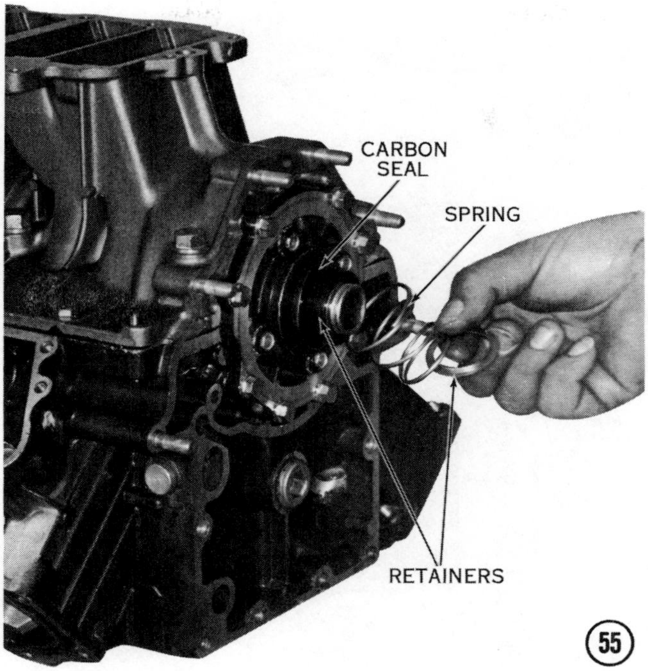
CARBON
SEAL
SPRING
RETAINERS

(55)

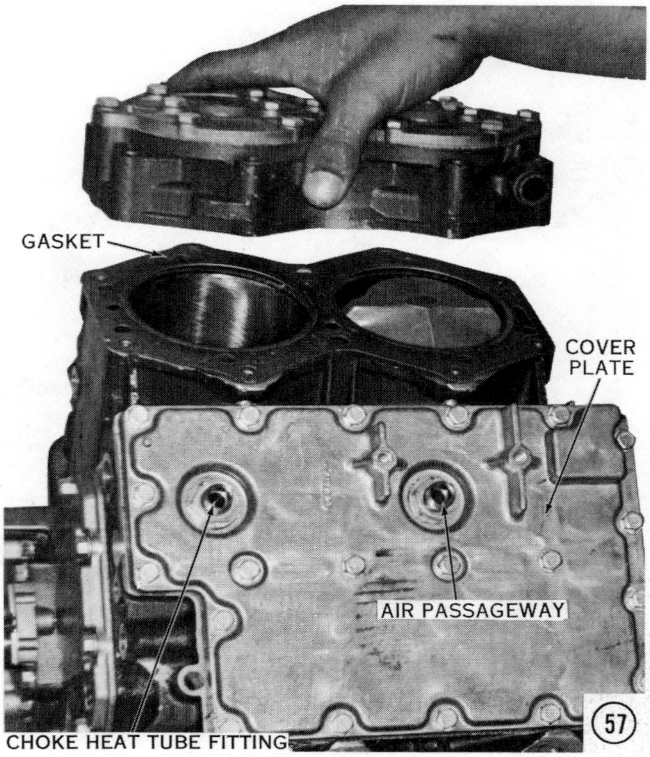
GASKET
COVER
PLATE
AIR PASSAGEWAY
CHOKE HEAT TUBE FITTING

(57)

(56) Install the upper crankcase head assembly, using new O-ring seals. Torque the bolts to 120–144 in-lbs.

(57) Position a new gasket on the block, and then install the exhaust port cover, tightening the retaining bolts securely. Place a new gasket on each side of the block, replace the heads, and then insert the cylinder head bolts, tightening them finger-tight. *CAUTION: Make sure that the temperature switch is installed in the starboard side cylinder head.*

(58) Torque the cylinder head bolts to 168–192 in-lbs., in the sequence shown. *NOTE: It is necessary to retorque the cylinder head bolts after the engine has been run and then cooled down.*

(59) Position a new gasket under each of the intake port covers, and then replace the covers. Tighten the retaining screws evenly. *CAUTION: Make sure that the intake port cover with the radius cut into the ribs is installed in the lower starboard side, as shown.*

(60) Inspect the reed-valve block to make sure that the valves are clean and lie flat against the block. The reed valves must not be bent away from their seating

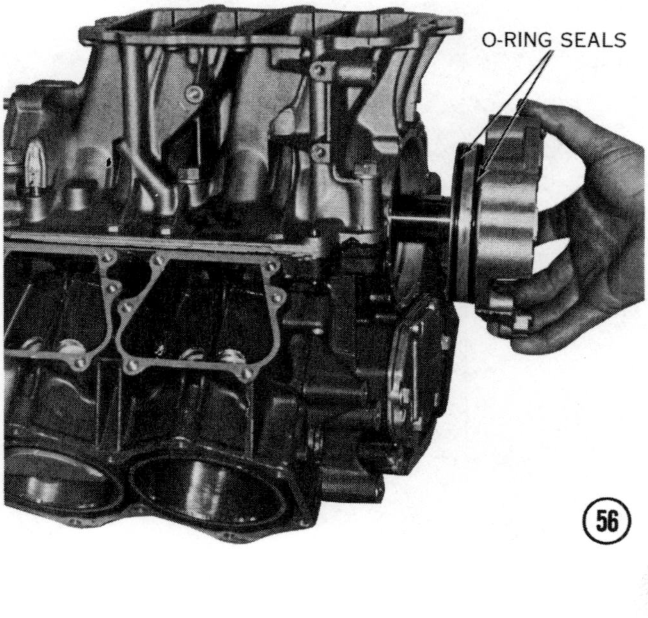
O-RING SEALS

(56)

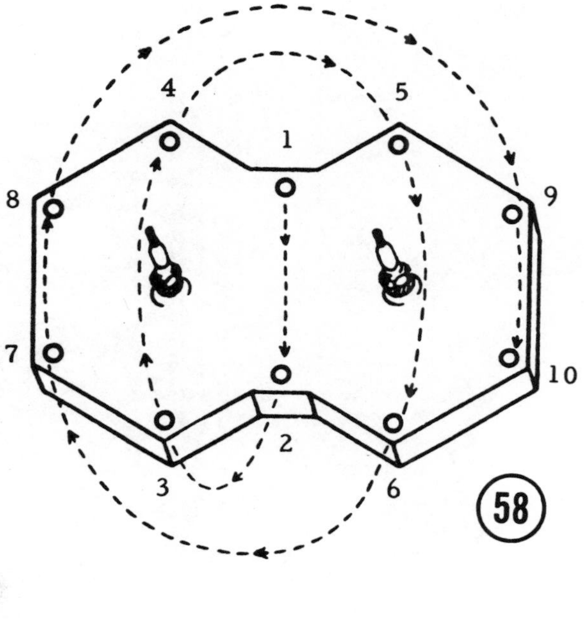
1
2
3
4
5
6
7
8
9
10

(58)

INTAKE PORT COVER

RADIUS

59

surfaces, or the engine will run irregularly. Slip the reed-valve block assembly into the crankcase, using a new gasket.

60

BOLTS

61

61 Position a new gasket over the reed-valve block, thread three of the retaining bolts into the casting, as shown, and then slide the carburetor over the three bolts. Install the rest of the bolts and tighten all ten securely.

62 Install the stator and the timing belt, tightening the three retaining screws securely.

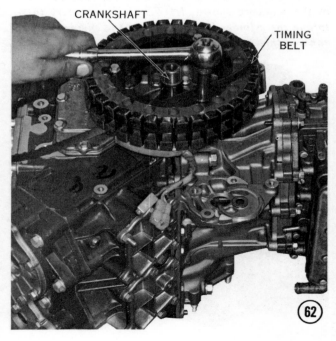

CRANKSHAFT

TIMING BELT

62

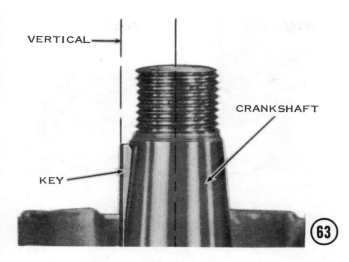

VERTICAL

CRANKSHAFT

KEY

63

63 Assemble the flywheel key to the crankshaft groove with the outer edge vertical, as shown.

64 Before installing the flywheel, check both tapered surfaces for burrs and nicks, which must be dressed off with a fine file. Clean both tapered surfaces with solvent and blow dry with compressed air. *CAUTION: This assembly must be perfectly dry. Any oil or grease on the taper will be spread by the rotating hub.* Hook the timing belt over the flywheel pulley, and then install the flywheel.

65 Tighten the flywheel retaining nut to 70–85 ft-lbs. of torque.

PULLEY

64

FLYWHEEL HOLDING TOOL

65

66 Bolt the cranking motor drive-end case assembly to the block with a single bolt and lockwasher, and then install the cranking motor. Secure it to the end case with the two through-bolts. Rotate the drive-end pinion to make sure that the armature turns freely as you tighten the through-bolts.

TIMING BELT INSTALLATION

NOTE: The belt timing instructions which follow are for the 1966 100 Hp engine. See Chapter 3, Tuning, for making the timing adjustments on other four-cylinder models.

67 Attach the distributor bracket to the block with the three bolts and flat washers, tightening the bolts

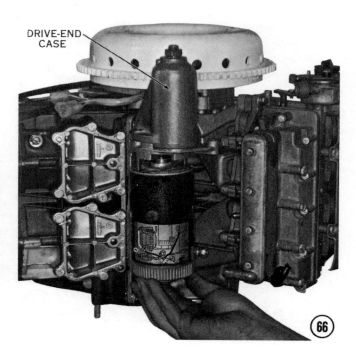

DRIVE-END CASE

66

⑥⑧ Turn the distributor pulley until the timing marks are aligned, as shown. Install the drive belt.

⑥⑨ Adjust the position of the distributor bracket so that the timing belt can be deflected 1/4″–3/8″ under a one-pound pressure, applied to the center of the belt. Tighten the distributor bracket mounting bolts securely.

⑦⓪ Replace the ring gear cover, tightening the retaining bolts securely.

⑦① Replace the breaker plate assembly, spacing the breaker points to 0.020″ for a preliminary adjustment.

finger-tight so that the timing belt tension can be adjusted later on. Rotate the flywheel so that the timing marks on the flywheel and the cylinder block are in line. *CAUTION: If the engine is attached to the motor leg, rotate the flywheel in a clockwise direction only to prevent damaging the water pump impeller.*

CONDENSER

BREAKER POINTS

71

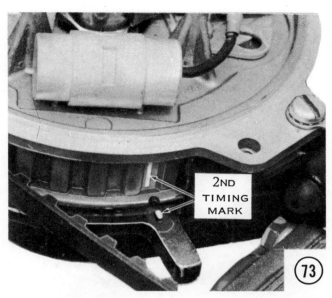

2ND TIMING MARK

73

BREAKER POINT ADJUSTMENTS

72 To time the first set of breaker points to piston movement, disconnect the breaker point lead and connect it to a self-powered test lamp. Connect the other test lead to a good ground on the breaker plate. Rotate the distributor housing to the fully advanced position so that the boss on the housing is against the rubber stop on the distributor bracket. *CAUTION: The distributor housing must be held in this position through the following breaker point adjustments.* Rotate the flywheel (clockwise only) so that the first timing mark on the distributor pulley lines up with the timing mark on the distributor housing. Loosen the lock screw, turn the gap adjusting screw until the breaker points close, and then turn it back again until they just open, as indicated by the test lamp going out. Recheck the adjustment by rotating the flywheel slightly in each direction. The breaker

points should open the instant the pulley mark passes the distributor timing mark. *NOTE: This times the first set of breaker points to the piston.*

73 To time the second set of breaker points to fire 90° apart, rotate the flywheel (clockwise only) a quarter turn (90°) until the mark on the distributor pulley lines up with the second timing (synchronizing) mark on the distributor breaker plate. Repeat the gap adjustment for the second set of breaker points so that they just open as the pulley mark passes the distributor second timing (synchronizing) mark.

74 Replace the rotor, making sure that it engages

TIMING MARKS

72

ROTOR

74

HEAT TUBE

(75)

GASKET

(77)

the indexing flat on the shaft properly and that it is
fully depressed. Inspect the distributor cap to be sure
that the rotor spring and brush are in place and that
the brush is free. To assure proper ventilation, make
sure that the ventilating screen in the distributor cap is
clean. Replace the distributor cap, making sure that the
locating lugs are indexed properly.

⑦⑤ Install the heat tube; one end is connected to
the automatic choke and the other end is connected to
the fitting on the exhaust port cover.

⑦⑥ Replace the rope starter plate. Tighten the three
screws securely.

(76)

(78)

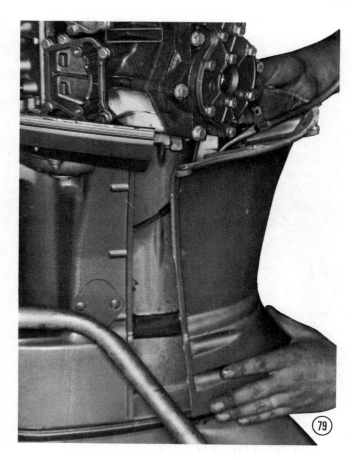

more easily engaged by bringing the powerhead into position, with the intake manifold facing slightly toward the port side, and then rotating the powerhead until the splines engage. *CAUTION: Don't rotate the driveshaft counterclockwise, or the water pump impeller vanes will be damaged.* Tighten the adaptor plate-to-powerhead retaining bolts securely.

⑦⑧ Replace the front cowl, install the retaining bolts and lockwashers, and then tighten them securely.

⑦⑨ Replace the motor leg rear cover. Insert the water discharge rubber boot into the hole in the cover. Install and tighten the Allen-headed bolts securely.

⑧⓪ Replace the rear cowl. Install the six retaining bolts and lockwashers, and then tighten them securely.

⑧① Install the fuel pump. Connect the inlet and outlet hoses and the pressure hose to the crankcase fitting. Connect all wires leading to the powerhead.

⑧② Install the tower shaft, tightening the bearing clamp screws securely. Check to see that the tower shaft turns freely. Install the throttle control shaft.

ADJUSTING THE DISTRIBUTOR LINKAGE

⑧③ Attach the linkage to the distributor. Turn the

⑦⑦ Make sure that the gasket surfaces of the powerhead and the powerhead adaptor are clean. Position a new gasket on the adaptor, and then lift the assembled powerhead with a chain hoist. Position it over the motor leg, using care to avoid damaging the splined ends of the crankshaft and driveshaft. *NOTE: The splines are*

PRESSURE LINE

INLET HOSE

THROTTLE CONTROL SHAFT

PLASTIC
BUSHING

TOWER SHAFT ⑧②

distributor to the fully advanced position by hand. With the shift lever in FORWARD gear, the inside surface of the control shaft arm should be parallel to the edges of the triangular projection on the control shaft bracket.

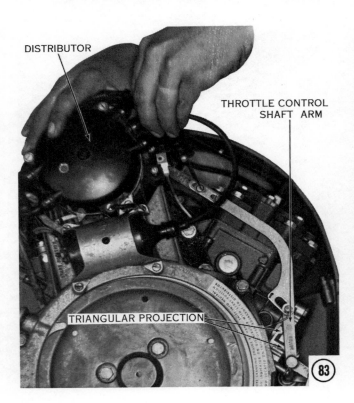

DISTRIBUTOR

THROTTLE CONTROL
SHAFT ARM

TRIANGULAR PROJECTION

⑧③

THROTTLE
ARM

THROTTLE
CAM

ROLLER

INDEX MARK

⑧④

If necessary, loosen the two linkage screws and make the adjustment while holding the distributor in the fully advanced position. Tighten the screws securely.

MAKING THE PICKUP ADJUSTMENT

⑧④ Check the position of the throttle with the cam

YOKE

CLEVIS PIN

THROTTLE
STOP

THROTTLE CONTROL ROD

⑧⑤

the cam and correctly aligned with the index mark. Tighten the screw. Recheck the adjustment. The cam follower must just begin to move as the index mark on the cam passes the centerline of the cam-follower roller.

85 Turn the tower shaft to the wide-open throttle position to see that the throttle arm is against the full-throttle stop. If necessary, make an adjustment by removing the clevis pin and turning the yoke on the throttle control rod until the throttle control shaft and the throttle arm reach their wide-open positions at the same time. *NOTE: The distributor must reach the fully advanced position at the same time.*

ADJUSTING THE SAFETY SWITCH

86 The safety switch on the distributor bracket prevents the cranking motor from being actuated with the throttle fully advanced. To adjust the switch, loosen the retaining screws and position the switch so that the contact points close at the midpoint of the cam slope. *NOTE: A sharp click can be heard when the switch contacts close.* Tighten the retaining screws. *NOTE: The switch contacts are normally open and must close to complete the cranking motor solenoid circuit.* Check the operation of the switch with a self-powered test lamp. When the switch button reaches the midpoint of the cam slope, the contacts must close and the test lamp should light.

86

by rotating the linkage from the closed to the wide-open position. The carburetor throttle must just begin to open as the center of the roller is opposite the index mark on the cam. If necessary, loosen the cam-adjustment screw, and then push the throttle arm to the closed position while holding the cam-follower roller in contact with

INLET FITTING

THERMOSTAT HOUSING

87

SLOT

88

through the cooling system and the ratio of coolant discharge to intake is controlled by a balanced action between the pressure control valve and the Vernatherm control element. When the powerhead and cooling system reach operating temperature (145°F.), the Vernatherm control element opens the thermostat valve, allowing heated water to discharge. The drop in pressure, produced by the opened thermostat valve, causes the pressure valve to close, preventing cooling system water from being recirculated through the water pump, and fresh water to be drawn through the water intake. This combined action controls water jacket temperature regardless of weather and water temperature.

⑧⑧ Install the lower retaining screw, and then slide the solid-state amplifier into position. Tighten the two screws securely.

⑧⑨ Install the spark plugs, using new gaskets. Support the wrench with the palm of your hand to keep it from tilting, which would crack the porcelain. Torque the spark plugs to 20 ft-lbs. Connect the high-tension wires to the spark plugs. *CAUTION: Make sure that the correct wires are connected by seeing that the number on the wire and the number stamped on the cylinder head agree.*

⑨⓪ Install the cranking motor solenoid.

⑨① Replace the fuse block and the low-tension wiring. Connect the terminal leads to the solenoid and the

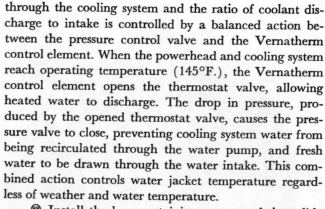

⑧⑦ Hook up the water hoses to the thermostat housing. The thermostat housing contains a pressure-release valve and spring, a Vernatherm control element, and a thermostat valve and spring. Circulation of water

FUSE BLOCK

RETAINING CLIP

TERMINAL BLOCK

(92) Install the hood and snap the latch closed. Run the engine in a test tank to make the tuning adjustments and to loosen it up. Use a 24/1 fuel/oil mixture for the first ten hours of operation. For the first ten minutes, operate the engine at a fast idle. Check the operation of the water pump to be sure that there is an adequate flow of coolant. Do not operate the engine above 3,000 rpm for the first hour. With an easy planing boat, it is desirable to bring the boat into planing position with full power and then reduce the throttle setting to 3,000 rpm. *CAUTION: Make sure that the boat maintains a planing attitude at this throttle setting.*

During the second hour of operation, bring the boat into a planing attitude, and then reduce the throttle setting to 4,000 rpm. During the second hour of operation, apply full power for a minute or two, and then return the throttle to a three-quarter setting (4,000 rpm) for a cooling period. *CAUTION: Avoid continuous full-throttle operation for extended periods during the next few hours.*

connectors to the alternator coil. Slide the terminal block into its retaining clip. Connect the primary wires to the ignition coil.

The outboard motor has extended man's leisure-time activities.

6
LOWER UNIT SERVICE

The lower unit of the 1.5, 3.0, 4.0, and 5.0 Hp engines is a nonshift type; it is necessary to turn the entire unit 180° to obtain reverse. The lower unit of the 6 through 33 Hp engines is manually shifted, the operator being able to select forward, neutral, or reverse gear by moving a shift lever. The 40 Hp engine can be optionally equipped with either a manually shifted or an electrically shifted lower unit. The lower units of the three-cylinder engine since 1968 and all four-cylinder engines since 1969 utilize hydraulic shifting. An oil pump, driven by the forward gear and using the lubricating oil in the gear case for shifting, is controlled by a solenoid; the solenoid operates a pump valve which forces the shifting dog clutch in the desired direction. Most of the larger engine sizes through 1968 can be shifted either mechanically or electrically.

All engines have a water pump, driven by the driveshaft, for cooling the engine and the lower unit.

EXHAUST RELIEF

Normally, exhaust gases are conducted down through the exhaust housing and out of the underwater outlet in the gear case. The siphoning action of the propeller and water provides an unrestricted escape for exhaust. In starting, however, water in the outlet creates back pressure that results in hard starting. Exhaust relief is provided by another outlet located in the water discharge passage above the water line. Since no water is discharged until after the engine is started, the exhaust gases will initially be discharged through the water outlet.

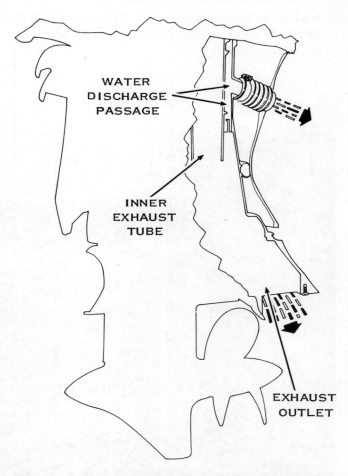

The water used for cooling the engine is discharged into the space between the exhaust housings and maintains a specified level when the engine is running. This chamber of water serves as an effective silencer, quiets the exhaust relief, and cools the outer housings. Normally, exhaust gases are conducted down through the inner exhaust tube and out through the underwater exhaust outlet. However, when starting the engine, the water in the exhaust housing creates back pressure which can cause hard starting. Exhaust relief is provided by an outlet in the water discharge passage above the water line. The initial flow of exhaust gases will pass out of this port until the water level rises to cut it off and force the exhaust out of the underwater outlet.

LOW SPEED   HIGH SPEED

The water pump impeller forces water through the powerhead and the gear case for cooling. At low speed (left), the impeller works as a displacement pump. At higher speeds (right), the water resistance keeps the blades from flexing and the pump acts as a circulator.

WATER PUMP

Water for cooling the powerhead is circulated by the water pump, located at the top of the gear case and driven directly by the driveshaft. The pump consists of a synthetic rubber impeller, which is keyed to the drive-shaft, and the pump housing, which is offset from the center with respect to the driveshaft. Because the housing is offset, the impeller blades flex as they rotate, varying the space between them. The pump inlet port, located in the stainless steel plate which forms the lower part of the pump housing, is open to the blades when the space between them is increasing. The pump outlet port, in the impeller housing, is open to the blades when the space between them is decreasing. Thus, at low speeds the impeller works as a displacement pump. At higher speeds, water resistance keeps the blades from flexing, and the pump acts as a circulator, enough water being provided by the forward motion through the water.

GEAR SHIFT

The three functions of forward, neutral, and re-

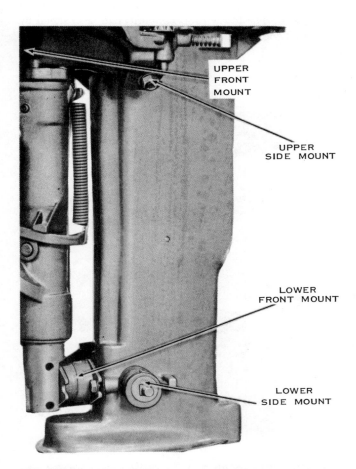

This illustration shows the locations of the rubber mounts used on the 18/20 Hp engines.

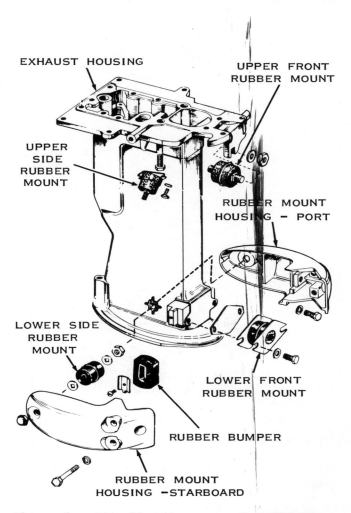

These are the positions of the rubber mounts on the 33 Hp engine.

verse operation are provided by the gear shift mechanism located in the lower gear case. The driveshaft pinion gear rotates constantly with the operation of the engine, driving two bevel gears which revolve freely on the propeller shaft. The shifter clutch dog is splined to the propeller shaft. In neutral operation, the shifter dog is centered between the two gears, which revolve in opposite directions, and remains motionless. In forward or reverse operation, the shift lever causes the shifter dog to engage either gear. Power is then transmitted from the pinion gear, through the shifter clutch dog, to the propeller shaft and propeller.

ENGINE MOUNTS

To minimize engine and driveshaft vibrations and to prevent them from being transmitted to the stern bracket and the boat transom, all of the larger outboard motors are supported by rubber mounts. If a mount cracks, or if the rubber shears off its metal plate, several troubles typically occur: misalignment and shifting prob-

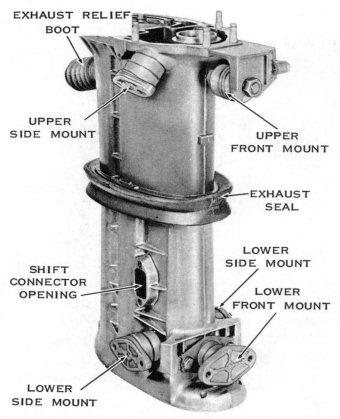

EXHAUST RELIEF BOOT

UPPER SIDE MOUNT

UPPER FRONT MOUNT

EXHAUST SEAL

LOWER SIDE MOUNT

SHIFT CONNECTOR OPENING

LOWER FRONT MOUNT

LOWER SIDE MOUNT

These are the locations of the rubber mounts on the 40 Hp engine.

lems, excessive vibration, and related vibration-caused troubles.

Service Procedures

To check for a broken engine mount, push against

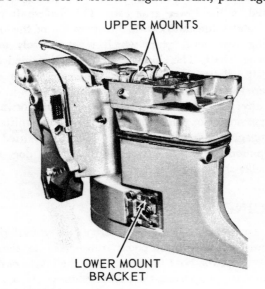

UPPER MOUNTS

LOWER MOUNT BRACKET

On the 55 Hp engine, the lower rubber mounts can be reached by taking off the lower mount covers.

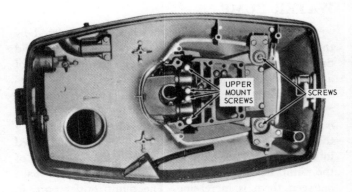

UPPER MOUNT SCREWS

SCREWS

The upper rubber mounts of the 55 Hp engine are shown here; it is necessary to take off the powerhead to change them.

the powerhead to see if it can be moved an excessive amount. Generally, a noise can be heard as the metal parts make contact.

To change an upper rubber mount on a two-cylinder engine, it is necessary to remove the front and rear exhaust covers. The lower mounts can be reached by taking off both lower mount covers.

To change an upper rubber mount of a three- or four-cylinder engine, it is necessary first to remove the powerhead. The lower rubber mounts can be reached by taking off the exhaust housing covers.

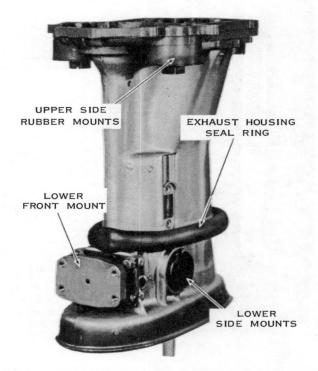

UPPER SIDE RUBBER MOUNTS

EXHAUST HOUSING SEAL RING

LOWER FRONT MOUNT

LOWER SIDE MOUNTS

The upper rubber mounts on a V-4 engine can be changed after taking off the powerhead. The lower mounts are accessible after removing the exhaust housing covers.

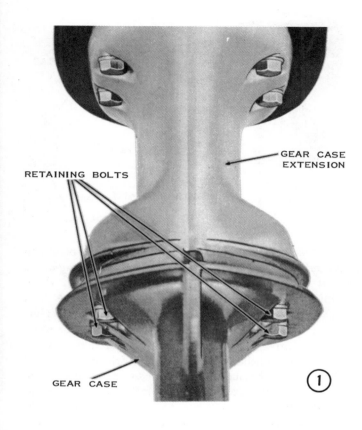

RETAINING BOLTS

GEAR CASE
EXTENSION

GEAR CASE

①

WATER PUMP
SCREWS

③

LOWER UNIT SERVICE PROCEDURES

The service procedures for the lower units will be covered in four sections according to shift, as follows: (1) nonshift, (2) mechanical shift, (3) hydraulic shift, and (4) electric shift. Each type of unit is covered with a complete set of step-by-step illustrated instructions.

SERVICING THE NONSHIFT TYPE LOWER UNIT

1.5, 3.0, 4.0 & 5.0 Hp Engines

① It is possible to remove the gear case without removing the powerhead or the exhaust housing. Do this by taking out the bolts holding the gear case to the exhaust housing or extension. Most models have four retaining bolts.

DISASSEMBLING

② Remove the propeller by taking out the cotter pin and then removing the propeller and drive pin. Drain the gear case.

③ Remove the water pump screws, and then lift the pump cover and driveshaft from the gear case. Take out the grommet from the water pump.

④ Remove the two screws holding the gear case head or bearing retainer to the case. Remove the head

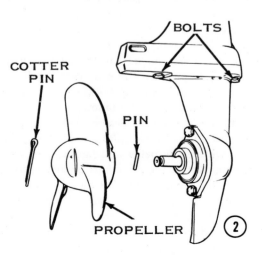

BOLTS

COTTER
PIN

PIN

PROPELLER

②

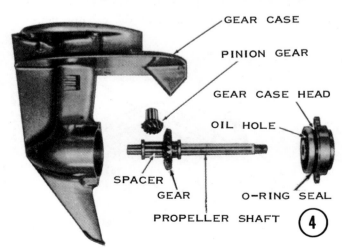

GEAR CASE

PINION GEAR

GEAR CASE HEAD

OIL HOLE

SPACER

GEAR

O-RING SEAL

PROPELLER SHAFT

④

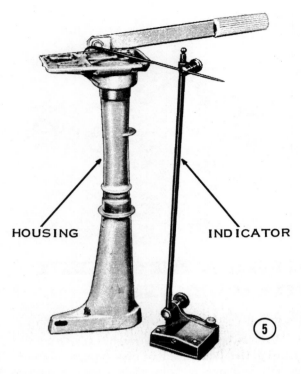

HOUSING   INDICATOR

⑤

or bearing retainer by pulling on the propeller shaft. Slide the gear case head or bearing retainer from the propeller shaft, and then remove the seals. Remove the driveshaft seal from the top of the gear case, using puller No. 377565.

CLEANING AND INSPECTING

Clean all parts in solvent and dry with compressed air. Don't use rags to dry the parts because of the danger of leaving lint. Remove gasket particles and dried cement with trichloroethylene. Discard all gaskets, oil seals, and O-ring seals. Always use new ones during assembly.

⑤ Check the flatness of the gasket surfaces and the parallelism of machined faces of the exhaust housing

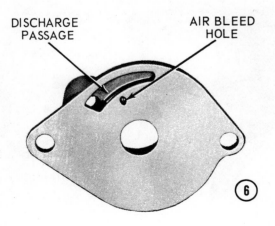

DISCHARGE PASSAGE   AIR BLEED HOLE

⑥

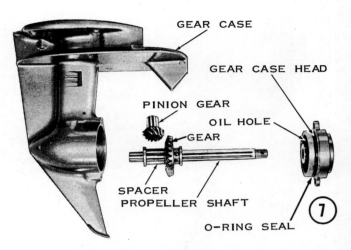

GEAR CASE

GEAR CASE HEAD

PINION GEAR

OIL HOLE

GEAR

SPACER

PROPELLER SHAFT

O-RING SEAL

⑦

and the gear case extension by using a surface plate and an indicator. *CAUTION: Don't attempt to straighten a bent housing; replace it.* Inspect the propeller shaft, pinion gear, and driveshaft splines for wear. A bent exhaust housing will cause excessive crankshaft spline wear. Inspect the bushings and thrust bearing for wear.

⑥ Inspect the impeller for wear or deterioration. Check the impeller drive pin on the driveshaft. Inspect the impeller chamber in the gear case for scoring, which will reduce the water output. Make sure that the air bleed hole in the cover is open. Inspect the water tube and the water intake holes for clogging or kinks, and clean them if necessary.

ASSEMBLING

⑦ Install a new seal on the top of the gear case. Press a new seal into the gear case head, and then place a new O-ring seal in position. *NOTE: Always lubricate new seals before assembling.* Oil the propeller shaft, and then slide the gear case head and spacer onto the shaft. Place the pinion gear in position in the gear case. Install the propeller shaft with the gear case head and spacer. *CAUTION: The gear case head has an oil hole which must face up. On the 1.5 Hp engine, the gear case head has a flat surface at the upper screw hole, which must face up.* Dip the gear case head screws in Perfect Seal #4, and then tighten them securely. Rotate the propeller shaft to check for binding.

⑧ Apply a fine bead of Sealer 1000 to the gear case, and then place the impeller plate in position. Place the driveshaft, with the impeller and housing, in position in the gear case. Rotate the driveshaft to engage the pinion gear. Install the impeller pin. Oil the impeller, and then slide it down the driveshaft, aligning it with the drive pin. Install the housing, twisting the driveshaft clockwise (as viewed from the top) in order to seat the impeller vanes in the proper direction of rotation. Attach the

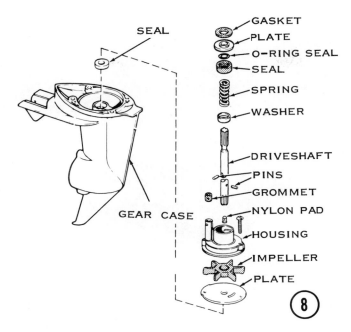

SEAL

GASKET
PLATE
O-RING SEAL
SEAL
SPRING
WASHER
DRIVESHAFT
PINS
GROMMET
NYLON PAD
HOUSING
IMPELLER
PLATE

GEAR CASE

(8)

impeller housing with the screws dipped in Perfect Seal #4, and then tighten them securely. Oil and install a new lower water tube grommet in the top of the water pump housing. Apply a light film of OMC Type A Grease to the propeller shaft, and then install the propeller, using a new drive pin and a new cotter pin to secure it.

SERVICING THE MECHANICAL-SHIFT TYPE LOWER UNIT

REMOVING

5.5, 6.0, 9.5, 18/20, 25, 33, 40, 65, 75, 80 & 85 Hp Engines

① It is possible to remove the lower gear case without removing the powerhead. However, if the exhaust housing is to be disassembled, it is necessary first to remove the powerhead. The gear case may be removed by taking off the upper engine cover and disconnecting the spark plug wires. Remove the exhaust housing cover plate to expose the shift rod connector. Take out the lower connector bolt.

② Remove the propeller, and then take off the five bolts holding the gear case or extension case to the exhaust housing. *NOTE: One bolt is at the top of the case, as shown, and four are reached from the underside.* Remove the gear case extension, if used.

DISASSEMBLING

③ Remove the three screws holding the water pump

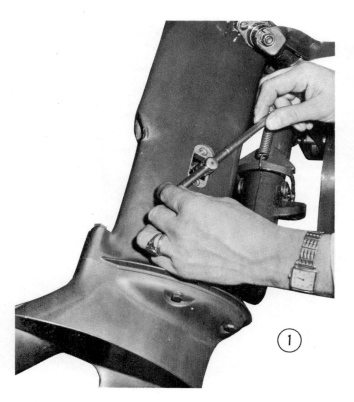

(1)

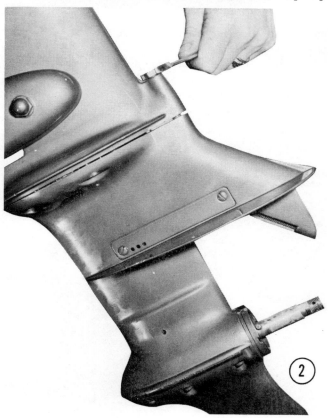

(2)

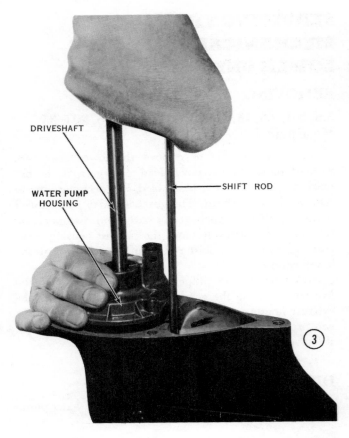

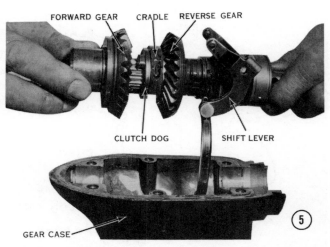

⑤ Swing the shifter lever and cradle out of the way. Lift the propeller shaft assembly from the gear case, and then remove the parts. Remove the seal from the gear case head and discard the O-ring seal. Remove the pinion gear and thrust washer from the upper gear case. *NOTE: If the bushing in the gear case is worn excessively, the entire gear case must be replaced.*

CLEANING AND INSPECTING

Clean all parts with solvent and dry with compressed air. Discard all oil seals, O-ring seals, and gaskets.

housing to the gear case, and then lift out the water pump assembly and driveshaft.

④ Remove the shift rod pivot pin and the six screws holding the gear case halves together. Separate the gear case halves.

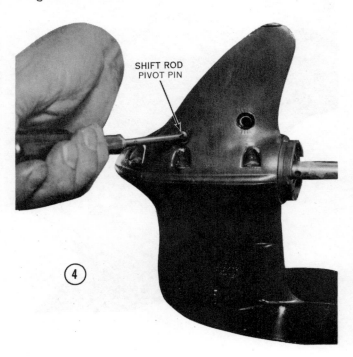

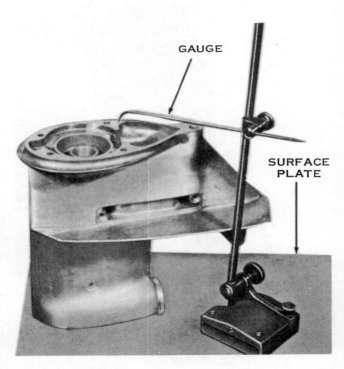

Check the parallelism of the gear case on a surface plate. If the gear case is bent, it must be replaced. Never try to straighten a bent gear case. Check the exhaust housing in the same manner.

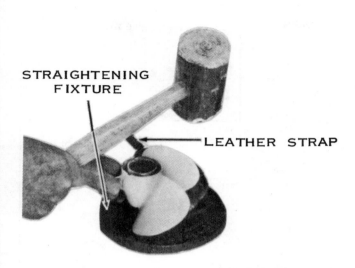

STRAIGHTENING FIXTURE

LEATHER STRAP

To straighten a bent propeller blade, use the special Tool No. 376934 and a piece of leather belting under the part of the blade that touches the fixture. Rap the high part of the blade smartly with a No. 3 rawhide mallet.

Inspect the driveshaft splines, drive gears, clutch dog, pinion gear, bearings, bushings, and thrust washers for wear or damage. Replace the clutch dog if the engagement surfaces are chipped or rounded.

Inspect the gear case and exhaust housing for nicks on the machined surfaces. Remove defects and resurface the faces on a surface plate, using No. 120 grit emery cloth and finishing with No. 180 grit cloth. Check the parallelism on a surface plate, using a gauge, as shown. Don't attempt to straighten a bent gear case.

Inspect the water pump impeller and replace it if the vanes are damaged or worn. Inspect the pump housing and plate for scores and pits. Check the water intake tube and screen for clogging or obstructions.

Inspect the propeller for nicks, broken blades, and cracks. Remove minor nicks with a file. *CAUTION: Don't attempt to weld a cracked or broken blade.* Check the pitch on a propeller block, Tool No. 376934. To straighten a bent blade, use a piece of leather belting under the part of the blade that touches the fixture. Rap the high part of the blade smartly with a No. 3 rawhide mallet. The leather allows a slight overbend to correct for the blade's normal tendency to spring back.

Check the rubber slip clutch, using the special fixture, Tool No. 378448, and a torque wrench. The clutch should start to slip at 100–160 ft-lbs.

ASSEMBLING

⑥ Replace the shift rod bushing and O-ring seal, using the special tool, No. 304515, and then install a new driveshaft seal, pressing against the lettered side of the

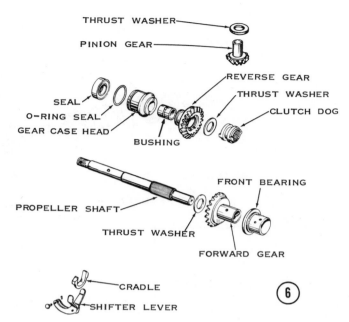

THRUST WASHER
PINION GEAR
REVERSE GEAR
SEAL
THRUST WASHER
O-RING SEAL
CLUTCH DOG
GEAR CASE HEAD
BUSHING
FRONT BEARING
PROPELLER SHAFT
THRUST WASHER
FORWARD GEAR
CRADLE
SHIFTER LEVER
⑥

seal. Oil the end of the shift rod, and then insert it through the shift rod bushing.

⑦ Install a new seal in the gear case head and a new O-ring seal in the groove. Assemble the clutch dog, thrust washers, gears, bushing, front bearing, and gear case head to the propeller shaft. Install the propeller shaft assembly in the gear case so that the gear case head and front bearing are seated over the dowel pin and matching groove. Place the cradle in the shifter dog, and then swing the shifter lever into position in the cradle.

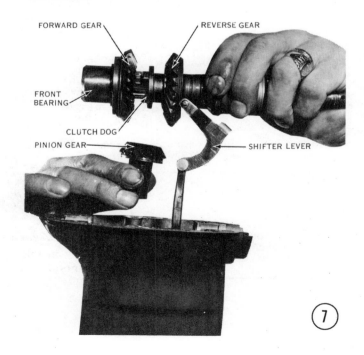

FORWARD GEAR
REVERSE GEAR
FRONT BEARING
CLUTCH DOG
PINION GEAR
SHIFTER LEVER
⑦

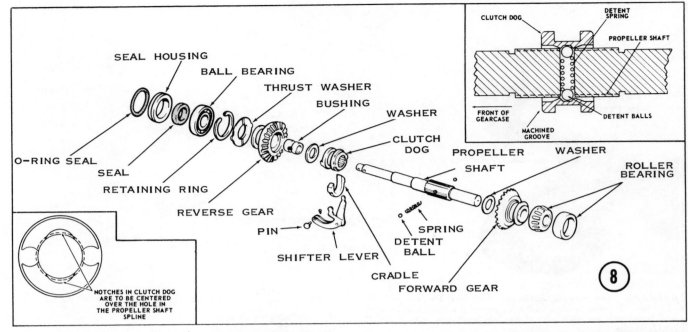

SEAL HOUSING
BALL BEARING
THRUST WASHER
BUSHING
WASHER
O-RING SEAL
SEAL
RETAINING RING
REVERSE GEAR
CLUTCH DOG
PROPELLER SHAFT
WASHER
ROLLER BEARING
PIN
SHIFTER LEVER
SPRING
DETENT BALL
CRADLE
FORWARD GEAR

CLUTCH DOG
DETENT SPRING
PROPELLER SHAFT
FRONT OF GEARCASE
MACHINED GROOVE
DETENT BALLS

NOTCHES IN CLUTCH DOG ARE TO BE CENTERED OVER THE HOLE IN THE PROPELLER SHAFT SPLINE

⑧

⑧ The propeller shaft for the 33 Hp engine varies in some details from the other engines' shafts, and these additional instructions are provided to assist in assembling the gear case for this model. Assemble the detent spring and the two detent balls to the propeller shaft, using OMC Needle Bearing Grease. Align the notches in the clutch dog with the detent balls in the propeller shaft as shown in the insert in the left corner. If the notches in the clutch dog appear to be off-center, rotate the clutch dog on the propeller shaft 180°. Slide the clutch dog forward onto the shaft and center it over the detent balls (which is the neutral position) as shown in the inset in the upper right corner. This will prevent accidental movement of the clutch dog during assembly and possible loss of the detent balls and spring. Assemble

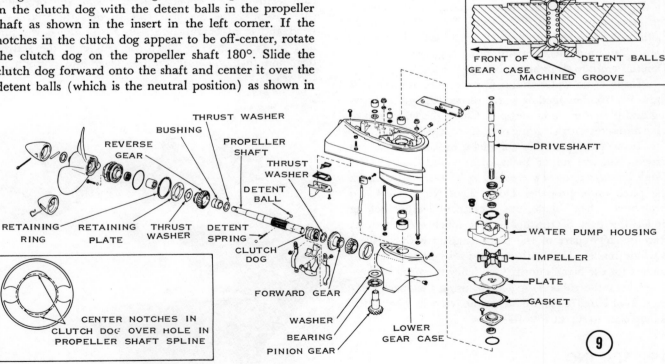

CLUTCH DOG
DETENT SPRING
PROPELLER SHAFT
FRONT OF GEAR CASE
DETENT BALLS
MACHINED GROOVE

THRUST WASHER
BUSHING
REVERSE GEAR
PROPELLER SHAFT
THRUST WASHER
DETENT BALL
RETAINING RING
RETAINING PLATE
THRUST WASHER
DETENT SPRING
CLUTCH DOG
FORWARD GEAR
WASHER
BEARING
PINION GEAR
LOWER GEAR CASE
DRIVESHAFT
WATER PUMP HOUSING
IMPELLER
PLATE
GASKET

CENTER NOTCHES IN CLUTCH DOG OVER HOLE IN PROPELLER SHAFT SPLINE

⑨

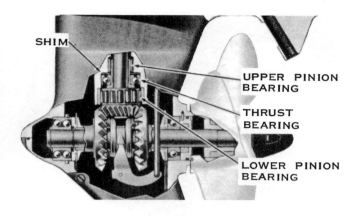

SHIM

UPPER PINION
BEARING

THRUST
BEARING

LOWER PINION
BEARING

The heavy duty gear case used on the larger engines has ball and roller bearings to support the parts.

the oil retainer housing, washers, gears, and bearings to the propeller shaft in the sequence shown. *CAUTION: The bronze side of the reverse gear thrust washer must face the gear.* Install the assembled propeller shaft into the gear case, with the tabs on the thrust washer facing up and down. Place the cradle, shifter lever, and shift rod in position.

⑨ The gear case and related parts of the 65 and 85 Hp engine lower units through 1968 are basically like the previous unit of the 33 Hp model, covered in Step ⑧. This illustration for the 65 Hp model is an exploded view for comparison.

⑩ Wash the machined faces of the gear case halves. Apply Sealer 1000 to the machined faces, and then lay a sealing strip in each groove. Cut the ends of the seal square and allow 1/32" to extend beyond the end of the

groove in order to provide a tight butt seal against the gear case head. Add a little sealer to the ends of the sealing strip. Apply a thin line of Sealer 1000 to the machined surfaces of the upper gear case. Place the bottom half of the gear case on the upper half, and then install both pairs of end screws after dipping them in Perfect Seal #4. Tighten the end screws enough to draw the gear case halves together. Install the shift lever pivot pin, using a new seal. Check the gear case seal for pinching between the gear case halves. Install the two center screws and gradually tighten all, alternating from side to side and working toward the end screws. Rotate the propeller shaft to check for free operation. Operate the shift mechanism to be sure that it operates properly.

⑪ Apply Sealer 1000 to the gear housing, and then position the impeller plate in the recess. Install the driveshaft, turning it to engage the pinion gear. Oil the impeller, and then slip it down over the drive pin. Install the water pump housing, turning the driveshaft clockwise so that the impeller blades slip into the housing in the proper direction. Dip the screws in Perfect Seal #4, and then tighten them securely. Install a new O-ring seal at the top of the driveshaft.

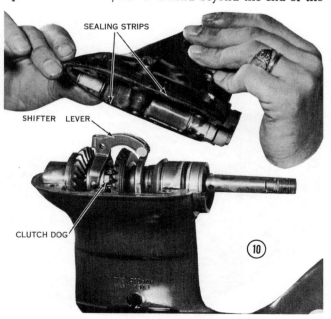

SEALING STRIPS

SHIFTER LEVER

CLUTCH DOG

⑩

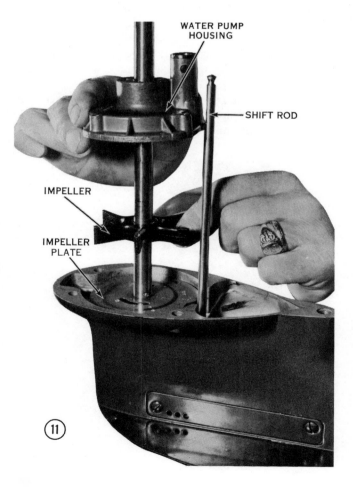

WATER PUMP
HOUSING

SHIFT ROD

IMPELLER

IMPELLER
PLATE

⑪

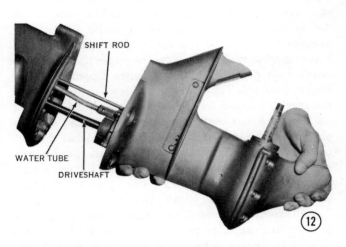

(12)

INSTALLING THE LOWER UNIT

⑫ Oil the upper end of the driveshaft and the lower end of the water tube. Place the shift lever in FORWARD gear. Bring the gear case into position under the exhaust housing, and then slide it up until the end of the driveshaft touches the crankshaft. *CAUTION: Alignment must be perfect to engage the driveshaft splines.* Turn the flywheel slightly in a clockwise direction to help in engaging the splines. Look between the gear case and extension housing to make sure that the water tube enters the grommet on top of the pump housing.

⑬ Attach the gear case to the exhaust housing with the bolts dipped in Perfect Seal #4. Four bolts are reached from the underside and one from the top. Re-

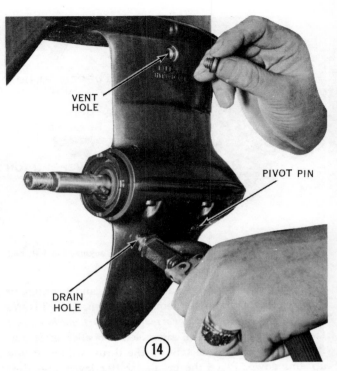

(14)

place the lower shift rod connector bolt. Replace the spark plug wires.

⑭ Remove the vent screw, and then fill the gear case through the drain plug hole with OMC Type C Lubricant. Add lubricant until it runs out of the vent hole, replace the vent plug, and then replace the drain plug. *CAUTION: Don't remove the pivot pin.*

⑮ Lubricate the propeller shaft with grease, and then install the propeller, shear pin, propeller nut, and cotter pin.

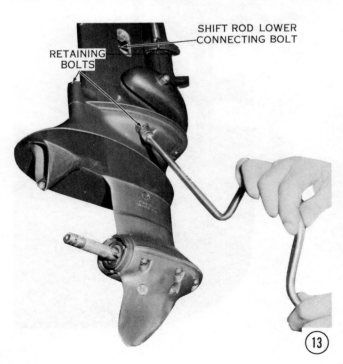

(13)

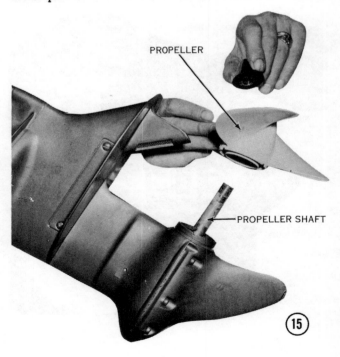

(15)

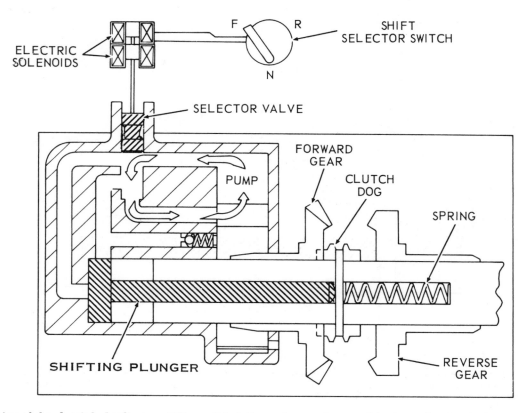

The shift mechanism of the electric-hydraulic gear shifting unit is in forward gear whenever there is an absence of oil pressure against the plunger. The engagement is made through spring pressure which forces the clutch dog to engage with the forward gear. Note how the selector valve is out of the hydraulic circuit, and the fluid circulates between the inlet and outlet ports of the pump itself.

SERVICING THE HYDRAULIC-SHIFT TYPE LOWER UNIT

55 Hp Engine (since 1968), 85 & 115 Hp Engines (since 1969)

This model contains an electric-hydraulic shift mechanism consisting of the usual gear case parts plus a vacuum switch, hydraulic pump, and selector valve. The hydraulic pump is mounted in the forward end of the gear case and is driven by the forward gear, using the gear case lubricating oil to supply the force needed for shifting. The solenoids operate the pump selector valve, which directs the hydraulic fluid to move the clutch dog to the selected position.

REMOVING

① The gear case can be removed from the exhaust housing and powerhead by disconnecting the spark plug wires. Drain the lubricant from the case. Slide back the

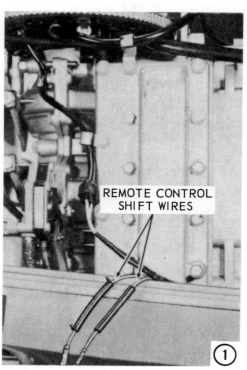

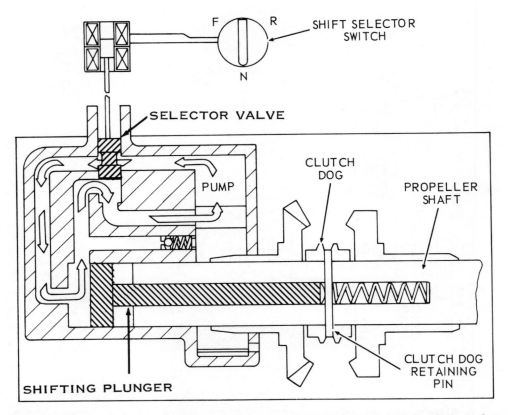

In neutral, the selector valve drops into the fluid circuit to direct the flow of fluid against the end of the plunger, where is just enough to balance the pressure of the shifting spring so that the plunger forces the clutch dog out of engagement with the forward gear. Note that the selector valve does not restrict the return flow of fluid to the pump intake.

insulating sleeve on the shift cable wires so that the terminals between the shift cable and the engine cable can be disconnected. *NOTE: The terminals are located on the port side, adjacent to the powerhead exhaust bypass cover.* Disconnect the terminals.

② Remove the four screws from the front exhaust cover and the two inside of the lower engine cover, and then take off the rear exhaust cover. Apply oil or liquid soap to the cable sleeve, which now can be pushed down through the hole in the exhaust housing.

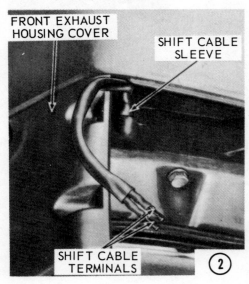

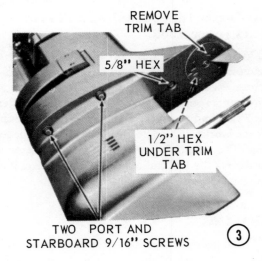

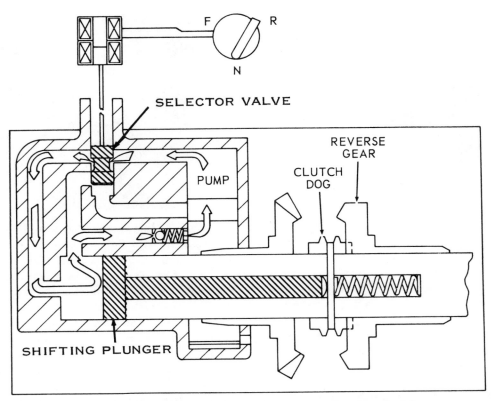

SELECTOR VALVE

PUMP

REVERSE GEAR

CLUTCH DOG

SHIFTING PLUNGER

In reverse gear, the shifter valve is depressed enough to restrict the return flow of fluid so that all of the pump pressure is directed against the shifting plunger, overcoming all spring tension so that the clutch dog is forced into reverse gear.

③ Scribe a mark on the gear case and adjustable trim tab so that it can be reinstalled in the same position. Remove the Allen-headed screw and the trim tab. Use a 1/2″ socket and short extension to remove the screw from inside of the trim tab cavity. Use a 5/8″ thin-wall socket to remove the countersunk screw, take out the four 9/16″ screws which hold the gear case to the exhaust housing, and then remove the gear case assembly. *CAUTION: Don't lose the plastic water tube guides, which are used to guide the water tube into the pump grommets during assembly.*

DISASSEMBLING

④ Remove the shift cable from the clamps around the pump housing. Take out the four screws holding the water pump housing to the case, and then slide off the housing and impeller. Remove the impeller drive key and the impeller plate. Remove the four upper drive-shaft bearing housing screws.

⑤ Remove the four screws, solenoid cover, and wave washer. Disconnect the shift cable leads. Lift the solenoids and plunger assembly from the gear case.

⑥ Remove the propeller nut, washers, and propeller. Take out the four bearing housing screws, using a long 1/4″ Allen wrench. Use a slide hammer with a hooked end to pull the bearing housing from the gear case.

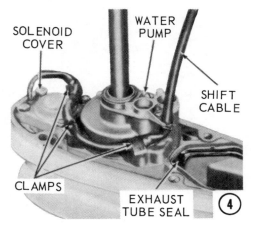

SOLENOID COVER

WATER PUMP

SHIFT CABLE

CLAMPS

EXHAUST TUBE SEAL

④

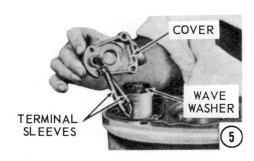

COVER

WAVE WASHER

TERMINAL SLEEVES

⑤

⑥

⑦ Slide the thrust washer and the thrust bearing from the propeller shaft. Remove the two Truarc rings.

⑧ Withdraw the propeller shaft, retainer plate, reverse gear, thrust washer, and clutch dog as an assembly.

⑨ Remove the pinion locknut from the bottom of the driveshaft by using the special holder, Tool No. 312752. With the locknut removed, take out the pinion gear thrust bearing and washer. Pull the driveshaft out of the gear case. Lift out the forward gear. Remove the Truarc ring holding the pump housing, and then take out the screen. Remove the oil pump from the gear case. If necessary, remove the lower driveshaft bearing.

⑩ Remove the piston from the oil pump, and then take out the cover screws and lockwashers. Lift off the pump cover. Remove the screw and screen from the cover. Remove the check valve and spring and the pump gears.

CLEANING AND INSPECTING

Clean all parts in solvent and dry with compressed

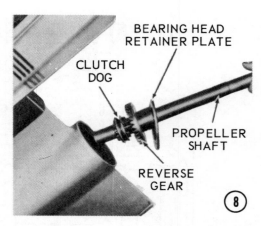

⑧

air. Wash needle bearings in solvent. Oil the bearings immediately with light spindle oil to prevent rusting. Rotate the bearings a few times after draining the excess oil, and then place them in a covered container until assembly. Discard any bearing that has rusted rollers or races. Worn, galled, or abraded surfaces can be caused by too loose a fit or a bearing locked by dirt. A fractured bearing ring can be caused by forcing a cocked bearing off a shaft.

⑪ Inspect the gear case for nicks on the machined surfaces. Remove the nicks and resurface the faces on a surface plate. Start with No. 120 emery cloth and finish with No. 180 cloth. Inspect and resurface the exhaust housing in a like manner. Replace the housing if it is bent. Check the parallelism on a surface plate, using a surface gauge. *CAUTION: Don't attempt to straighten a bent case; replace it.* Inspect the driveshaft splines for wear. A bent lower unit can cause extensive damage to

TRU-ARC PLIERS

⑦

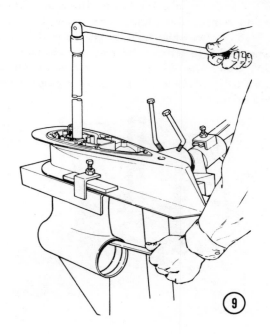

⑨

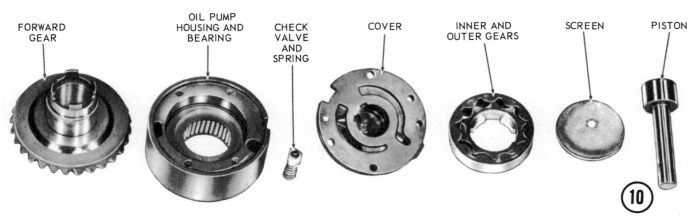

FORWARD GEAR   OIL PUMP HOUSING AND BEARING   CHECK VALVE AND SPRING   COVER   INNER AND OUTER GEARS   SCREEN   PISTON

⑩

the driveshaft splines. Also, a bent exhaust housing may cause the upper driveshaft splines to wear excessively and may also damage the crankshaft splines. Check the drive gears, pinion gear, and thrust washers and bearing for wear.

Replace all oil seals, O-ring seals, and gaskets. Always use a new upper pinion bearing and upper drive-shaft bearing as well as new propeller shaft housing bearings, if they have been removed.

⑫ Inspect the propeller for nicks, broken blades, and cracks. *CAUTION: Don't attempt to weld cracked or broken propeller blades.* Remove minor nicks with a file. Check the pitch on a propeller block. To straighten a bent blade, use a piece of leather strap or belting under the part of the blade that touches the fixture. Rap the high part of the blade smartly with a No. 3 rawhide mallet. The leather allows a slight overbend to correct for the blade's natural tendency to spring back.

Inspect the water tubes for obstructions. Check the

water pump impeller and replace it if the vanes are damaged. Inspect the water pump housing and the housing plate. Replace either if scored or pitted. Check the water intake screen.

Check the oil pump screen. Inspect the oil pump

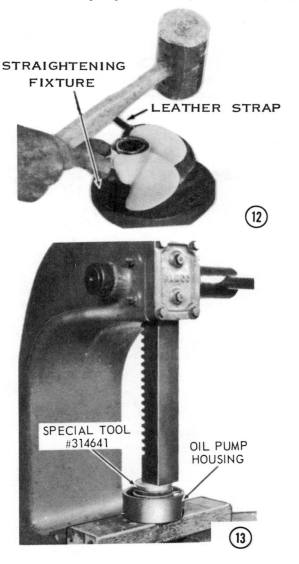

STRAIGHTENING FIXTURE

LEATHER STRAP

⑫

SPECIAL TOOL #314641

OIL PUMP HOUSING

⑬

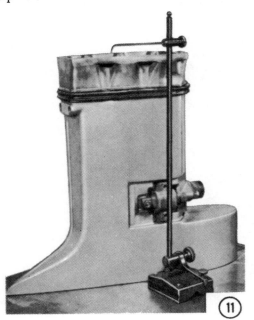

⑪

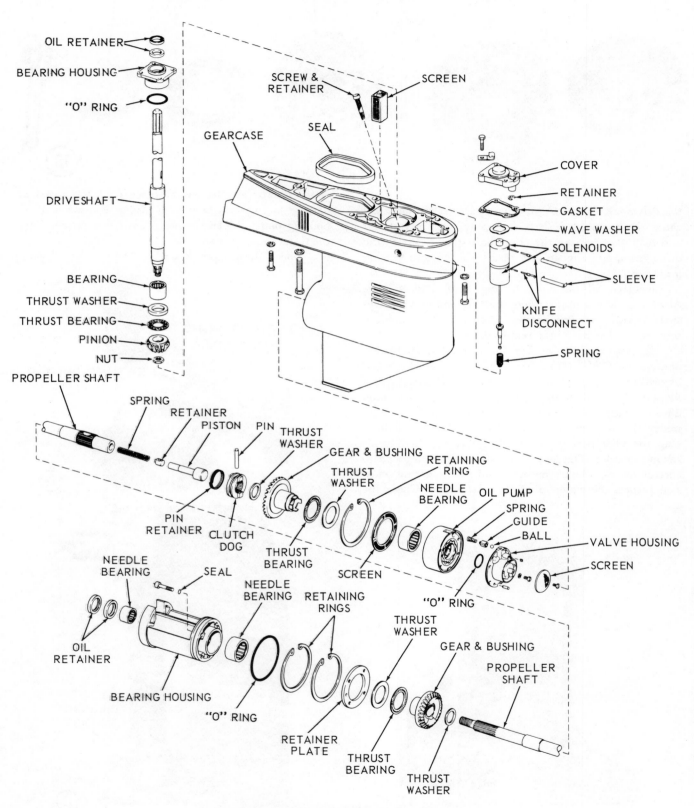

OIL RETAINER

BEARING HOUSING

"O" RING

DRIVESHAFT

BEARING

THRUST WASHER

THRUST BEARING

PINION

NUT

PROPELLER SHAFT

SCREW & RETAINER

SEAL

GEARCASE

SCREEN

COVER

RETAINER

GASKET

WAVE WASHER

SOLENOIDS

SLEEVE

KNIFE DISCONNECT

SPRING

SPRING

RETAINER

PISTON

PIN

THRUST WASHER

GEAR & BUSHING

THRUST WASHER

RETAINING RING

NEEDLE BEARING

OIL PUMP

SPRING GUIDE

BALL

VALVE HOUSING

SCREEN

PIN RETAINER

CLUTCH DOG

THRUST BEARING

SCREEN

"O" RING

NEEDLE BEARING

SEAL

NEEDLE BEARING

RETAINING RINGS

THRUST WASHER

GEAR & BUSHING

PROPELLER SHAFT

OIL RETAINER

BEARING HOUSING

"O" RING

RETAINER PLATE

THRUST BEARING

THRUST WASHER

Exploded view of the hydraulic-shift type of lower unit.

ASSEMBLY MARKS

THRUST WASHER AND BEARING NOT VISIBLE

FORWARD GEAR (14)

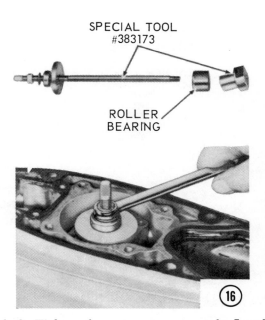

SPECIAL TOOL #383173

ROLLER BEARING

(16)

gears, housing, and cover for wear. Check the solenoid coil windings and shift cable leads for continuity. The solenoid windings should have 5–6 ohms resistance. Use the low-ohm scale of an ohmmeter.

ASSEMBLING

⑬ If removed, install a new roller bearing in the oil pump housing, using the special tool, No. 314641. Install the check valve in the smaller end of the spring, and then position the parts in the oil pump housing.

⑭ Install the oil pump gears in the housing. *CAUTION: One side of each gear has a mark; both marks must be on the same side when installed in the housing.* The surface of the pump gears and housing must be parallel when the forward gear, thrust bearing, and washer are installed. Install the pump cover, gasket,

and shaft. Tighten the cover screws securely. Install the screen on the cover.

⑮ Slide the assembled pump into the gear case, locating it on the pin and seating it as far forward as possible. *CAUTION: Unless properly seated, the solenoid plunger will not fit into the pump valve.* Install the large screen against the pump, with the loops facing out. Install the retaining ring, with the flat side toward the pump. Use Truarc pliers to install the retaining ring.

⑯ Install the lower driveshaft bearing, using bearing installer, Tool No. 383173. Place the bearing on the driver, with the lettered side of the case toward the driver. Insert the tool (with the large washer, bearing,

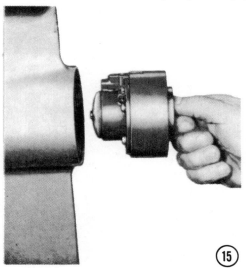

(15)

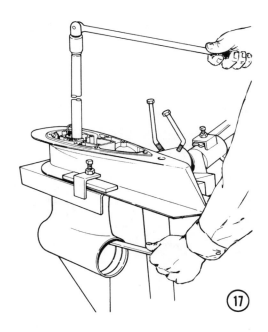

(17)

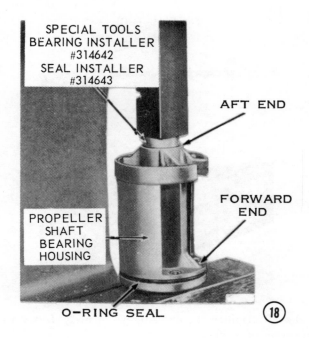

SPECIAL TOOLS
BEARING INSTALLER
#314642
SEAL INSTALLER
#314643

AFT END

FORWARD
END

PROPELLER
SHAFT
BEARING
HOUSING

O-RING SEAL

⑱

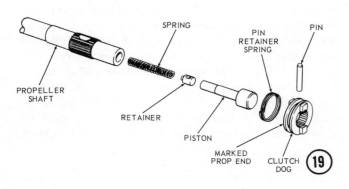

SPRING

PIN
RETAINER
SPRING

PIN

PROPELLER
SHAFT

RETAINER

PISTON

MARKED
PROP END

CLUTCH
DOG

⑲

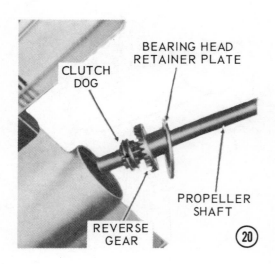

CLUTCH
DOG

BEARING HEAD
RETAINER PLATE

PROPELLER
SHAFT

REVERSE
GEAR

⑳

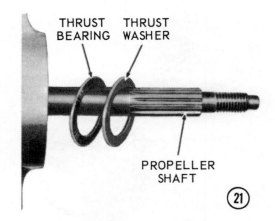

THRUST
BEARING

THRUST
WASHER

PROPELLER
SHAFT

㉑

washer, and nut) through the top of the gear case. Thread the rod into the driver. Tighten the nut to draw the bearing into the case.

⑰ Install the thrust washer, bearing, and forward gear as an assembly. Install the driveshaft, thrust washer, bearing, and pinion gear, using a special holding socket, Tool No. 312752, and then torque the nut to 40–45 ft-lbs.

⑱ If removed, install new bearings in the propeller shaft bearing housing. For the large bearing, use Tool No. 314641. For the small bearing, use Tool No. 314642. Install new seals back to back, with the lips of one seal facing out and those of the other facing in.

⑲ To assemble the clutch dog, insert the spring and retainer in the propeller shaft. Install the clutch dog on the shaft. *NOTE: One face of the clutch dog has the mark PROP END on the side, and this face must be installed toward the propeller end of the shaft.* Depress the spring and retainer, and then insert the pin. Secure the pin with the retainer spring.

⑳ Assemble the reverse gear and bearing housing retainer plate on the propeller shaft, and then insert the assembled shaft into the gear case.

㉑ Install two Truarc rings in the gear case. Position the thrust bearing and thrust washer on the reverse gear.

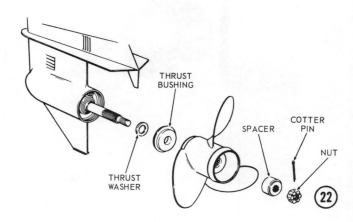

THRUST
BUSHING

THRUST
WASHER

SPACER

COTTER
PIN

NUT

㉒

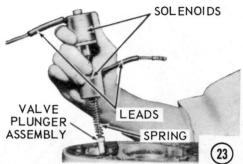

SOLENOIDS

VALVE PLUNGER ASSEMBLY

LEADS

SPRING

㉓

SERVICING THE ELECTRIC-SHIFT TYPE LOWER UNIT

40, 75, 85 (through 1968), 90 & 100 Hp Engines

These models contain an electric-shift gear case in which an electromagnet attracts the free end of a spring to a clutch hub when the coil is energized. The revolving spring wraps itself tightly around the hub to establish a direct coupling with the propeller shaft. When the NEUTRAL button is depressed, the electromagnet is de-energized and the drive spring resumes its normal position, with the spring floating on the clutch hub.

It is possible to remove the upper and lower gear case without removing the powerhead. However, if it is necessary to disassemble the exhaust housing, the powerhead must be removed first.

REMOVING THE LOWER UNIT

① To take off the propeller, remove the cotter pin, and then slide off the rubber cap.

② Take out the drive pin and the thrust washer under it. Slide the propeller from the shaft.

③ Drain the lubricant by taking out the drain plug and the filler plug.

㉒ Install a new seal in the driveshaft bearing housing, using a seal driver, Tool No. 314640. Position a new O-ring seal on the bearing housing, and then install the housing, with the bottom marking facing down. Secure it with the four Allen-headed screws dipped in Perfect Seal #4. Tighten the screws securely. Lubricate the propeller shaft, and then install the propeller.

㉓ Install the solenoid assembly, making sure that the plunger valve enters the oil pump body. *CAUTION: Don't force it.* Apply Perfect Seal #4 to both sides of the solenoid cover gasket, and then position the gasket on the gear case. Connect the shift cable leads, and then slide the sleeves over the terminals. Position the leads down in the gear case. Place the wave washer on top of the solenoid, and then install the solenoid cover.

㉔ Apply Sealer 1000 to the bottom edge of the impeller plate, and then position the plate in the gear case. Insert the impeller drive key in the driveshaft. Install a new oil pump seal in the impeller housing cover. Insert the water tube extension in the pump and into the grommets. Attach the cover to the impeller housing. Slide the impeller over the driveshaft. If the impeller is new, either side can be facing up. Install the pump housing, using a seal protective sleeve. Oil the impeller blades and rotate the driveshaft clockwise while sliding the housing over the impeller. Secure the pump housing with screws dipped in Perfect Seal #4. Route the shift cable around the water pump and secure it in the clamps.

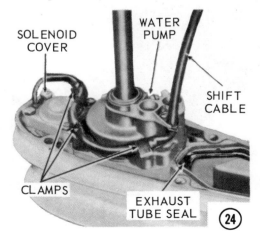

SOLENOID COVER

WATER PUMP

SHIFT CABLE

CLAMPS

EXHAUST TUBE SEAL

㉔

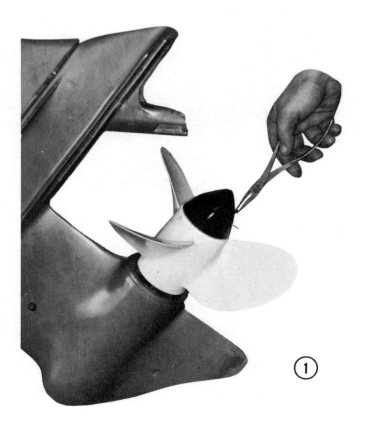

①

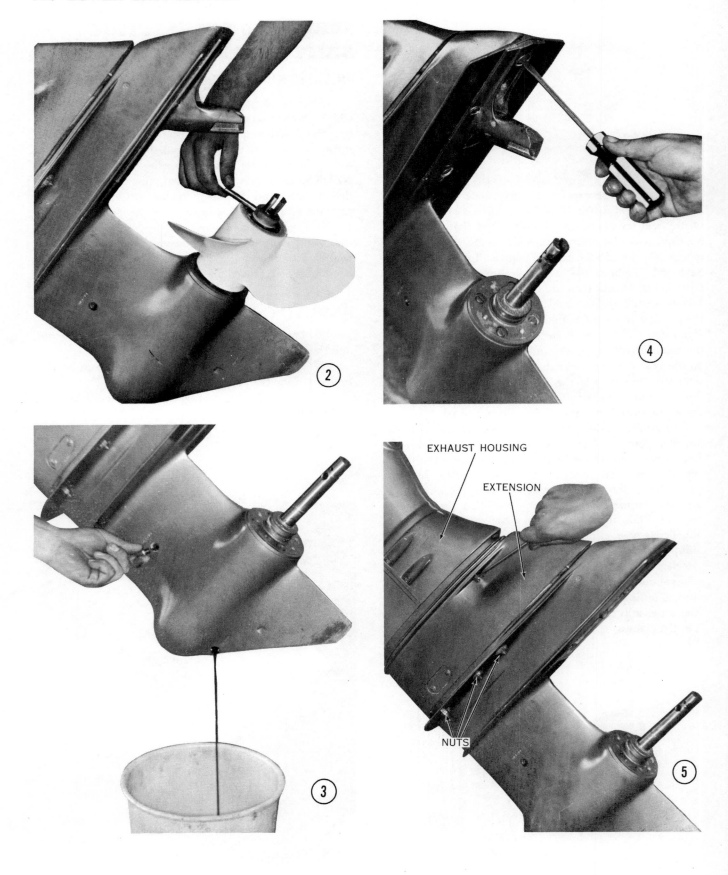

EXHAUST HOUSING

EXTENSION

NUTS

④ Remove the four retaining screws, and then take off the water intake.

⑤ Remove the two bolts and the six nuts holding the gear case and extension to the exhaust housing.

⑥ Remove the hood. Slide back the insulating sleeves on the shift cable wire so that the terminals can be disconnected.

⑦ Attach a chain hoist to support the weight, and then pull the gear case and extension housing from the exhaust housing while you carefully guide the shift wires through the exhaust housing.

DISASSEMBLING

⑧ Remove the O-ring seal, the shim, and the extension tube.

⑨ Remove the water pump housing screws and the housing. Lift out the water tube and grommets. Take out the water pump impeller and the Woodruff key. Remove the short screw, and then take off the impeller plate and gasket from the gear case extension.

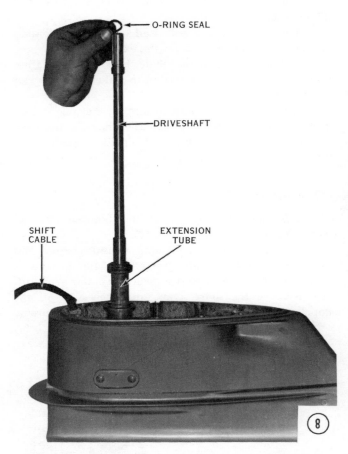

O-RING SEAL

DRIVESHAFT

SHIFT CABLE

EXTENSION TUBE

(8)

(10)

⑩ Remove the hex-headed bolts which hold the extension to the gear case. The lower one can be reached through the water intake opening.

⑪ Slide the extension away from the gear case to expose the shift cable connector sleeves, which must be slid back to expose the connectors. Remove the pilot ring.

⑫ Reach in with a hook and pull out the two magnets, which are used to collect iron filings. Remove the clamp holding the blue reverse coil lead. Remove the thrust plate, bracket, and oil line. Lift out the thrust bearing.

WATER PUMP HOUSING

(9)

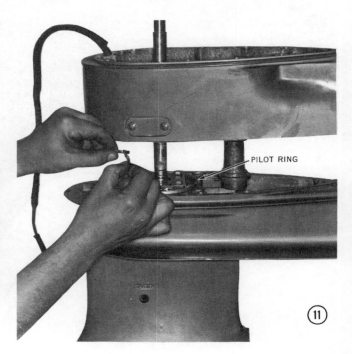

PILOT RING

(11)

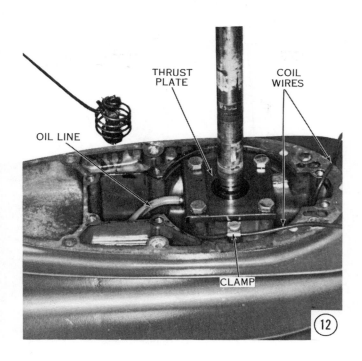

OIL LINE

THRUST
PLATE

COIL
WIRES

CLAMP

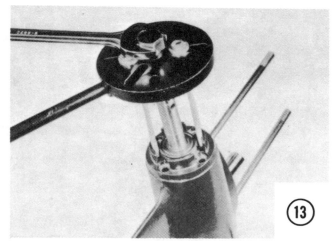

⑬ Remove the gear case head by taking out the four bolts holding it in place. It may be necessary to use a puller if the gear case head is tight.

⑭ Remove the thrust bearing and thrust washers from the propeller shaft. Remove the Truarc retaining ring, using Tool No. 311879.

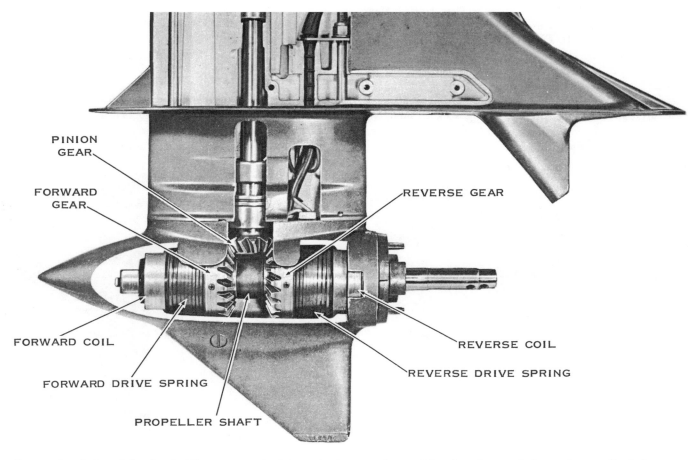

PINION
GEAR

FORWARD
GEAR

REVERSE GEAR

FORWARD COIL

REVERSE COIL

FORWARD DRIVE SPRING

REVERSE DRIVE SPRING

PROPELLER SHAFT

Cross-sectioned view of the electric-shift gear case. The drive spring is wrapped around the selected gear to lock it to the propeller shaft.

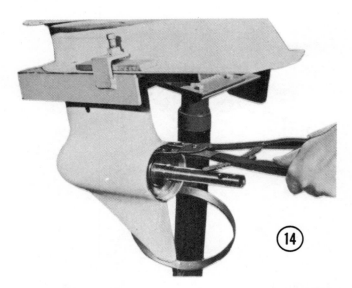

(14)

⑮ Feed the blue wire from the reverse coil down through its passageway before attempting to remove the coil and lead assembly. *CAUTION: Don't attempt to remove the reverse coil and lead assembly without first feeding this wire through its passageway, or you will cut the wire.* After the coil wire is out, insert two gear case head screws into the opposite sides of the coil and carefully rock it out. Remove the propeller shaft, reverse gear, clutch hub cover, brass washer, and clutch spring as an assembly. *CAUTION: Make sure that the cam lobe on the shaft clears the oil pump plunger.* Remove the oil pump plunger, spring, and body assembly by lifting it straight up and out of its bore.

⑯ Remove the pinion locknut from the bottom of the driveshaft with a special holding socket, Tool No. 312752. Pull the driveshaft out of the case, and then remove the pinion gear.

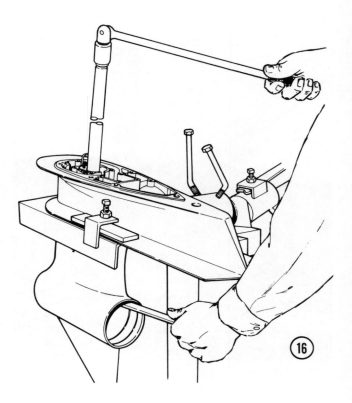

(16)

⑰ Remove the forward gear, clutch hub, and spring as an assembly. Remove the forward coil and lead assembly, using the special remover, Tool No. 380658. After the coil is loose, make sure that the coil wire is free, and that the knife-disconnect does not get stuck in the passageway leading to the gear cavity. Remove the front propeller shaft bearing. Attach the bearing cup remover, Tool No. 380657, to the bearing cup, and then attach a slide hammer to the puller to remove the bearing cup.

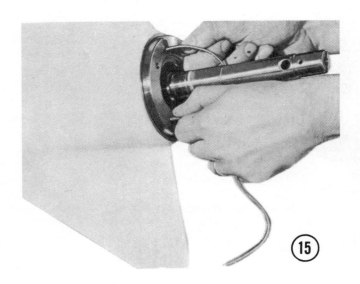

(15)

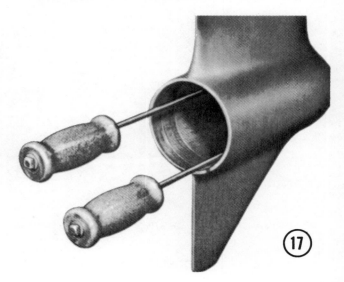

(17)

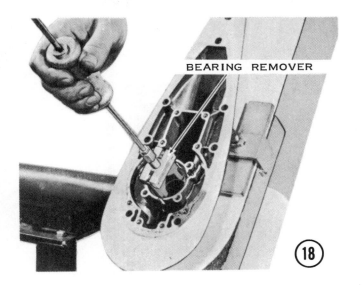

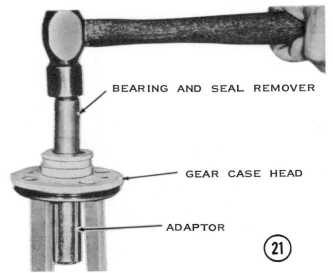

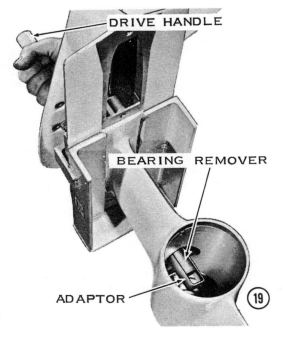

⑱ Attach a bearing remover, Tool No. 380657, to the upper needle bearing assembly. Next, attach a slide hammer and pull the needle bearing, as shown. Remove the oil deflector.

⑲ Place the adaptor, Tool No. 380659, on the roller bearing. Attach a remover, Tool No. 311885, to the handle of Tool No. 311880, and then drive the roller bearing out, as shown.

⑳ To disassemble the forward or reverse gear assembly, remove the Truarc retainer. Slide the gear, spacer, and clutch spring off the hub. Remove the bearing. *NOTE: The forward gear assembly contains a bronze bearing, while the reverse gear assembly contains a needle bearing with 40 needles. In addition, the reverse gear assembly has a sleeve around the clutch spring.* Remove the setscrews in the gear and clutch assembly. Clean the setscrews, gears, spacers, and clutch springs with a degreasing solvent and allow the parts to dry.

㉑ To disassemble the gear case head, place it on a

The magnets collect iron filings, and this prevents the particles from being circulated with the lubricating oil.

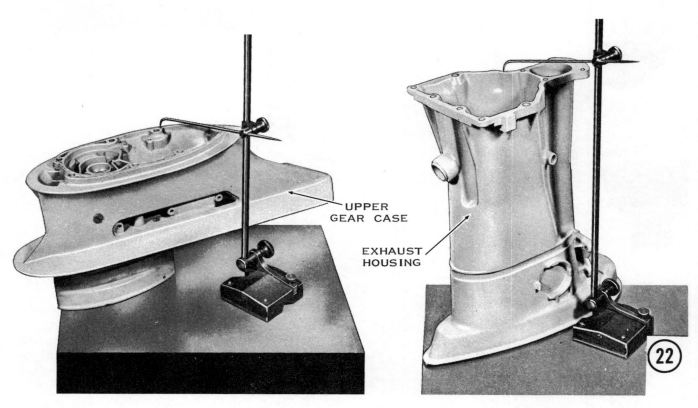

UPPER
GEAR CASE

EXHAUST
HOUSING

22

suitable support, and then drive out the needle bearing assembly, using Tool No. 380659. Remove the two seals in the gear case head. Note the direction of the seal lips for assembly purposes. *CAUTION: The oil seals must not be reused.*

CLEANING AND INSPECTING

Clean all parts with solvent and dry with compressed air. Discard all oil seals, O-ring seals, and gaskets. Discard the upper pinion bearing, the upper driveshaft bearing, and the gear case head bearing, if these have been removed, because the thin steel case housing the needles will be damaged in removal.

㉒ Check the parallelism on a plate with a surface gauge and a scriber. A drill press table will serve, using the spindle as a gauge. *CAUTION: Do not attempt to straighten a bent gear case; replace it.* Inspect the gear case for nicks on the machined surfaces. Remove nicks and resurface the faces on a surface plate. Start with No. 120 grit emery cloth and finish with No. 180 grit. Inspect the driveshaft splines for wear. A lower unit bent from striking a submerged obstruction can cause extensive damage to the driveshaft. Replace the shaft if it is worn or bent.

Inspect the water tubes for obstructions or kinks, which may restrict the water flow. Check the opening of

the 3/32″ hole in the inlet water tube. This sprays a fine mist of cooling water on the shift cable. If it is clogged, serious damage can occur.

㉓ Inspect the propeller for nicks, broken blades, and cracks. *CAUTION: Do not attempt to weld cracked or broken propellers.* Remove minor nicks with a file. *NOTE: The aft side of the propeller is flat while the other side is rounded. File the blades accordingly to retain the shape.* Check the pitch on a propeller pitch block. To straighten a bent blade, use a piece of leather strap or belting under the part of the blade that touches the fixture. Rap the high part of the blade smartly with

23

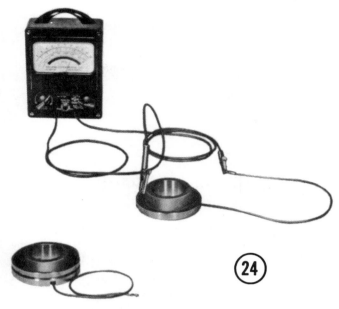

a No. 3 rawhide mallet. The leather allows a slight overbend to correct for the blade's tendency to spring back. Check the rubber slip clutch, using the propeller torque fixture assembly, Tool No. 378448, with torque shaft, Tool No. 308114.

Inspect the water pump impeller and replace it if the vanes are damaged or worn. Inspect the pump housing for scoring and replace it if damaged. Inspect the impeller housing plate and replace it if scored or pitted.

Inspect the drive gears, pinion gear, and thrust washers for wear. Replace any that are worn.

Wash needle bearings in solvent, and oil immediately with clean, light spindle oil to prevent rusting. Inspect the bearings for wear. Replace if worn.

㉔ Check the electromagnet coil windings on an ohmmeter or ammeter. The resistance should be approximately 6 ohms, or 2.0–2.4 amps if an ammeter is used. Check the shift cable leads for continuity. Check for shorts between the green and the blue (forward and reverse) leads which could cause both coils to operate at once. The green lead is for the FORWARD gear range and the blue lead is for the REVERSE.

ASSEMBLING

㉕ To assemble the gear case, install two new seals, using a seal installer, Tool No. 311877, attached to a drive handle, Tool No. 311880, as shown. The seals should be installed so that, when the assembly is completed, the lips of the seals will point away from each other. Install the gear case head needle bearing, using an installer, Tool No. 311869, attached to a drive handle, Tool No. 311880.

㉖ Slip the spacer and clutch spring into the gear.

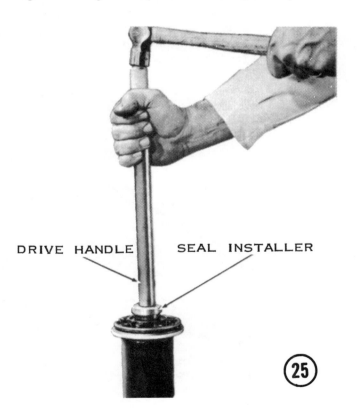

DRIVE HANDLE   SEAL INSTALLER

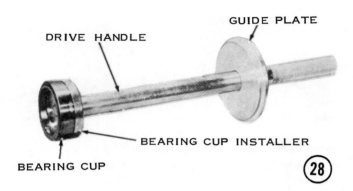

DRIVE HANDLE

GUIDE PLATE

BEARING CUP INSTALLER

BEARING CUP

(28)

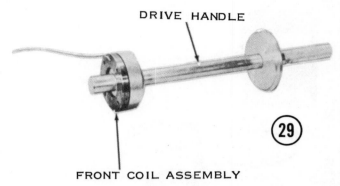

DRIVE HANDLE

(29)

FRONT COIL ASSEMBLY

Make sure that the spring engages the gear properly. Apply Loctite Sealant "D" sparingly to the threads of each screw. *CAUTION: One drop is the maximum to use. Don't allow the Loctite to enter any moving parts.*

㉗ Torque the setscrews to 15–20 in-lbs. on gears with 8–32 × 5/32″ setscrews or to 30–35 in-lbs. on gears with 10–32 × 3/16″ setscrews. Bake the gear and clutch spring assembly at 300°F. for 20 minutes. Install the bronze bearing in the forward gear. Install the clutch hub on the gear and spring. Install the retaining ring, lettered side up. *CAUTION: In the event that the bronze bearing becomes cocked on the hub, do not force the assembly by wringing or tapping.* Apply needle bearing grease to the rear clutch hub bearing surface, and then place 40 needles around the hub. *NOTE: With the 40 needles in place, a slight gap between the first and last needle is normal.* Install the sleeve over the spring, with the flanged end facing the coil. Assemble the hub and gear, and then install the retaining ring. Install the gear case extension seals flush with the upper and lower casting surfaces, lips facing out. If removed, apply oil to the shift cable and pull the upper end up through the bottom of the extension until the lower end is seated in the casting. Install the retainer, and then slide the sleeve over the cable and down to the retainer.

㉘ Install the bearing cup from the propeller shaft bearing assembly, using an installer, Tool No. 311872, attached to a drive handle, Tool No. 311880. The guide from the front coil installer, Tool No. 380691, should be placed on the drive handle to press in the bearing cup. Install the roller bearings. *NOTE: Assembly will be facilitated if a small amount of oil is used in assembly.*

㉙ Assemble the front coil and lead assembly installer, Tool No. 380691 and No. 311880. Place the coil and lead assembly on the body of the installer, as shown. Attach an extra lead with a knife-disconnect to the front coil lead. Feed this wire into the gear case and up through the forward coil lead opening. Be careful not to damage the connection between the coil and lead. Insert the coil and installer into the gear case so that the coil lead is at the top of the coil. Carefully pull the

attached lead while feeding the coil into the gear case. Drive the forward coil in until it seats. Remove the installer tool and the extra length of wire. With the coil installed, use an ohmmeter to check the resistance, which should be 6 ohms. An infinite resistance reading indicates an open circuit, such as a broken wire. Readings less than specifications indicate a short circuit to ground. Install the oil deflector, open side up, in its cavity, making sure that the notches in the side of the deflector line up with the drilled holes in the gear case.

㉚ Place the upper needle bearing on the installer, Tool No. 311876, and the lower roller bearing on the pilot from Tool No. 380758. Place the stud No. 312019 from Tool No. 380759 through the driveshaft opening. The end of the stud with 1/2″ of thread must be at the bottom. Place the lower roller bearing into the gear case and attach the installer to the stud. Place the upper needle bearing (and the bearing installer) on the top of the stud. Next, place the 3/8″ flat washer and the 3/8″–16 hex nut from the roller bearing installer, Tool No. 380758, on the stud. Draw up on the nut until both bearings are seated.

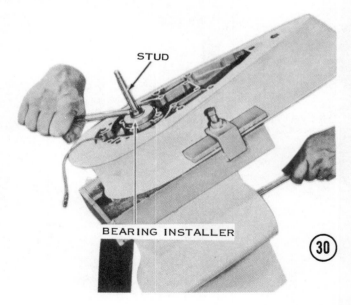

STUD

BEARING INSTALLER

(30)

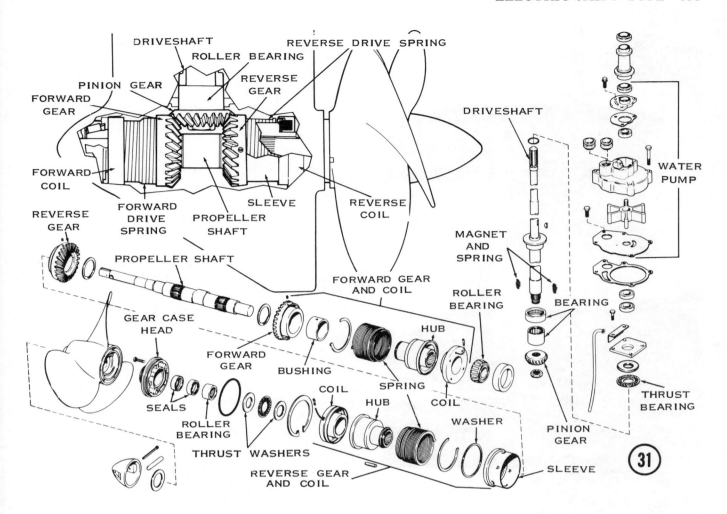

Figure 31 labels: DRIVESHAFT, ROLLER BEARING, REVERSE DRIVE SPRING, PINION GEAR, REVERSE GEAR, FORWARD GEAR, DRIVESHAFT, WATER PUMP, FORWARD COIL, FORWARD DRIVE SPRING, PROPELLER SHAFT, SLEEVE, REVERSE COIL, REVERSE GEAR, MAGNET AND SPRING, PROPELLER SHAFT, ROLLER BEARING, BEARING, FORWARD GEAR AND COIL, GEAR CASE HEAD, FORWARD GEAR, HUB, BUSHING, SPRING, COIL, HUB, COIL, PINION GEAR, THRUST BEARING, SEALS, COIL, WASHER, ROLLER BEARING, THRUST WASHERS, REVERSE GEAR AND COIL, SLEEVE

③① Install the forward gear, clutch, and spring assembly. Install the driveshaft and the pinion gear. Torque the locknut to 70–80 ft-lbs. Install the oil pump and plunger, and then replace the propeller shaft. *CAUTION: Make sure that the pump cam faces away from the pump.* Turn the shaft slightly to engage the forward gear hub splines. Install the reverse gear, clutch, and spring assembly on the propeller shaft. *CAUTION: Align the splines with the propeller shaft. Don't force it. If the splines are aligned, the gear should slip into place easily.* Install the washer in the rear coil. *NOTE: Grease it to help in assembly.* Install the rear coil and lead assembly in the gear case. Before inserting the coil, make sure that the lead is at the top of the coil. After the coil is installed, feed the coil lead up through its passageway. With the coil installed, use an ohmmeter to check the resistance, which should be 6 ohms. Install the coil retaining ring (with the opening up) using pliers, Tool No. 311897. Install the thin thrust washer, the thrust bearing, and the second thrust washer on the propeller

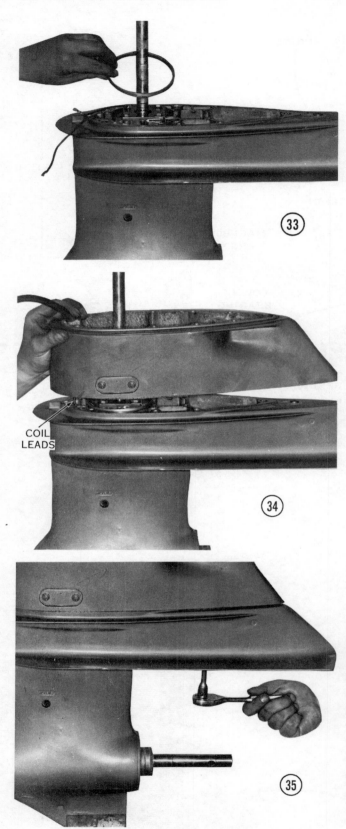

③③

④④ COIL LEADS

③⑤

shaft. *NOTE: When installing the thrust washers, the one with the chamfer on the inner diameter goes nearest the coil. It should be noted also that this washer is the thinner of the two.* Install the gear case head. Align the countersunk holes in the gear case head with the tapped holes in the rear coil, and then seat the gear case head with a mallet. Install the four screws and tighten them securely.

㉛ Clamp the blue reverse coil lead to the gear case, and then install the thrust bearing, plate, oil line bracket, and oil line.

㉜ Replace the two magnets which are used to collect iron filings, and then position the extension-to-gear case alignment ring on the case. Locate the coil leads in the front of the gear case cavity.

㉝ Apply Perfect Seal #4 to the gasket, and then position the gasket on the gear case. Place a seal protector sleeve over the splined end of the driveshaft and apply oil to the sleeve. Slide the gear case extension over the sleeve and down the driveshaft until the coil leads can be connected to the shift cable. Connect the leads, and then slide the insulating tubing over the terminals. *CAUTION: Make sure that the terminals are completely covered.* Push the cable down into the gear case, and then lower the extension onto the case. *CAUTION: Make sure that the leads are not pinched.*

㉞ Attach the extension to the gear case with three

WATER TUBE

③⑥

hex-headed bolts, two from the top and one from the bottom. *NOTE: The larger screw attaches the aft section of the extension through the water intake and exhaust cavity.* Check the shift cable with a meter to see if it is pinched.

③⑥ Install a new grommet on the water tube and a new grommet in the water pickup. The flat-sided upper grommet slides over the longer end of the tube, the round grommet over the intake end. The grommets have a lip on one side, and the tube must butt against the grommet lips.

③⑦ Push the lower grommet into the water intake, and then install the water intake while positioning the upper grommet into the receptacle provided for it in the gear case. Attach the water intake with four screws.

③⑧ Apply Perfect Seal #4 to both sides of the impeller housing plate and the gasket, and then position it on the extension housing. Attach the plate with a short hex-headed screw in the corner of the plate. Align the plate with the holes. Install the Woodruff key in the driveshaft.

③⑨ Position the impeller in the water pump housing. Oil the impeller blades, and then rotate the driveshaft clockwise while sliding the assembly into place.

④⓪ Slide the extension tube over the driveshaft, with the marked end facing up. Position a new O-ring seal in the groove below the splines on the driveshaft.

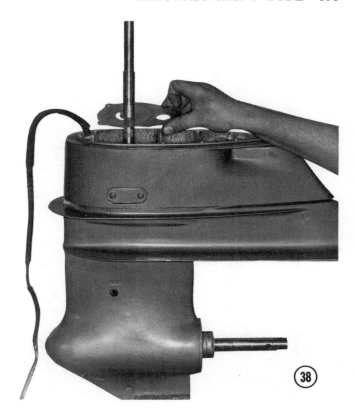

(38)

WATER TUBE

(37)

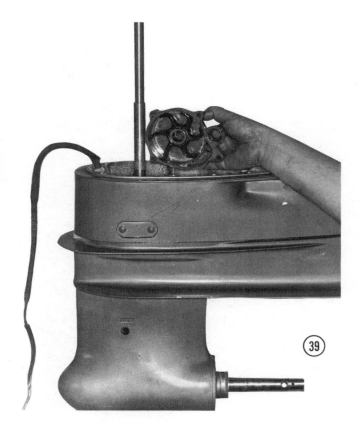

(39)

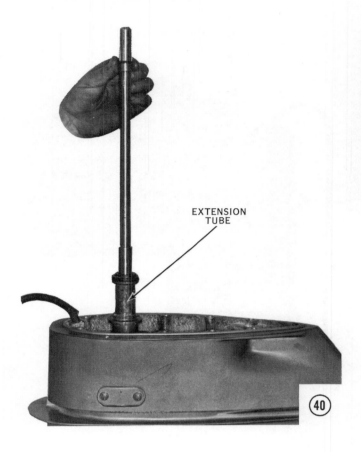

EXTENSION
TUBE

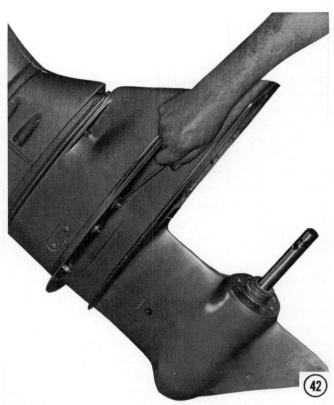

㊶ Apply Perfect Seal #4 to both sides of a new gasket, and then position the gasket over the studs on the exhaust housing. Attach a piece of baling wire to the shift cable, and then thread the wire through the exhaust housing so that you can pull the shift cable through as you slide the gear case into position. *CAUTION: Make sure that the water tubes enter the grommets. CAUTION: Turn the powerhead flywheel only clockwise to align the crankshaft and driveshaft splines. This will avoid damage to the water pump impeller.*

WIRE

SHIFT
CABLE

GASKET

6 OHMS
RESISTANCE

METER BLACK
LEAD TO GROUND

METER RED
LEAD TO
COIL LEAD

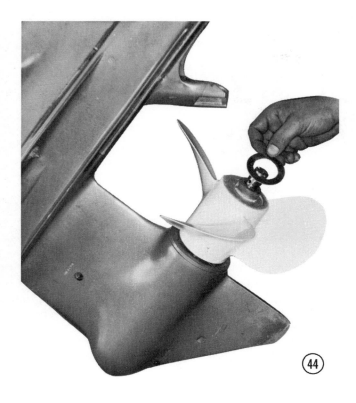

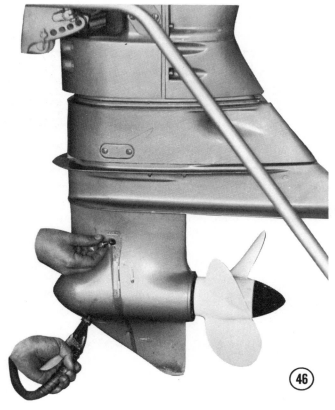

④② Secure the gear case and extension with two bolts and lockwashers and six nuts. Torque the bolts to 28–32 ft-lbs. and the nuts to 24–26 ft-lbs.

④③ Check the shift cable leads with an ohmmeter to test for an open or short circuit. Connect the forward coil green lead to the ohmmeter and ground the other test probe. If the circuit is correct, the ohmmeter will register 6 ohms. If the reading is less than 6 ohms, the coil or wire is shorted. Test the reverse coil circuit in the same manner. Secure the shift cable to the power-head with the thermostat screw and clamp. Connect the leads, and then slide the insulating sleeves over the terminals.

④④ Grease the propeller shaft with gear lubricant, and then slide the propeller over the shaft. Install the spacer.

④⑤ Align the holes through the propeller and shaft, and then insert the drive pin. Replace the rubber cap, aligning the holes. Install a new cotter pin to secure the assembly.

④⑥ Fill the gear case with OMC Type C gear lubricant until it runs out of the vent hole. Replace the vent and drain plugs, tightening them securely.

7
ELECTRICAL SYSTEM SERVICE

The first outboard motors were started by pulling on an attached rope, and even today most small engines still are started in that way. With the advent of the larger, higher-compression engines, though, it became necessary to replace the rope starter with an electric cranking system.

Since a starting motor requires a large amount of current, it is necessary to have a fully charged battery for the starting system. The battery can be externally charged or the engine optionally can be equipped with an alterna-tor, which charges the battery while the engine is operat-ing.

With the addition of the battery, the next logical improvement was to change the ignition system from a magneto type to a battery-ignition system. The latest improvement has been to replace the conventional igni-tion system with a capacitor-discharge type, using a solid-state amplifier. Ignition system service is covered in Chapter 3, Tuning for Performance. All other electrical system service is covered in this chapter.

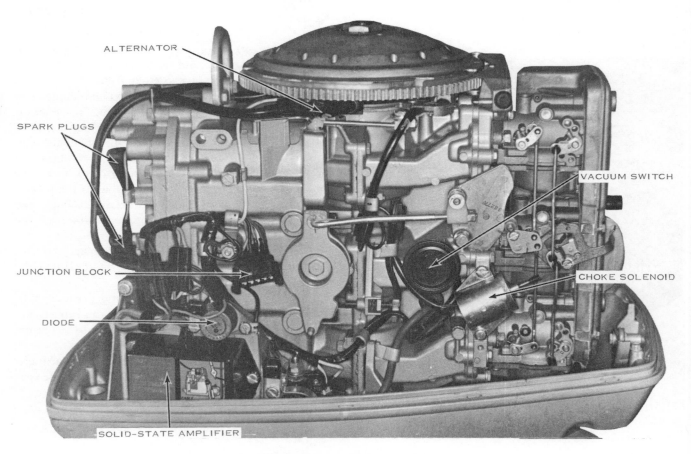

Electrical components on the three-cylinder engine.

DESCRIPTION

The electrical system consists of four circuits: the generating circuit, the starting circuit, the choke circuit, and the ignition circuit.

GENERATING CIRCUIT

Permanent magnets and a stator are located within the flywheel. The alternating current generated in the stator windings passes to the rectifier which, in turn, changes the alternating current into direct current. The negative side of the rectifier is grounded. The positive side goes through the internal harness plug to the battery. The negative side of the battery is connected, through the connector, to the ground of the engine.

STARTING CIRCUIT

The starting circuit consists of the cranking motor and the starter-engaging mechanism. The solenoid is a heavy-duty switch used to carry the heavy current from the battery to the starting motor. The solenoid is actuated by turning the ignition key to the START position.

CHOKE CIRCUIT

The choke is activated by a solenoid that attracts a plunger to close the choke valves. It is energized by turning the ignition key to the START position and holding the choke switch in the ON position until the engine starts.

Electrical system components used on the V-4 engine.

IGNITION CIRCUIT

The ignition circuit varies with engine type. The one- and two-cylinder engines have flywheel-type magnetos. The three-cylinder engine has a CD (Capacitor-Discharge) type of ignition system with two sets of breaker points located under the flywheel. They are used to actuate a solid-state amplifier for generating about 25,000 volts for firing the spark plugs. V-4 engines have had three different types of ignition systems. Initially, the four-cylinder engine had a belt-driven magneto, which was replaced in some models by a belt-driven distributor and a battery-ignition system. Since 1967, the 100 Hp engine (and 115 Hp engine in 1969) has had a CD type of ignition system with a pulse generator in place of the conventional breaker points. Since 1968, all other three- and four-cylinder engines use the CD type of ignition system with breaker points. All engines with CD ignition require surface-gap type spark plugs.

Ignition system service is covered in Chapter 3, Tuning for Performance. All other electrical system service is covered in this chapter.

TROUBLESHOOTING

Trouble in the electrical system often is first evidenced by failure of the starter to operate, and may be caused by failure of any one or more of the electrical components. If the ammeter does not indicate charge with the engine running, or if the battery fails to retain enough charge to start the engine, the first things to check are the condition of the battery, polarity of the battery, and electrical connections throughout the circuit. A large percentage of electrical failures are caused by loose or dirty electrical wiring connections, especially in the starting circuit.

BATTERY

For best performance, use a 12-volt, 60-ampere hour battery, or better, with a minimum of two-minutes cold starting capacity at 300 amperes discharge, zero degrees Fahrenheit, and a 10-second voltage reading of 7.5 volts. Frequently, poor starting is traceable to a battery with specifications not conforming to recommendations. *CAUTION: Correct battery polarity is extremely important. The battery must be connected so that its negative (−) post is connected to ground. If the positive (+) post is connected to ground, the rectifier diodes, voltage suppressor, and pulse pack may be damaged.*

TESTING A BATTERY

The condition of the battery cells may be checked quickly and accurately by following the light-load test procedure. Before starting the test, add water as necessary to bring the electrolyte to the proper level. Place a load on the battery by holding the starter switch on for three seconds. It makes no difference whether the starter turns the engine or not. However, if the engine does start, turn off the ignition key to stop it immediately.

Establish an 8- to 10-ampere load by turning the ignition switch to the ON position. Turn on the lights or other accessories as necessary. After one minute, with an 8- to 10-ampere load still on, read the individual cell voltages with a voltmeter having a 0.01-volt scale division. *NOTE: After testing, close the openings in the sealing compound made by the probes of the voltmeter.*

If any cell reads 1.95 volts or more, and the difference between the highest and lowest cell reading is less than 0.05 volt, the battery is good and is sufficiently charged. If the cell readings are both above and below 1.95 volts, and the difference between the highest and lowest reading is less than 0.05 volt, the battery should be recharged. If any cell reads 1.95 volts or more but there is a difference of 0.05 volt or more between the highest and lowest cell, the battery should be replaced.

If the reading for each cell is less than 1.95 volts, the battery is too low to test properly; however, this does not necessarily indicate a defective battery. A battery in this condition should be boost-charged but not fully charged at this time, and the light-load test repeated. If the battery is found to be good after boost-charging, it should be fully recharged before being returned to service. If none of the cells comes up to 1.95 volts after the first boost charge, the battery should be given a second boost. Batteries which do not come up after the second boost-charge should be replaced.

BATTERY CHARGING

Boost-charge 12-volt batteries at 50 amperes for 20 minutes. *CAUTION: Do not boost-charge the battery more than this amount for the light-load test.* If batteries are to be fully charged by means of a "quick charger," the charging rate must be "tapered" (reduced to a safe limit) when the electrolyte temperature reaches 125°F., or when gassing becomes excessive. *CAUTION: Failure to do so may harm the battery.*

If the battery is to be slow-charged, adjust the electrolyte to the proper level by adding water, and then charge the battery at five amperes until it is fully charged. A full charge of the battery is indicated when all cell gravity readings do not increase when checked

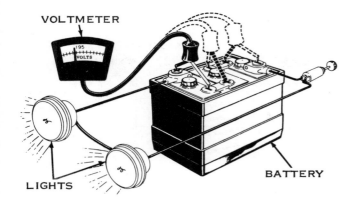

VOLTMETER

LIGHTS

BATTERY

The battery can be tested by turning on the lights and accessories until there is an 8–10 ampere load and then measuring the individual cell voltages, as discussed in the text.

at three intervals of one hour, and when all cells are gassing freely. Plenty of time must be allowed for slow-charging. Charging periods of 24 hours or more are often required.

BATTERY CARE

The battery should be kept charged at all times. The state of charge should be checked by making specific gravity readings with a hydrometer. It is suggested that specific gravity readings and checking for replacement of water be made every two weeks. If the battery has been standing for 30 days, it should be recharged before being placed in service.

The specific gravity of the battery electrolyte should be checked with a battery hydrometer which has a built-in thermometer and correction chart. No other method is accurate in determining the condition of a battery. Note, also, that a hydrometer reading is not accurate if water has been added recently, due to the fact that the water has not had a chance to mix thoroughly with the electrolyte.

The proper water level should be maintained at all times. If water is added in freezing weather, the battery should be charged to a full charge at once or the water may freeze and crack the battery case. Only pure distilled water should be added to the battery to replace water lost through evaporation. *CAUTION: Never add acid except when acid has been lost by spilling.*

Install the battery near the engine. For mounting the battery, use a frame securely fastened to the boat. A loose battery may shift in the boat, damaging itself or other equipment. Tighten the hold-down nuts evenly until the battery is secure. If the hold-down nuts are tightened too much, distortion and damage to the battery case will result.

STARTING MOTOR

The electric starting system consists of the starting motor, starter and choke switches, starter and choke solenoids, safety switch, and the necessary cables and wires with their connectors. The starting motor supplies cranking power to the engine by converting electrical energy into mechanical power, which is transmitted through the drive pinion gear and the flywheel ring gear to crank the engine. The starter switch controls the operation by activating the starter solenoid, which makes the circuit between the battery and starting motor.

The starter solenoid completes the circuit through a movable contact disc which strikes two terminal contacts that are connected to the starting motor circuit. The solenoid contains many turns of wire which, when energized by the starter switch, exert a magnetic pull on the solenoid plunger, causing it to move the contact disc against the terminal contacts.

The starting motor drive pinion is disengaged when at rest and is made to mesh with the flywheel ring gear by the rotation of the starting motor armature. After the engine has started, the starter pinion is driven faster than the starting motor shaft and moves down the screw shaft and out of mesh with the flywheel.

The safety switch opens the starting motor circuit, preventing accidental engaging of the starting motor whenever the throttle lever is set beyond the START position. The switch is operated by a plunger which rides on a cam on the lower distributor housing.

Due to the construction of the starting motor, maintenance operations are generally limited to periodic checking for looseness of the mounting. Unless it is certain that the starting motor requires attention, do not remove it. A thorough check should be made of the battery, cables, starter solenoid, and switch. Check the starting motor by using the no-load test. With 12.0 volts applied to the starting motor, the maximum current should be 60 amperes, and the minimum speed should be 8,000 rpm.

OVERHAULING THE STARTING MOTOR

REMOVING
18/20, 25, 33, 40 & 55 Hp Engines

① Disconnect the battery lead at the starting motor. Remove the three cap screws holding the starting motor bracket and the mounting bracket to the crankcase, and then lift the starting motor and bracket off the bracket studs. On the 55 Hp model, it is necessary to remove the air silencer because one of the mounting screws is

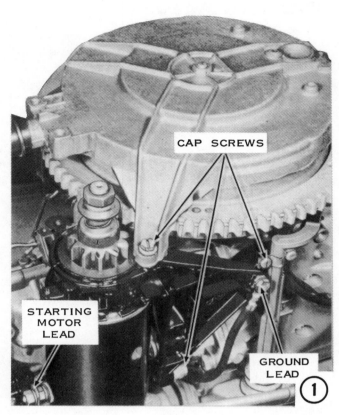

CAP SCREWS

STARTING MOTOR LEAD

GROUND LEAD

①

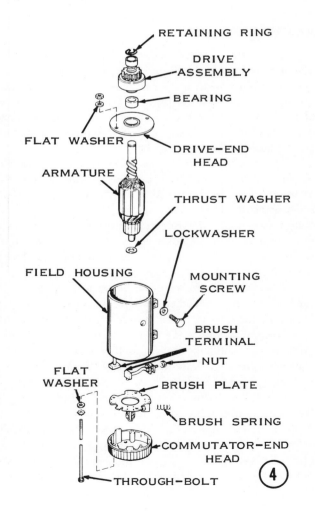

DRIVE-END HOUSING

TOP CAP SCREW

THROUGH-BOLTS (UNDERNEATH)

STARTER LEAD

②

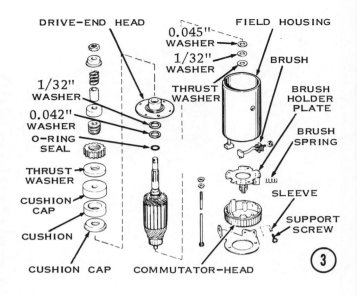

DRIVE-END HEAD

FIELD HOUSING

0.045" WASHER

1/32" WASHER

BRUSH

1/32" WASHER

0.042" WASHER

O-RING SEAL

THRUST WASHER

BRUSH HOLDER PLATE

BRUSH SPRING

THRUST WASHER

CUSHION CAP

CUSHION

CUSHION CAP

COMMUTATOR-HEAD

SLEEVE

SUPPORT SCREW

③

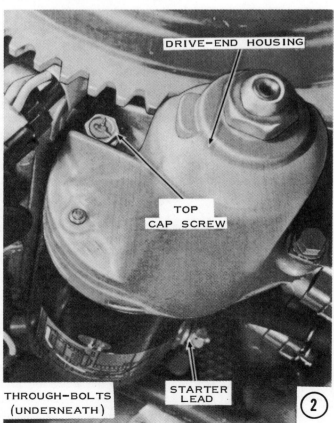

RETAINING RING

DRIVE ASSEMBLY

BEARING

FLAT WASHER

DRIVE-END HEAD

ARMATURE

THRUST WASHER

LOCKWASHER

FIELD HOUSING

MOUNTING SCREW

BRUSH TERMINAL

NUT

FLAT WASHER

BRUSH PLATE

BRUSH SPRING

COMMUTATOR-END HEAD

THROUGH-BOLT

④

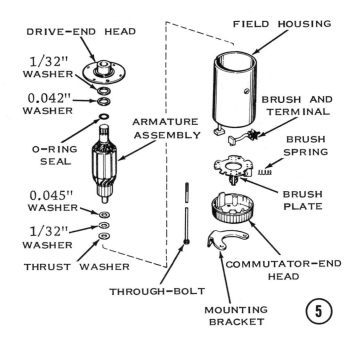

DRIVE-END HEAD

1/32" WASHER

0.042" WASHER

ARMATURE ASSEMBLY

O-RING SEAL

0.045" WASHER

1/32" WASHER

THRUST WASHER

THROUGH-BOLT

FIELD HOUSING

BRUSH AND TERMINAL

BRUSH SPRING

BRUSH PLATE

COMMUTATOR-END HEAD

MOUNTING BRACKET

⑤

behind the air silencer. Remove the two through-bolts, and then separate the starting motor from the bracket.

All V-4 Engines

② Disconnect the battery lead to the starting motor. Loosen the two through-bolts, and then slide the starting motor down so that the splines disengage from the drive-end housing. If it is necessary to remove the drive-end housing, take out the top screw, and then lift the housing from the powerhead.

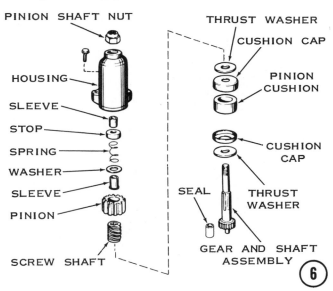

PINION SHAFT NUT

HOUSING

SLEEVE

STOP

SPRING

WASHER

SLEEVE

PINION

SCREW SHAFT

THRUST WASHER

CUSHION CAP

PINION CUSHION

CUSHION CAP

SEAL

THRUST WASHER

GEAR AND SHAFT ASSEMBLY

⑥

DISASSEMBLING

18/20, 25, 33 & 40 Hp Engines

③ Remove the drive-end head from the field assembly, and then lightly tap on the commutator-end head with a rubber mallet. Remove the brushes and springs from the holders.

55 Hp Engine

④ This exploded view shows that the pinion gear can be removed by taking off the retaining ring, sleeve, and spring. The other parts are removed as in the previous unit.

All V-4 Engines

⑤ The starting motor for the larger engines comes apart when the two through-bolts are removed.

⑥ If necessary, the drive can be disassembled by taking off the nut at the top of the drive housing, which will release the parts.

CLEANING AND INSPECTING

Clean all parts with a solvent-soaked rag. *CAUTION: Don't dip electrical parts in solvent, or you will damage the insulation.*

⑦ Clean the commutator with grade 00 sandpaper. If the surface is worn or deeply pitted, it should be turned in a lathe. Check the armature on a growler for shorted turns by holding a hacksaw blade over the laminations while slowly turning the armature. If the hacksaw blade vibrates, the armature coils are shorted.

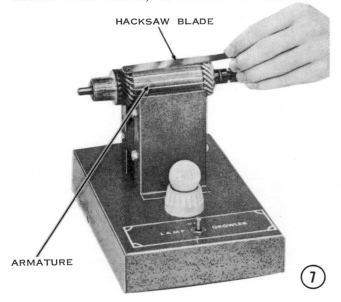

HACKSAW BLADE

ARMATURE

⑦

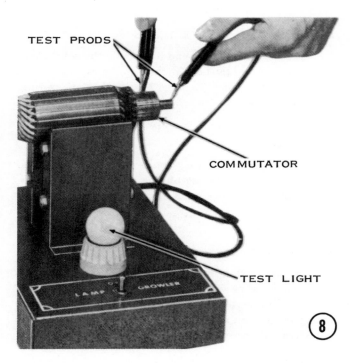

TEST PRODS

COMMUTATOR

TEST LIGHT

⑧

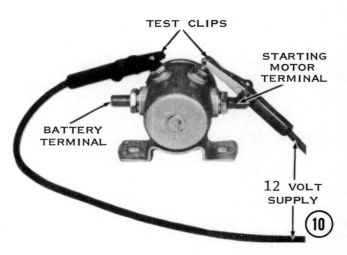

TEST CLIPS

STARTING MOTOR TERMINAL

BATTERY TERMINAL

12 VOLT SUPPLY

⑩

Check the insulating segments between the commutator bars for a short, which will give the same indication. This type of short circuit can often be corrected by digging out the metallic piece causing the trouble.

⑧ Check the commutator for ground by touching one test prod to the commutator and the other to the shaft. If the test lamp lights, the armature is defective.

⑨ Check the field windings with a test light for continuity and ground. Check for continuity by touching the test prods to both brushes; the test lamp should light. To test for ground, place one of the test prods on the metal part of the housing and the other on one of the brushes. If the test lamp lights, the field windings are grounded.

⑩ The starter solenoid is a sealed unit. To test it, apply 12 volts to the small terminals, and the solenoid plunger should click as it operates.

ASSEMBLING

⑪ To facilitate assembly of the starting motor, insert the brushes and brush springs in the holders. Tie them in place with a piece of fine wire. Assemble the brush holder and armature to the field housing, and then remove the wires. Replace the commutator- and drive-end heads to complete the assembly. Use the exploded views for assembling the parts of the drives.

⑫ Check the starter current draw after installing it on the engine by connecting an ammeter in the ground circuit. Under a cranking load, the motor current draw must not exceed 120 amperes (140 amperes on the

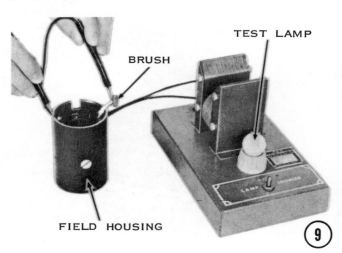

TEST LAMP

BRUSH

FIELD HOUSING

⑨

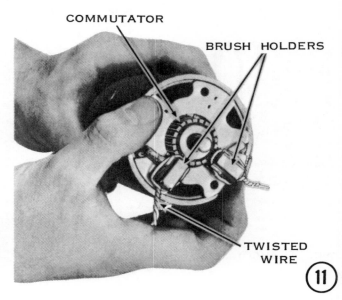

COMMUTATOR

BRUSH HOLDERS

TWISTED WIRE

⑪

four-cylinder models). Without a load, the current draw should be 60 amperes at 10.0 volts, and the minimum speed should be 8,000 rpm.

DC CHARGING CIRCUIT

33 & 40 Hp Engines

The charging system consists of a DC generator,

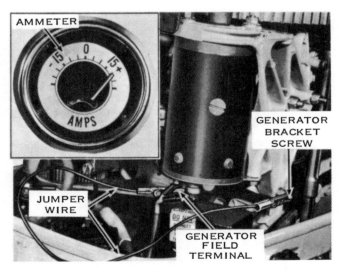

Troubleshooting the DC generator used on the 33 and 40 Hp engines can be accomplished by grounding the generator field terminal with a jumper wire. If the generator now charges, the trouble is in the regulator, as discussed in the text.

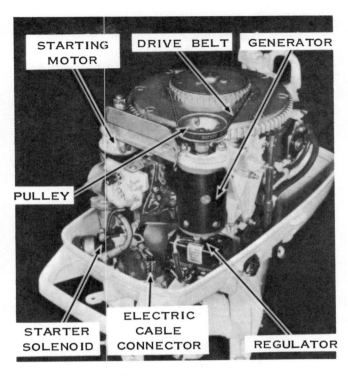

The generator used on the 33 and 40 Hp engines is a belt-driven, fully regulated DC unit.

voltage regulator, and battery. The three functions of the regulator are: (1) to prevent the battery from discharging through the generator when the engine is idling or stopped (cut-out relay), (2) to limit the charging current to a safe value (current regulator), and (3) to limit the voltage to a safe value (voltage regulator).

OUTPUT TESTS

Connect a voltmeter across the battery terminals, using the 15-volt scale. The voltmeter should indicate a voltage of 12.6 for a fully charged battery. Start the engine and run it about 3,500 rpm; the voltage should rise to the regulated setting, which should be 14.0–15.0 volts.

If the voltage does not rise, then the generator or regulator is at fault. The trouble can be isolated by grounding the field terminal with a jumper wire while the engine is operating at 3,500 rpm. If the regulator is defective, the generator output will now rise to about 10 amperes and the voltage should rise above 16 volts. This is because the regulator has been removed from the circuit by the jumper wire, and the generator is now operating without any regulation. *CAUTION: Don't run the engine with the jumper wire in place, or you will burn up the generator.*

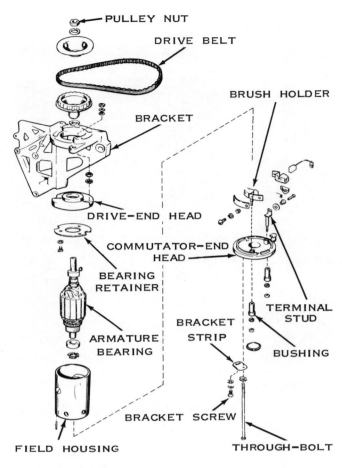

- PULLEY NUT
- DRIVE BELT
- BRUSH HOLDER
- BRACKET
- DRIVE-END HEAD
- COMMUTATOR-END HEAD
- BEARING RETAINER
- ARMATURE BEARING
- BRACKET STRIP
- TERMINAL STUD
- BUSHING
- BRACKET SCREW
- FIELD HOUSING
- THROUGH-BOLT

Exploded view of the DC generator used on the 33 and 40 Hp engines.

REMOVING THE GENERATOR

Remove the generator pull flange by taking off the attaching nut and lockwasher. Loosen the through-bolt nuts to permit releasing the belt tension. Lift the drive belt off the pulley. Disconnect the generator armature and field leads. Remove the nuts from the generator bracket studs. Remove the attaching bolt holding the ring gear guard to the generator bracket, and then lift the bracket and generator from the powerhead as an assembly.

DISASSEMBLING THE GENERATOR

Remove the pulley. Take off the bracket strap from the mounting bracket by taking out the attaching bolt. Remove the nuts, lockwashers, and through-bolts from the generator. Hold the generator with the shaft end facing down, and then drop it lightly on a soft wooden block until the heads separate. Remove the drive-end head and armature. Remove the terminal stud nuts, and then take off the commutator-end head.

CLEANING AND INSPECTING

Check the bearings for roughness or play. Replace any bearing that shows signs of excessive looseness. *CAUTION: Don't wash or lubricate the ball bearings because they are factory-packed with a special lubricant.*

Check the brushes for wear; replace them if they are worn to half of their original length.

Check the fields and armature with a growler and test lamp for a short, a ground, or an open circuit.

ASSEMBLING

Assemble the armature, bearing, and bearing retainer to the drive-end head. Install the brushes in their holders. Place the armature and drive-end head in position in the field housing. *NOTE: The dowel pin in the head must be aligned with the notch in the case.*

Install the terminal stud bushings and nuts. Attach the generator to the mounting bracket, leaving the nuts on the through-bolts loose enough to allow for adjusting the drive belt tension. Install the bracket strap attaching screw. Place the key and pulley on the generator shaft.

INSTALLING

Attach the armature and field leads to the studs on the bottom of the generator. *NOTE: The holes in the*

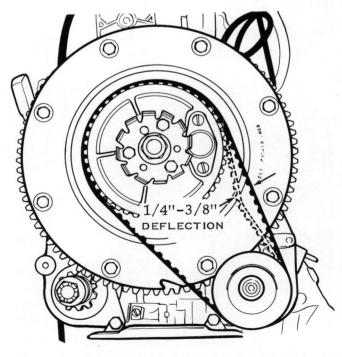

1/4"-3/8" DEFLECTION

The generator drive belt should deflect 1/4"–3/8" under moderate finger pressure.

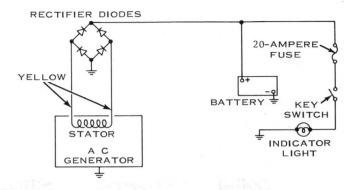

Wiring diagram for the 9-ampere alternator charging circuit.

lead terminals and the terminal studs are different sizes to prevent incorrect assembly. Position the generator and bracket assembly on the powerhead studs. Install the stud nuts, but don't tighten them. Push the generator bracket toward the rear of the engine until the stops on back of the generator bracket make contact with the two machined pads on the cylinder. Tighten the mounting bracket nuts.

Place the belt on the generator pulley. Install the pulley flange, lockwasher, and nut. Adjust the drive belt tension by pivoting the generator until the belt deflects 1/4"–3/8" under finger pressure. *NOTE: The strap and one bolt hole in the bracket are slotted for this adjust-*

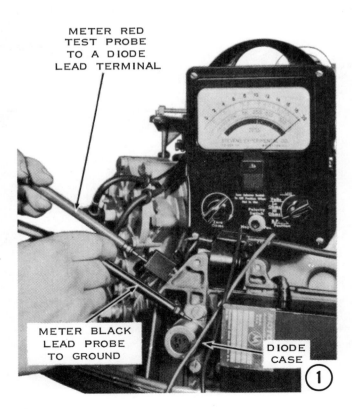

① METER RED TEST PROBE TO A DIODE LEAD TERMINAL

METER BLACK LEAD PROBE TO GROUND

DIODE CASE

ment. Tighten the nuts and capscrews securely. *CAUTION: The generator bearings will wear excessively if the belt tension is too tight.*

AC CHARGING CIRCUIT

All Three- and Four-cylinder Engines

The charging circuit consists of an alternator, a rectifier, and a battery. The alternator is made up of two parts, the flywheel, with cast-in magnets, and the stator assembly, which is bolted to the crankcase. The stator is made up of a circular field winding with 12 coils wound over laminated iron cores. The flywheel, with cast-in magnets, turns around this assembly, inducing alternating current in the coils. A rectifier converts the alternating current into direct current.

Two types of charging circuits are used, a 9-ampere and a 15-ampere system. Both contain bridge-type rectifiers and have similar charging circuits. The 15-ampere charging circuit has, in addition, a transistorized voltage regulator and a charge indicator light.

SERVICING THE NINE-AMPERE CHARGING CIRCUIT

CHECKING THE RECTIFIER DIODES

① Turn the test meter control knob to the HIGH OHMS position. Disconnect the diode yellow and green leads at the connector. Connect the ohmmeter red test lead to one of the diode terminals and the black test lead to the rectifier case (ground). Note the meter reading and then reverse the test leads. A normal diode will show a reading with the test leads connected in one direction and no reading in the other direction. An infinite (very high) reading in both checks indicates that the diode is open circuited. A zero reading in both tests indicates that the diode is shorted. Repeat the tests for the other diodes by connecting the test leads between the other diode leads and the rectifier case.

CHECKING THE STATOR WINDINGS

② To check the stator windings for ground, disconnect the yellow leads at the powerhead. Connect the red meter test lead between either yellow lead and the black meter test lead to ground. A reading indicates that the windings are grounded. To test the stator windings for continuity, turn the ohmmeter control knob to the LOW OHMS position and connect the meter test leads between the two yellow stator leads; the meter should

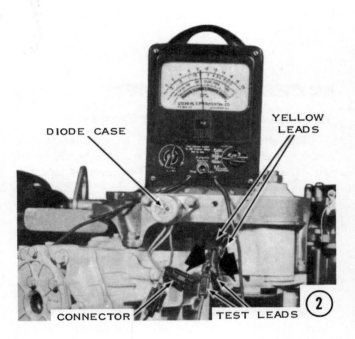

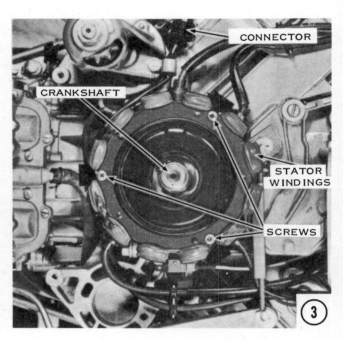

read 0.75 ±0.2 ohm if the windings are good. An infinite reading means that the windings are open circuited.

REPLACING THE STATOR WINDINGS

③ If the stator windings are defective, the stator can be replaced by removing the flywheel with a puller, Tool No. 378103. Disconnect the stator lead connector, remove the three retaining screws, and then lift the stator from the powerhead. Place a new stator in position, and attach it with the three screws dipped in Loctite. Torque the screws to 48–60 in-lbs. Reconnect the stator lead connector.

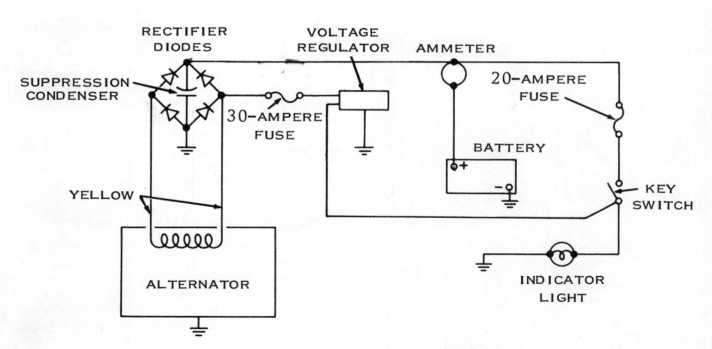

Wiring diagram for the 15-ampere alternator charging circuit.

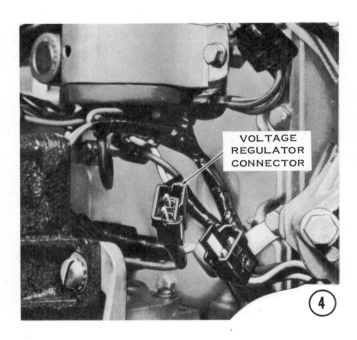

VOLTAGE REGULATOR CONNECTOR

④

CHECKING THE RECTIFIER DIODES

⑤ To check the rectifier diodes, turn the test meter knob to the HIGH OHMS position. Disconnect the three wire plugs. Connect one meter test lead to one of the yellow wire diode terminals and the other meter test lead to the diode case. Note the meter reading, and then reverse the test leads. A normal diode will show a reading with the test leads connected in one direction and no reading in the other direction. An infinite (very high) reading in both tests indicates that the diode is open circuited. A zero reading in both tests indicates that the diode is shorted. Repeat the test procedure for the other diodes by connecting the test leads between the other yellow wire spade terminal and the diode case. Then connect the test leads between one yellow terminal and the brown terminal. The meter must read in only one direction.

CHECKING THE STATOR WINDINGS

⑥ To check the stator windings on the engine, disconnect the leads at the powerhead. With the test meter on HIGH OHMS, connect the test lead to either yellow

SERVICING THE FIFTEEN-AMPERE CHARGING CIRCUIT

CHECKING THE VOLTAGE REGULATOR

④ With the solid-state voltage regulator used, there can be only two types of failures: (1) no output, resulting in an undercharged battery, or (2) too much output, resulting in an overcharged battery. The following tests must be performed with a fully charged battery and with the engine running at 3,000–3,600 rpm. If the battery is undercharged and the ammeter does not indicate a charge, stop the engine and disconnect the regulator leads at the connector in the regulator circuit. *CAUTION: Make sure that all accessories are turned off because the uncontrolled voltage during the test could damage the accessories.* Restart the engine and run it at 3,000–3,600 rpm. If the ammeter now shows a full charge, the stator windings are good but the regulator must be replaced. If there is no ammeter reading, check the stator windings.

If the battery is overcharged, check the 30-ampere fuse in the voltage regulator line. If the battery is consistently being overcharged (ammeter indicates continuous maximum charge or the battery uses excessive amounts of water), then check the battery voltage by running the engine at 3,000–3,600 rpm with all accessories turned off. Check the battery voltage and, if it is in excess of 15 volts, replace the regulator.

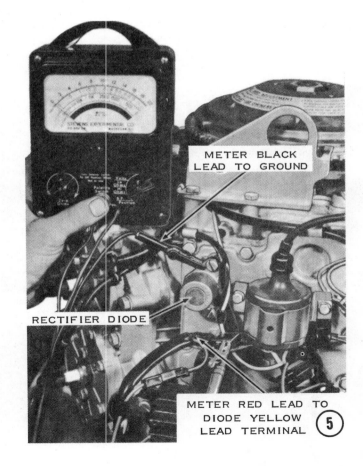

METER BLACK LEAD TO GROUND

RECTIFIER DIODE

METER RED LEAD TO DIODE YELLOW LEAD TERMINAL ⑤

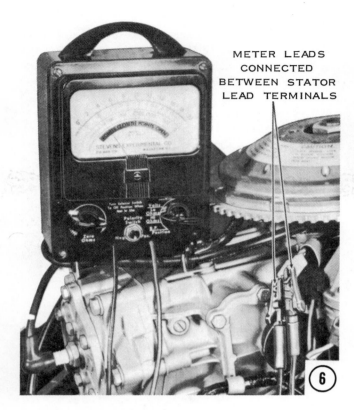

METER LEADS CONNECTED BETWEEN STATOR LEAD TERMINALS

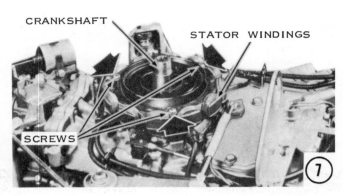

CRANKSHAFT

STATOR WINDINGS

SCREWS

stator lead and the other test lead to a good ground. An infinite reading indicates that the windings are not grounded. To check the stator windings for continuity, turn the test meter control knob to the LOW OHMS position. Connect the two test leads to the two stator yellow leads and the meter should read 0.5 ±0.2 ohm if the windings are good. An infinite reading indicates that the windings are open circuited.

REPLACING THE STATOR WINDINGS

⑦ If the stator windings have to be replaced, remove the flywheel. Disconnect the stator lead connectors. Remove the three screws, and then lift the stator from the powerhead. Place a new stator winding in position and attach it with three screws dipped in Loctite. Tighten the screws to 48–60 in-lbs. of torque. Replace the flywheel, and then reconnect the stator lead connectors.

A dependable engine requires periodic maintenance.

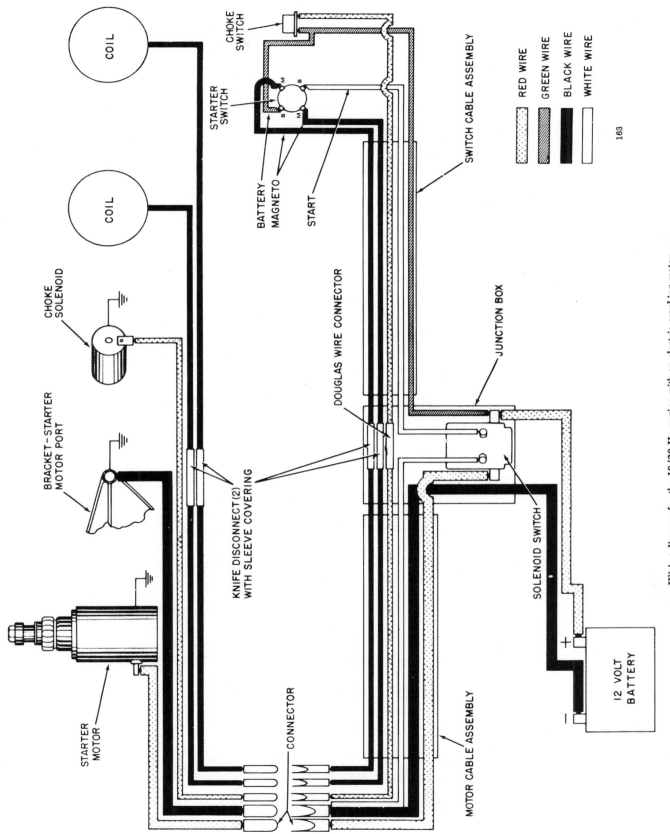

COIL

COIL

CHOKE SWITCH

STARTER SWITCH

BATTERY MAGNETO

START

SWITCH CABLE ASSEMBLY

RED WIRE

GREEN WIRE

BLACK WIRE

WHITE WIRE

163

CHOKE SOLENOID

BRACKET - STARTER MOTOR PORT

DOUGLAS WIRE CONNECTOR

JUNCTION BOX

KNIFE DISCONNECT (2) WITH SLEEVE COVERING

STARTER MOTOR

CONNECTOR

SOLENOID SWITCH

MOTOR CABLE ASSEMBLY

12 VOLT BATTERY

Wiring diagram for the 18/20 Hp engine with an electric cranking motor.

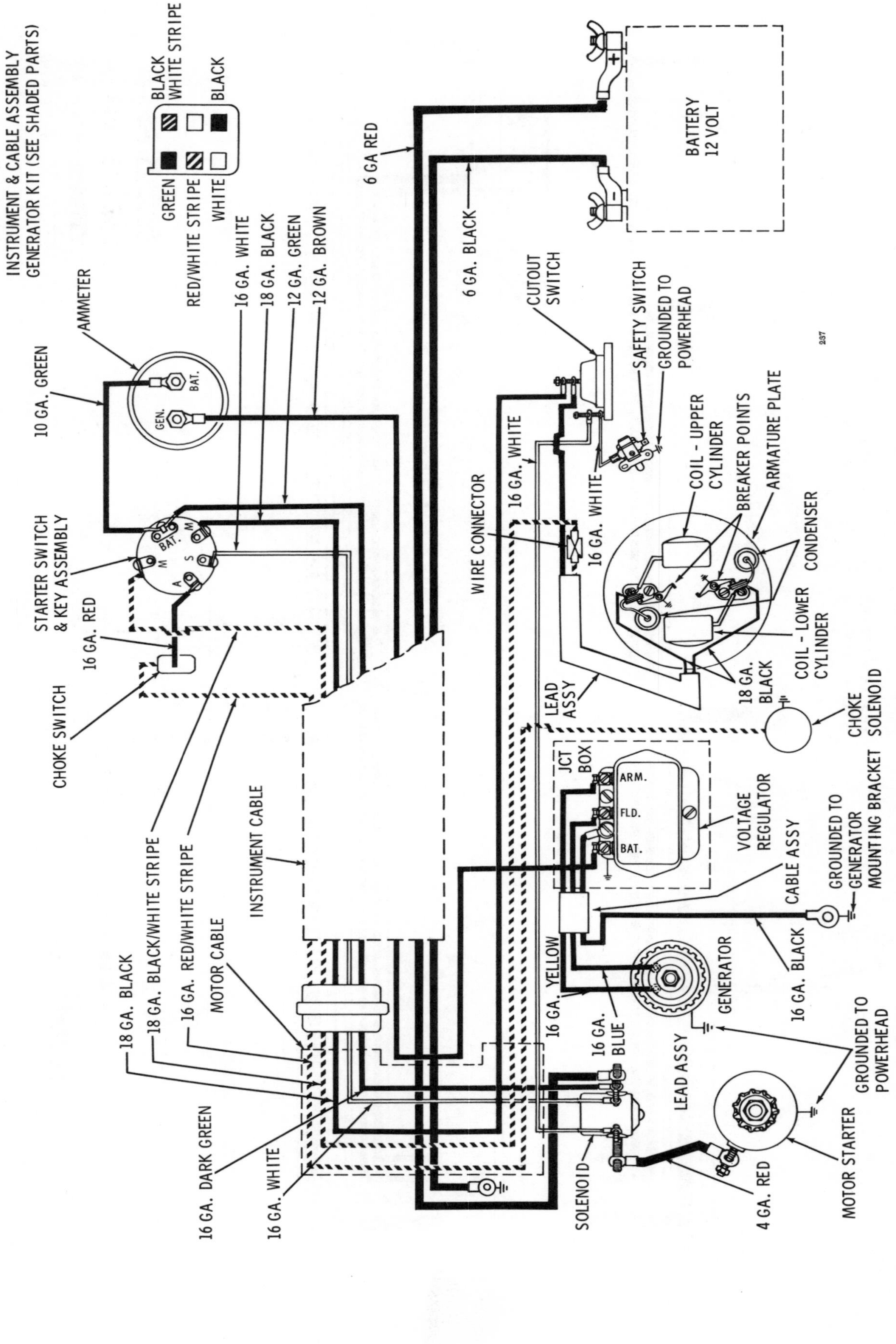

Wiring diagram for the 33 Hp engine with a DC generator.

INSTRUMENT & CABLE ASSEMBLY
GENERATOR KIT (SEE SHADED PARTS)

AMMETER

GREEN

RED/WHITE STRIPE

WHITE

BLACK
WHITE STRIPE

BLACK

10 GA. GREEN

16 GA. WHITE

18 GA. BLACK

12 GA. GREEN

12 GA. BROWN

6 GA RED

BATTERY
12 VOLT

6 GA. BLACK

CUTOUT
SWITCH

SAFETY SWITCH

GROUNDED TO
POWERHEAD

STARTER SWITCH
& KEY ASSEMBLY

BAT. M

M   S

A

16 GA. RED

CHOKE SWITCH

16 GA. WHITE

16 GA. WHITE

WIRE CONNECTOR

COIL - UPPER
CYLINDER

BREAKER POINTS

ARMATURE PLATE

CONDENSER

COIL - LOWER
CYLINDER

18 GA. BLACK

CHOKE
SOLENOID

LEAD
ASSY

JCT
BOX

ARM.

FLD.

BAT.

VOLTAGE
REGULATOR

GROUNDED TO GENERATOR
MOUNTING BRACKET

CABLE ASSY

INSTRUMENT CABLE

16 GA. BLACK

GENERATOR

16 GA. YELLOW

16 GA.
BLUE

LEAD ASSY

GROUNDED TO
POWERHEAD

18 GA. BLACK

18 GA. BLACK/WHITE STRIPE

16 GA. RED/WHITE STRIPE

MOTOR CABLE

16 GA. DARK GREEN

16 GA. WHITE

16 GA. WHITE

SOLENOID

4 GA. RED

MOTOR STARTER

237

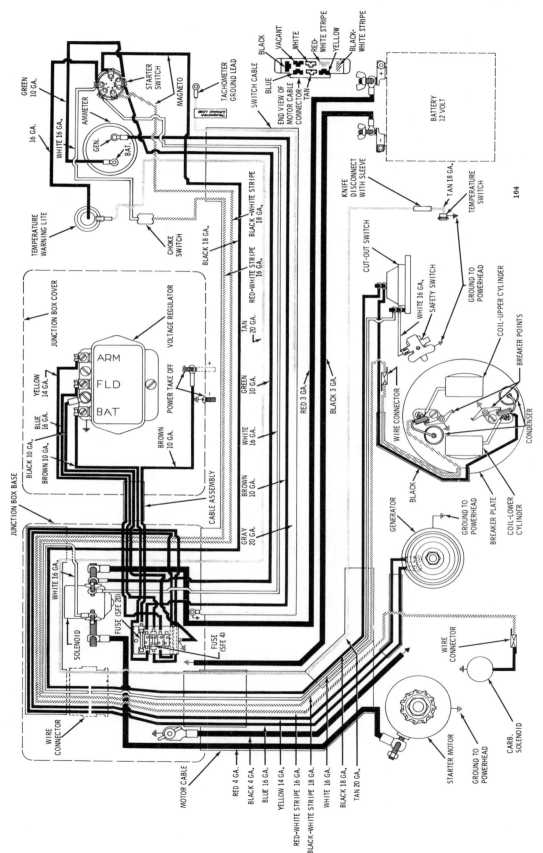

Wiring diagram for the 40 Hp engine with a DC generator.

164

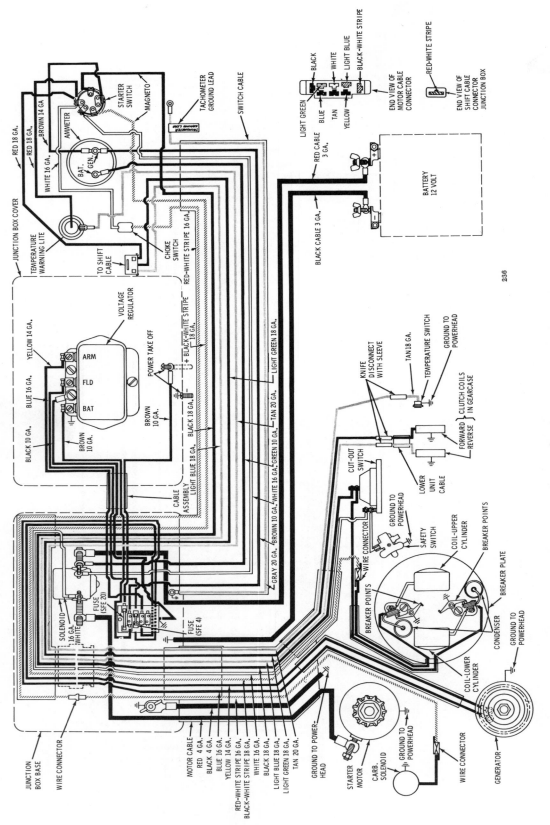

Wiring diagram for the 40 Hp engine with an electric shift.

58771

Wiring diagram for the 55 Hp engine.

Wiring diagram for the 60 Hp model.

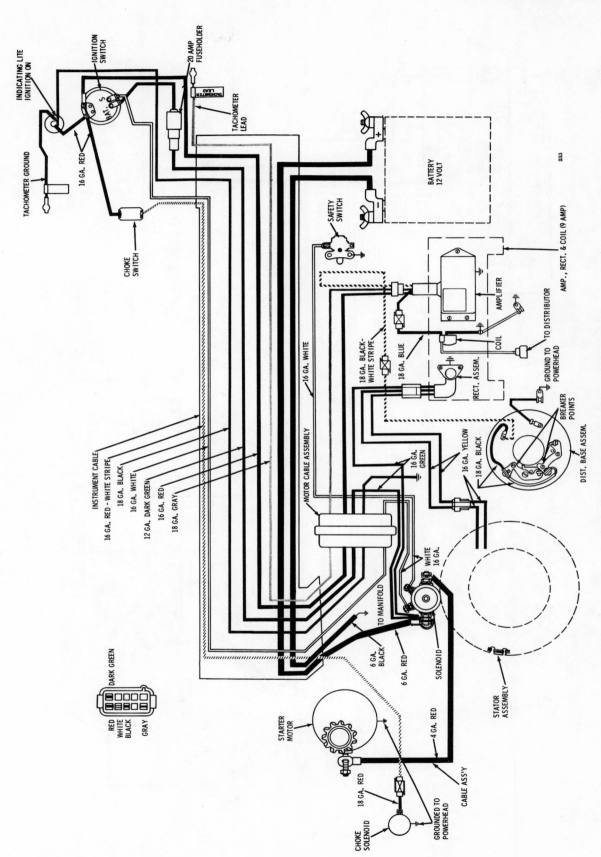

Wiring diagram for the 65 Hp engine.

Wiring diagram for the 75 Hp model with a distributor.

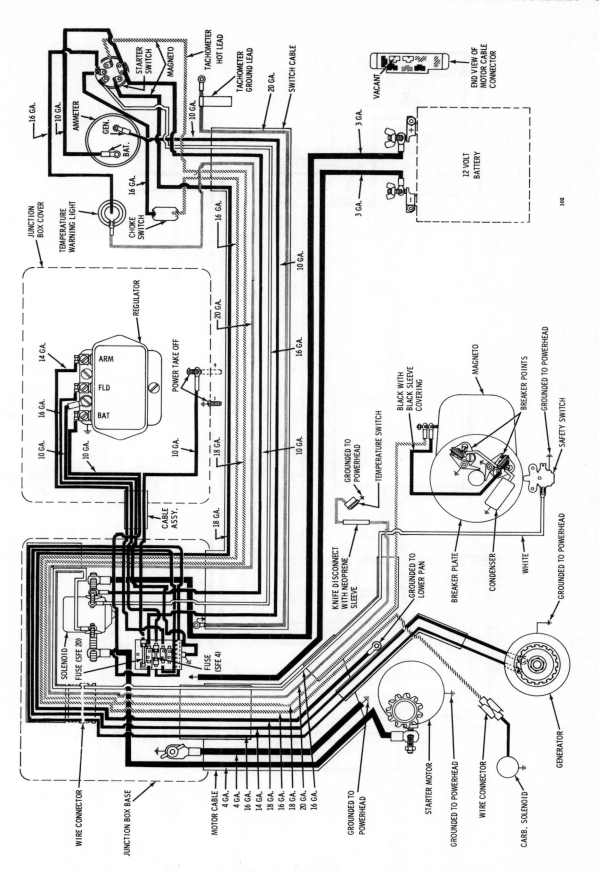

Wiring diagram for the 75 Hp engine with a magneto.

Wiring diagram for the 80 Hp engine with a magneto.

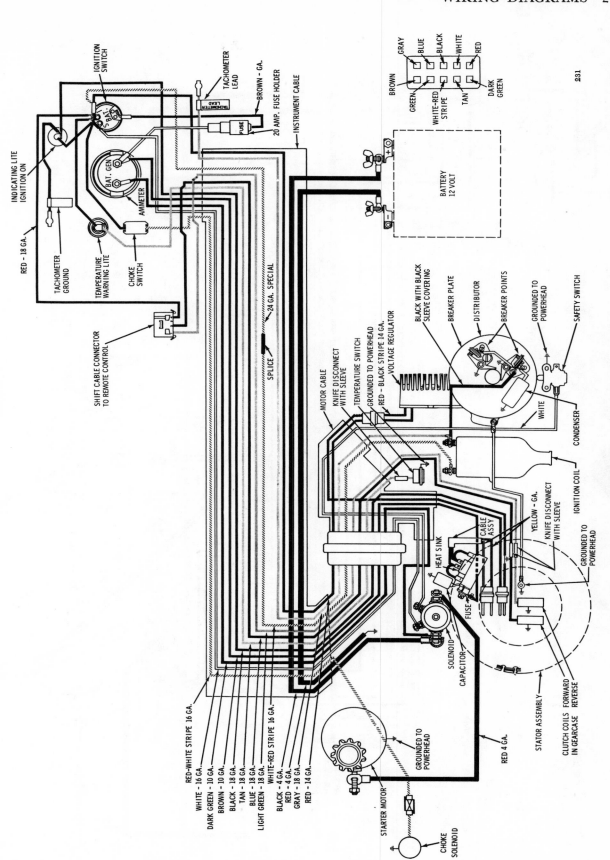

Wiring diagram for the 80 Hp engine with a distributor.

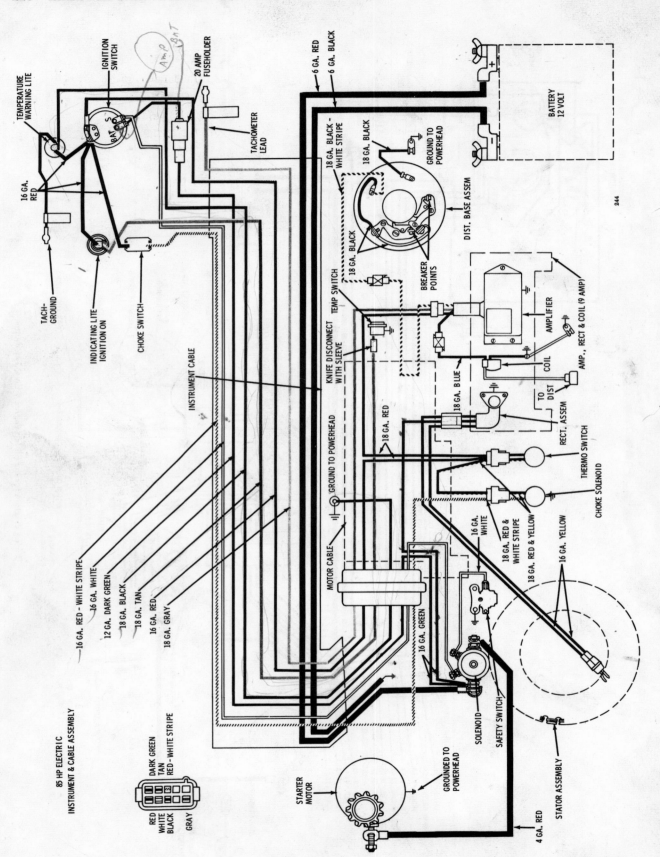

Wiring diagram for the 85 Hp engine.

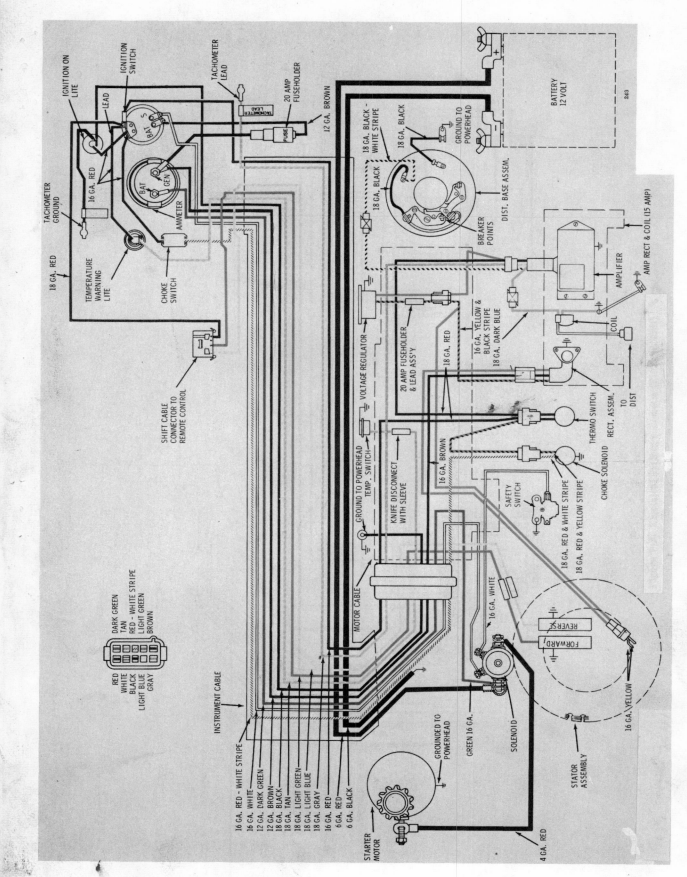

Wiring diagram for the 85 Hp engine with an electric shift.

242

Wiring diagram for the 90 Hp engine.

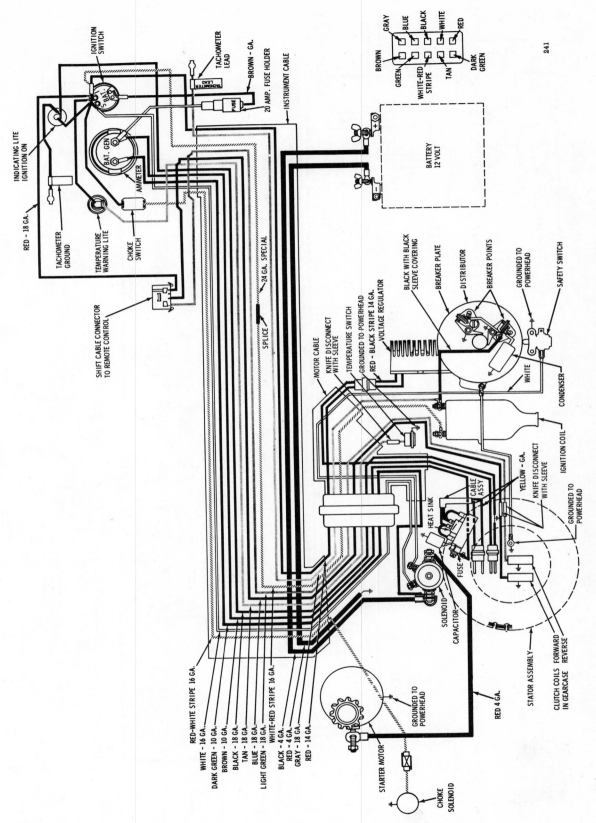

Wiring diagram for the 1966, 100 Hp model with a distributor and breaker points.

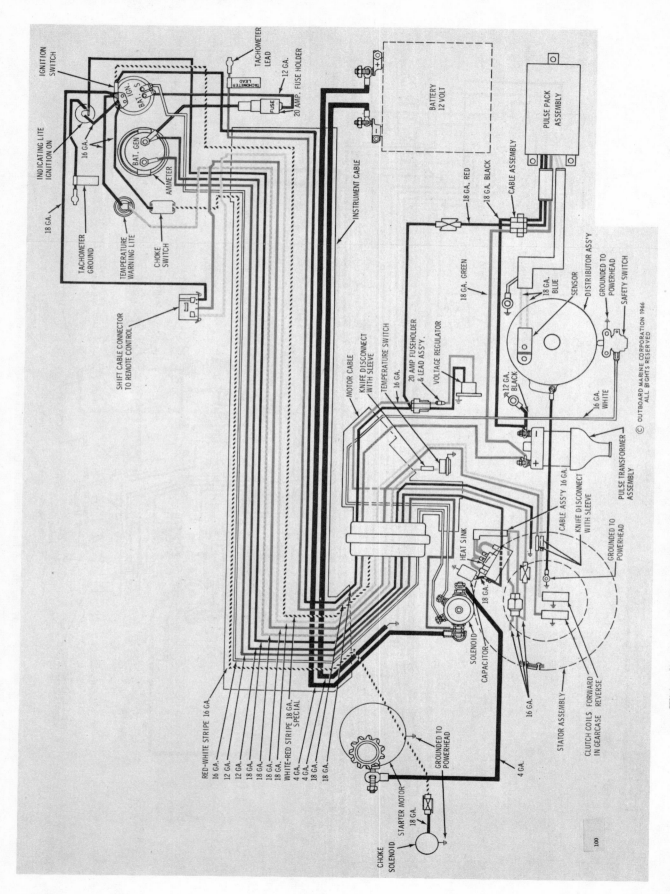

Wiring diagram for the 1967, 100 Hp model with a distributor containing a pulse generator for the CD ignition system.

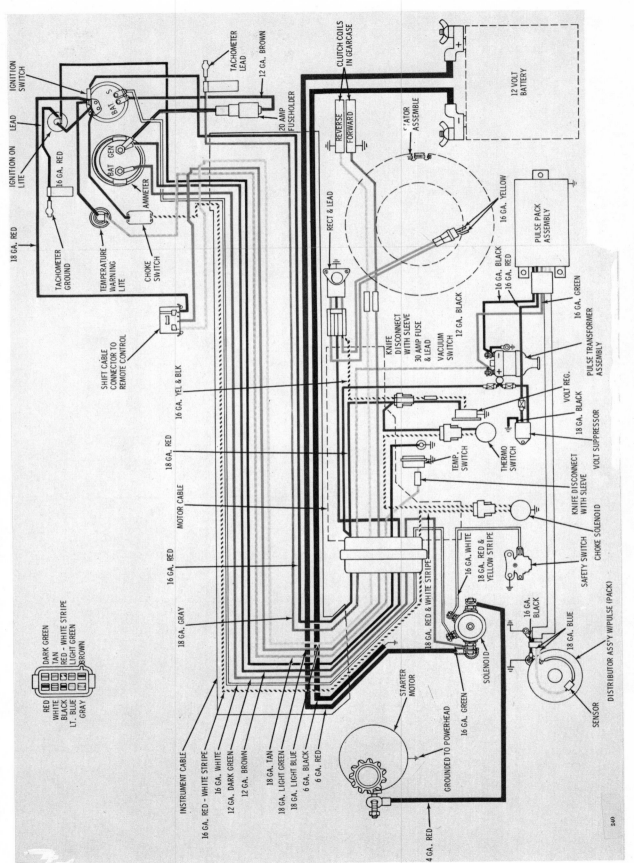

Wiring diagram for the 1968, 100 Hp model with a pulse generator (under the flywheel) for the CD ignition system.